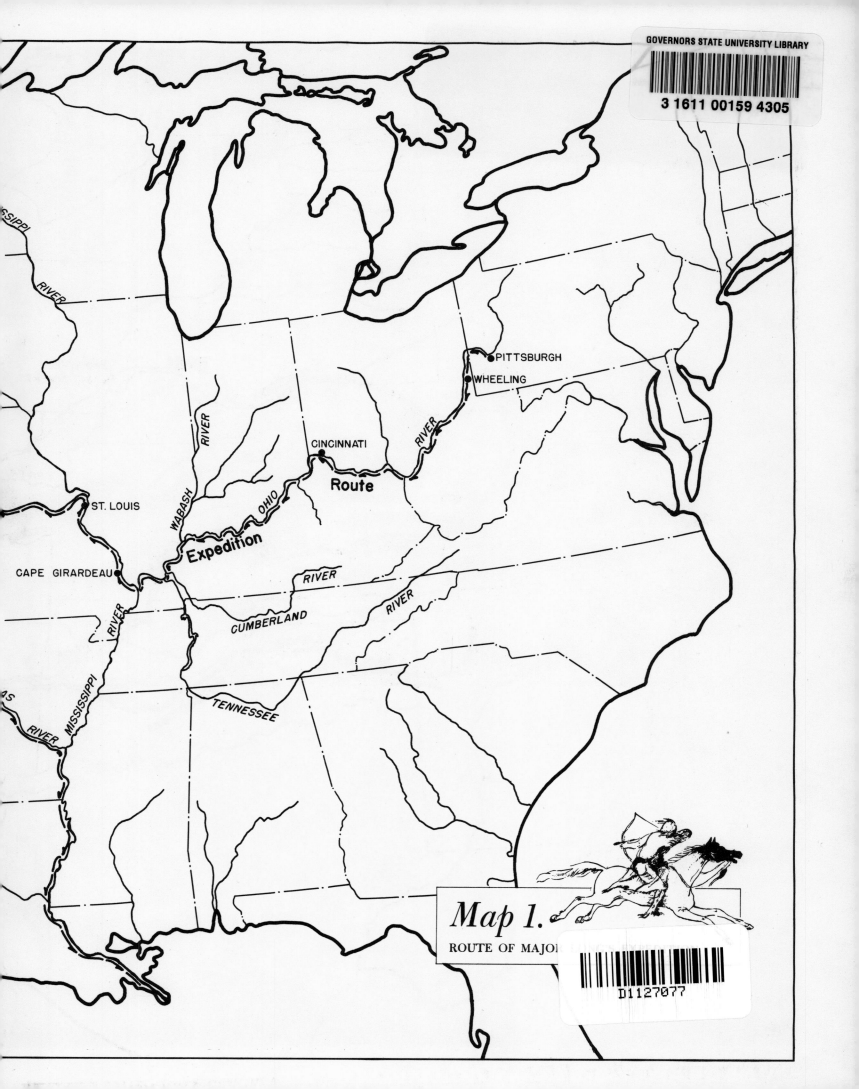

ST. LOUIS

CINCINNATI

Route

PITTSBURGH

WHEELING

RIVER

WABASH RIVER

OHIO

Expedition

CAPE GIRARDEAU

RIVER

CUMBERLAND

RIVER

MISSISSIPPI

RIVER

TENNESSEE

MISSISSIPPI

RIVER

Map 1.

ROUTE OF MAJOR

MEMOIRS OF THE

AMERICAN PHILOSOPHICAL SOCIETY

HELD AT PHILADELPHIA

FOR PROMOTING USEFUL KNOWLEDGE

VOLUME 52

TITIAN RAMSAY PEALE

1799-1885

The American Philosophical Society

INDEPENDENCE SQUARE • PHILADELPHIA

1961

JESSIE POESCH

And His Journals of
The Wilkes Expedition

Preface

Many types of scholarly approaches are available to the student of cultural history. One of the more satisfying is the biographical study. In preparing this study I have tried to present a straightforward narrative of the life of a man who could never be singled out as a great or creative leader yet who made the scholar's beloved "contribution" to the science and art of his day. I have followed where the facts have led, and often they shaped their own story. He and his family and friends were nineteenth-century people who did indeed see themselves in a romantic light. At the same time, and in no contradiction to their noble and romantic sentiments, these people were among the vanguard who pushed forward those developments of science, scientific theory, and industry which have shaped the twentieth century. Peale himself was a proud, independent, often difficult individual, possessed with an avid curiosity and zest for life. At times the story of his life reads like an exciting adventure story. His career illuminates many problems and preoccupations of scholarship in the natural sciences in the nineteenth century, including the dichotomy that often existed between the field observer and the "closet" naturalist. His extant journals of the Wilkes Expedition are published here, in Part II, for the first time in their entirety. They provide us with a detailed record of the activities of this artist-naturalist while a member of this remarkable enterprise.

It is a pleasure to name some of the many persons and institutions who have helped to make this study possible: I should particularly like to thank the persons responsible for the Henry Francis DuPont Winterthur Museum Program in Early American Culture, under whose aegis I began this study, and the Penrose Fund of the American Philosophical Society, whose generosity made it possible to bring it to completion. Professor Joseph Ewan of Tulane University, Mr. Charles Coleman Sellers of Dickinson College, and Dr. Ernest Moyne of the University of Delaware have each read the manuscript in two different stages and have given invaluable suggestions and counsel. Maurice and Venia Phillips of the Academy of Natural Sciences in Philadelphia have been generous with their time and counsel and have guided me to pertinent materials. Others who have given helpful suggestions and criticisms or have allowed me to study their collections, or both, include Dr. John Munroe, Dr. and Mrs. Charles M. James, Dr. David B. Tyler, Dr. Anthony N. B. Garvan, Dr. Robert Cushman Murphy, Miss Jacqueline Hoffmire, Mrs. Joseph Carson, Mr. Carl Schaefer Dentzel, Miss Ida Edelson, Mr. Robert R. Peale, Mrs. Coleman Sellers Mills and the late Mr. Mills, Mr. Harry Peale Haldt, Mrs. Joseph Peale, and the late Mr. Edmund Bury. Several of these people have become warm personal friends.

Mrs. Gertrude Hess, Mrs. Ruth Duncan, and Mr. Murphy Smith, all of the staff of the Library of the American Philosophical Society, have been more than helpful in facilitating my use of the rich manuscript collections of that institution, upon which so much of this study is based. The librarians of the following institutions have all been most helpful: the Historical Society of Pennsylvania, the Library Company of Philadelphia, the Academy of Natural Sciences of Philadelphia, the Library of Congress, the American Museum of Natural History, the Smithsonian Institution, the Frick Art Reference Library, the Western Americana Collection of Yale University Library, the William Henry Smith Memorial Library of the Indiana Historical Society, the National Archives, the Haverford College Library, the Museum of Comparative Zoology at Harvard University, and the Southern Historical Collection of the University of North Carolina. I should like to thank each of these institutions for permission to quote from their materials, and especially to thank the Library of Congress for permission to publish Peale's Wilkes Expedition journals.

Mrs. Patricia Pugh Reifsnyder shared with me the difficult task of proofreading the journals against the original manuscript. Mrs. Eleanor Freisem typed this entire study with care and competence. To both I am exceedingly grateful. Finally, I should like to thank my many personal friends who shared or tolerated my enthusiasm for this project and who assuaged me during occasional moments of exasperation. For the final form of this study and for any errors, I alone am responsible.

J. P.

Philadelphia, 1960.

Contents

Illustrations

FIG. 1. Oil painting, portrait of Titian R. Peale. *ca.* 1825–1835. Inscription on back reads, "T.R. Peale—by himself with a little help from his brother Rembrandt. Mrs. T. R. Peale to John Hoffmire, Red Bank, 1886." Courtesy of the American Museum of Natural History.

Part One

TITIAN RAMSAY PEALE

I

Introduction

THE STORY of the frontiersman and of the settler and his family, pushing westwards to new lands, is a familiar one in the annals of American history. As a part of this movement, and usually as a vanguard, were men of the East who went West, and who came back. Among these were men who went for a specific purpose, to perform specific tasks, and to bring back information about the new areas—information about trade routes and trade possibilities, information about the kind of soil and the products of new lands.

These purposeful travelers were talented men, both curious and contemplative, eager to explore new frontiers of knowledge as well as of land. With their mental abilities they combined great physical courage and a sense of adventure. In their packs, or in their seabags if the sea was their frontier, they carried varied and sometimes seemingly odd kinds of equipment. These would include the compass, chronometer, and surveying instruments, the botanist's boxes, butterfly nets, dredges, casks, spirits, and notebooks and paintbrushes along with guns and ammunition. In the carefully recorded notes, the measurements, the maps, the drawings, and the specimens they brought back they knew they were making a contribution to "useful knowledge," knowledge which today would be variously classified under specialized categories of learning such as geography, anthropology, ethnology, zoology, biology, geology, and mineralogy. Meriwether Lewis and William Clark were among the most notable leaders of men in this character. Others would include Stephen H. Long, Zebulon Pike, John C. Fremont, and, on the sea, Charles H. Wilkes.

The artist-naturalist was often one of the specialized and intrepid travelers who made up the membership of exploring expeditions. Beginning at least with the quickening of intellectual life and the literal widening of horizons which occurred during and following the Renaissance, one can regularly find records of artists whose particular task was to accompany imperial or scientific expeditions and to record what they saw—the flora and fauna, the manner of living and the appearance of strange people. Their paints and inks provided the first visual images of new lands, new peoples, new birds and beasts.

In North America this tradition can be traced to Jacques Le Moyne and John White, who accompanied French and English expeditions to these shores in 1564 and 1585, respectively. Among artists of the eighteenth and nineteenth centuries one could readily list a dozen or more whose work served the dual purposes of providing visual records which contributed information and which satisfied a desire for beauty. Mark Catesby, John James Audubon, George Catlin, and Karl Bodmer are some of the best known. Some of these men were trained as both artists and natural scientists (according to the standards of the day). They recorded flora and fauna, geographical sites, Indian life, and thus provided important documents of interest to learned men and those interested in the new sciences both here and abroad, as well as practical knowledge helpful to the settlers who were to follow in their footsteps and to the government. In their passion for accuracy and in their eagerness to record all they saw, these artists frequently created excellent drawings and paintings well worth attention today.

Titian Ramsay Peale, youngest son of Charles Willson Peale, was such an artist-scientist. His life span extended from 1799 to 1885. In his lifetime he was not only to record new information about the birds and animals of many and far-away places, but he was also to share in and contribute to the development of that new tool of the documentary artists, the camera. Not a giant of his time, his life and his work nonetheless have a compelling interest. Perhaps his very failures make him worthy of study. He experienced both the joy and satisfaction of achievement as well as the bitterness of defeat; the account of his life illuminates the story of the stumbling, faltering development of natural science and art in nineteenth-century America.

Peale grew up in the stimulating atmosphere of Philadelphia, then the most important scientific center in the United States. Early made aware of the West, he was to be among the first to explore the upper reaches of the Red and Arkansas Rivers, and to be a passenger on the first steamboat to travel the upper

Missouri. Home again, the fashionable and rising young man of Philadelphia shared in the amateur enthusiasms of a romantic age. Later, as a member of the Wilkes Expedition, he witnessed and participated in America's push for dominance in world trade. His career frustrated, and the widespread enthusiasm for natural history gone from the American scene, he secured a job in the United States Patent Office, presiding over the introduction of new mechanisms that made for the industrialization of an expanding and war-torn land. His private life continued to be devoted to recording nature through paintings, drawings, and the camera—only in private life could he continue to pursue the interests developed in his youth.

"NATURE and ART" was inscribed upon an open book represented in an advertisement of the Philadelphia Museum, better known as Peale's Museum, appearing in *Poulson's American Daily Advertiser* of November 3, 1821. It was an appropriate emblem for a Peale family institution. Certainly the study of nature and the pursuance of art were the two guiding forces in Titian Peale's life. It is fitting and natural that a son of Charles Willson Peale should be so guided. These two forces were, in fact, close to family gods. Members of the Peale family served them in diverse ways.

Painting and museum management were the two major occupations of that many-sided man, Charles Willson Peale, whose life story is described in detail in Charles Coleman Sellers' excellent biography.[1] First self-taught, and then trained in London by Benjamin West, the elder Peale became a prominent artist of the Revolution. He painted many of the military and political leaders of the day as well as numerous members of the leading families of Maryland, Pennsylvania, and New Jersey. In art, his aim was to imitate nature. Though his ideal was to rise to the sublime effects of "history painting," he devoted himself chiefly to the representational painting of portraits, and his greatest joy seems to have come from creating an accurate and recognizable likeness.

From art imitating or representing nature, he turned to its glorification in his new Museum. The Museum ticket proclaimed:

The Birds & Beasts will teach thee! Admit the Bearer to Peale's Museum, containing the Wonderful works of NATURE and Curious Works of ART.[2]

Peale was not a profound scholar, but he attempted to present the works of nature in an attractive and correct fashion. In so doing, he contributed much to the enthusiastic amateur interest in natural history that existed in some circles in the new republic at the turn of the century. There was almost a missionary zeal in the joyful eagerness with which he proclaimed this union of God and nature. This was an expression of his own deistic faith. At the same time, he never lost sight of the profit motive and put his artistic abilities to practical use in creating varied and new displays that would draw the public. Peale's Museum was an attractive, interesting, dignified place, where Philadelphia matrons or Quakers in town for Yearly Meeting might appropriately spend an afternoon or evening. For several decades it was the most important respository of objects of natural history in Philadelphia. The growing body of scholars in that community came to the Museum to study the specimens there, wrote about and discussed them, and made contributions to the collection.

In the large and close-knit family of the Peales, the sons almost inevitably learned and shared the activities of the father. The briefest sketch of some of their activities reveals how they fulfilled these, while their very names reflect the father's interests in art, science, and nature. The oldest son, Raphaelle, did his stint in the Museum, possibly damaging his body permanently in the process of preserving specimens with arsenic. He was professionally an artist, however, and what living he earned was largely from the brush. Present-day art critics would probably consider him the most talented of the family. For him art and nature were most nobly served when he painted nature's forms in still life—the forms of humble fruits and vegetables delineated with a skill that reveals the artist's heightened abilities of perception. These he painted again and again, even though these paintings failed to provide an adequate income. Today the artistic merit of these paintings is recognized, and they are much sought after.

Rembrandt Peale thought in large, grand words and phrases. He, too, earned his living chiefly by painting, though he ventured into museum-directing for a time. He went abroad several times to study in the academies and salons of Europe, and to him "Art" and "Nature" always began with capital letters. Nature was a thing to ponder and to discuss in learned fashion. Art was a means of glorifying and recording with dignity the virtues of great heroes. Art was a means of representing the sublime, the best, in Nature.

Rubens, the youngest son of the first wife of Charles Willson Peale, was a humbler and more practical person. He was a museum manager and farmer. He loved God's earth and its products. In his youth he and his friends rambled over the countryside collecting minerals. It was he who first systematically organized the mineral collection in Peale's Museum. When the family moved to a farm in Germantown in 1810, it was he who helped his father design and plant a flourishing garden that became a showplace of the community. Having dabbled with oils and watercolor occasionally as a youth, he passed many hours of his old age in painting flowers, fruits, and birds. These are somewhat naive and stiff, but possess considerable charm.

[1] Sellers, Charles Coleman, *Charles Willson Peale*, 2 v., Philadelphia, *Memoirs Amer. Philos. Soc.* **23** (1 & 2), 1947. This work will hereafter be cited as Sellers, *CWP*.
[2] *Ibid.* **2**: 270.

Another son of the first family, Titian Ramsay I, died when a youth of eighteen. He was one of his father's chief assistants in the museum. Clearly an intelligent and talented boy, he had at that youthful age contemplated a pioneering study of the insects of North America, and had written a short manual on miniature painting.[3]

Charles Linnaeus and Franklin, the first two sons by Peale's second wife, turned more to the mechanic arts. Linnaeus was a mill-keeper, farmer, soldier, sailor, and museum manager. He died in his thirties, and had never really found himself vocationally. Franklin, a person of gentle disposition, rose to become Chief Coiner of the United States Mint after serving an apprenticeship in a machine shop, and then sharing with his brother, Titian, the subject of this biography, and

---

[3] The subject of this study is the second Titian Ramsay Peale. Since the first lived such a short time, and since it would be confusing constantly to refer to Titian Ramsay Peale II, a nomenclature he did not use, he will be called Titian Ramsay Peale throughout this study. When referring to the first Titian, Titian Ramsay Peale I will be used.

The manuscript manual on miniature painting is in the collection of the American Philosophical Society Library. This institution will hereafter be cited as APS.

another son of the second marriage, the management of the Museum. Franklin's marriage to the niece of Stephen Girard meant financial independence; he later became a railroad president. In his later years he was known and loved in Philadelphia as a civic leader, and especially for his love of and devotion to music and for his leadership in the Musical Fund Society. An archaeological collection of the art of the Stone Age was yet another of his leisure-time passions. In his old age he maintained a warm and friendly correspondence with his brother Titian. They shared many common interests related to the pursuance of the arts, science, and the study of nature.

Equally within the family circle was Charles Willson Peale's brother, James Peale. Though less dominant as a personality than his brother, he developed into an artist of equal, or even greater, skill. During his long and fruitful career he painted portraits, still lifes, and landscape scenes with skill and taste. Several of his children, James, Jr., Anna, and Sarah Miriam painted for profit.

Creativity, curiosity, affection, an interest in art, science, and nature—these qualities were embedded in the matrix of Peale family life. The life of the son, Titian Ramsay Peale, was formed by them.

II

A Home In
Philosophical Hall

BORN in Philadelphia's Philosophical Hall where his family lived as caretakers, Titian Ramsay Peale called this building home for eleven years. Here he saw and knew some of America's leading students of the new scientific knowledge. Here he saw his father's artist friends come and go. In his old age he could appropriately say that it was here that he had imbibed a taste for Nature (it was always on their tongues in just such phrases) and for truth, which was to last throughout his life.[1]

His date of birth seems to have been November 2, 1799. It is written so in the family copy of Pilkington's *The Gentleman's and Connoisseur's Dictionary of Painters*,[2] in which births and deaths of other members of the family are also recorded. Titian Peale, however, long believed himself to have been born on October 10, 1800.[3] Burial records show October 10, 1799 as his birth date, and Peale in his old age apparently reported this as the correct date. He was the next to youngest of Charles Willson Peale's children by his second wife.[4] The boy was named after an older brother who had died in New York City during the yellow fever epidemic of 1798.[5] The first name was a typical selection of the elder Peale, who named many of his children after well-known artists. Colonel Nathaniel Ramsay, from whom the middle name derived, was a brother in-law and lifelong friend of the elder Peale.

At the time of the child's birth Charles Willso Peale was fifty-eight years of age. For more than a decade he had been devoting most of his energies and enthusiasms to building up a museum of natural history and art. His friend Colonel Ramsay seems to have first suggested it when he observed that the public might be as interested in viewing the bones of the mastodon, which Peale had been asked to draw, as in the collection of portraits of Revolutionary heroes which Peale was displaying in his painting room.[6] In 1794 the family and the museum had been removed to Philosophical Hall. Peale, a member of the American Philosophical Society, was allowed to use certain of the rooms for exhibits, and to house his own family in the other rooms. His lease required him to serve as Librarian and as a caretaker or curator of objects for the Society. Two spacious second-floor rooms were reserved for the Society's use; Peale's duties included keeping these neat and clean.[7]

By 1802 Peale's Museum had expanded, and permission was received to install it in the nearby State House, known better now as Independence Hall. Here it was to remain until 1827, and while at this location it was an important and well-known Philadelphia institution.[8] The Museum was a family project, with practically all members helping in one way or another.

In 1799 Titian R. Peale's mother was thirty-four years of age. Elizabeth DePeyster Peale was a plump woman with a good singing voice, the daughter of a

---

[1] Speech of Titian Ramsay Peale (hereafter referred to by his initials TRP) at meeting in his honor, Minute Book, May 18, 1881. MS, United Bowmen Collection, Historical Society of Pennsylvania.

[2] London, 1770. The family copy is at the APS.

[3] TRP to an unknown correspondent, March 22, 1879. MS, New-York Historical Society, lists all the children of Elizabeth DePeyster Peale and records his own birthdate as October 10, 1800. This is the date used by Albert Charles Peale in his biographical study, Titian R. Peale, 1800–1885, *Bull. Philos. Soc. Wash.* **14:** 317–326, 1905. An undated manuscript which has recently come to light at the Pennsylvania Academy of the Fine Arts, from TRP to an unknown correspondent reads: "Mrs. Peale made a mistake in giving you my age. I was born Octr 10th 1799. Mrs. P. joins in kind regards."

[4] Records, Bringhurst Undertakers, Philadelphia.

[5] Sellers, *CWP* **2:** 106.

[6] *Ibid.*, **1:** 239.

[7] Phillips, Henry, Jr., Old minutes of the Society, from 1743 to 1838, *Proc. Amer. Philos. Soc.* **22:** 221–222, 1884.

[8] Peale, Titian R., *Circular of the Philadelphia Museum containing directions for the preparations and preservation of objects of natural history*, 5, Philadelphia, 1831.

Fig. 2. State House Yard, 1800. By William Birch. Over the door of Philosophical Hall in the center background a sign reads, MUSEUM. Two years later the Museum expanded into the State House itself, occupying all the upper floors. Courtesy of Fairmount Park Art Association.

New York merchant. It was in Peale's Museum that she first met Charles Willson Peale in 1791, the year in which they were married.[9] She presided over the family of motherless children of Peale's first wife, Rachel Brewer Peale, and within a few years became the mother of a good-sized family of her own. At the time of Titian Peale's birth the children at home included the two youngest of the first family, Rubens and Sophonisba, then fifteen and thirteen years of age. Titian's own brothers and sisters numbered three: Charles Linnaeus, aged five; Benjamin Franklin, aged four; and Sybilla Miriam, a baby of two. In 1802 another daughter, Elizabeth DePeyster, was born. There is no doubt that the mother of this second family was a proud and sensitive spirit. In the family correspondence one is made aware of her over-sensitive feelings when the father gently reprimands an older child for thoughtlessness or encourages another to write to his new step-mother.

The three oldest offspring of Charles Willson Peale were already young adults. Angelica Peale Robinson was farthest removed from the family circle; she and her merchant husband lived in Baltimore. Though she kept in constant touch with the family by letter, her husband cared little for the activities of the Peale family and she rarely saw them. Both Raphaelle and Rembrandt had recently married and had begun independent careers. Their children were often in the home of the grandparents, making a lively gathering at Philosophical Hall.

In the early 1800's Raphaelle made frequent trips away from Philadelphia, attempting to earn his livelihood. One year he was in Virginia, painting miniatures and taking profiles by the hundreds. At another time he was in Baltimore, taking charge of an exhibition of one of the mastodon skeletons which his father had exhumed in upper New York state. Boston and Geor-

---

[9] Sellers, *CWP* 2: 24–26.

gia were also included in Raphaelle's itinerary. Talented and personally lovable, given to drink, he was in and out of the family home; and he was always living on the edge of poverty.

Rembrandt was a soberer individual and close to his father's activities. In 1802 he and his younger brother Rubens were off to England where they exhibited, not too profitably, one of the mastodon skeletons. Of all the members of the family, Rembrandt was the one to turn most towards Europe for his inspiration and his values. In subsequent years he was to make several more trips to Europe—to England, France, and Italy. He was to visit many of the important museums of Europe, to meet many of the leading artists and scientific men of the day, and to paint many of the latter for the Museum in Philadelphia.

It was a cosmopolitan and mildly eccentric family and their horizons were broad. Not only did different members of the family travel widely, but most of the important visitors to Philadelphia came to know the genial and lively Mr. Peale; one finds mention of such acquaintanceships in many travel journals of the time. Peale painted the portrait of one such visitor, Baron von Humboldt, for the Museum gallery.[10] The two enjoyed animated conversation ranging over many fields of knowledge. To men such as the Baron and Thomas Jefferson, the elder Peale poured out his embryonic ideas and dreams of a national museum, ideas which were to become more specific in the second decade of the century. He nursed a dream for the establishment of a center of learning for the new nation, and in his mind a well-organized collection was basic to such a center. He knew his collection was probably the best of its kind in America and equal to many in Europe, and he hoped it could become part of such a center. His concern was based on both practical and altruistic motives. His zeal for the advancement of knowledge was sincere; the Museum was an economically sound venture and the aging (in years if not in spirit) man was anxious to establish the Museum in such a way that the numerous members of his family could continue to profit from it.

Though the Museum was well known for amusing and delightful entertainment, such as the showing of the fanciful transparencies painted by the Peales, it was equally well known for the natural history collection, and in this latter field a very real contribution was made to the scientific knowledge of the day by father and sons. Peale and his sons devoted much care to classifying and labeling their many specimens of natural history. The collection grew rapidly, and they were often far behind in this work. A scientific historian has pointed out that had C. W. Peale taken the time to publish colored figures and a descriptive catalog of his "wonders," many new species now credited

to others might bear the name of Peale. His greatest contribution, and one which probably exceeded all others of his time, was in awakening a wide public interest in natural history, especially ornithology.[11]

His dream was to make his Museum a repository for "a comparative view of each genus . . . of the old and new world."[12] His collection of birds was excellent, and he was glad to have it used by such students of nature as Alexander Wilson, who was then at work on his *American Ornithology*, which represented the first attempt to classify and figure all the known American species.

Wilson was but one of Philadelphia's outstanding students of nature whom the Peales, including the boy Titian, knew. Wilson had been a Scottish weaver and poet in the manner of Burns who had come to America in 1794. Schoolteaching provided him with a livelihood during his first years in the new land. A new impetus was given to his life when, in 1802, he first met William Bartram, the sensitive and eccentric Philadelphia naturalist and acquaintance of C. W. Peale. Bartram encouraged the younger man's interest in observing and collecting birds, gave him free access to the Bartram library, and encouraged him to draw and paint. Wilson made rapid strides in his new studies, and before long had conceived the idea of producing as complete as possible a survey of American ornithology. It was probably in these years that Wilson first met the Peales and came to know the Museum on Chestnut Street. Rubens Peale, in his later years, recorded the story of their first meeting as he remembered it:

> My father & I frequently went gunning before breakfast to shoot Birds to stuff for the Museum, using guns with small bores and the finest mustard seed shot, doing them as little injury as possible. . . . [One time when they had spread some of their catch out upon a sheet of paper] a young man approached who enquired concerning them and he told me I had shot a favourite bird that sang every day near his window. His name was Alexander Wilson, he taught schull in the woods in a small log cabben near the Darby Road on the property of Wᵐ Bartram. . . . I gave Mr. W an invitation to see the Museum, and he came the next saturday afternoon, I don't remember ever to have seen any one so much delighted especially with the birds. I produced my pictures of birds and from that time he regularly came to the Museum on sat. aftⁿ or Sunday, he became quite expert in drawing. This induced him to publish a work on Ornithology and printed by Mr. Wᵐ Bradford. We were ever afterwards bosom friends to his death.[13]

The close friendship with the Peales is reflected throughout the text of Wilson's monumental nine-volume pioneer work on *American Ornithology*, pub-

---

[10] CWP to Mrs. Nathaniel Ramsay, Sept. 7, 1804, CWP Letterbook ⅏ 5, 131. MS, APS. Unless otherwise cited, all manuscripts are at the American Philosophical Society Library. Charles Willson Peale will hereafter be cited as CWP.

[11] Burns, Frank L., Charles W. and Titian R. Peale and the ornithological section of the old Philadelphia Museum, *Wilson Bulletin* **44**: 23–35, 1932. Other sources for this section are CWP to Thomas Jefferson, Feb. 26, 1804, CWP Letterbook ⅏ 5, 18; and CWP to James Madison, April 30, 1809, CWP Letterbook ⅏ 10, 52–54.

[12] CWP to Dr. Mitchell, July 26, 1803, CWP Letterbook ⅏ 4, 72.

[13] Rubens Peale's Autobiographical Notes, 41–42, MS, APS.

lished in the years between 1808 and 1814. Many of the birds described and drawn by Wilson were in the Museum collection; in many other cases Wilson reports giving his specimens to the Museum. In one of his many references to Charles Willson Peale, Wilson gave special praise to Peale's role as a disseminator of knowledge:

> . . . Mr. Charles W. Peale, proprietor of the Museum in Philadelphia, . . . as a practical naturalist, stands deservedly first in the first rank of American connoisseurs; and . . . has done more for the promotion of that sublime science than all our speculative theorists together. . . .[14]

Wilson, applying the standards of the embryonic scientific studies, tried to be scrupulously accurate and objective in his descriptions and drawings. He, like T. R. Peale who was to follow in his tradition, spent long hours in the forests and fields observing, and was a "solitary, exploring pilgrim." According to his standards, such field observation was imperative and, while he felt it should be supplemented with book learning, he also felt the latter could never take the place of it. He inveighed against the closet naturalists:

> Should there appear in *some* of the following accounts of our native birds, a more than common deficiency of particulars as to their manners and migration, he would beg leave to observe, that he is not engaged in copying from *Museums* the stuffed subjects they contain; nor from books or libraries the fabulous and hearsay narratives of *closet naturalists*. A more laborious, and, as he trusts, a more honorable duty is prescribed him. He has examined the stories of living Nature for himself; and submitted with pleasure, to all the difficulties and fatigues incident to such an undertaking.[15]

Wilson articulated his own standards clearly.

> Well authenticated facts deduced from careful observation, precise descriptions, and faithfully pourtrayed representations drawn from living nature, are the only true and substantial materials from which we can ever hope to erect and complete the great superstructure of science;—without these all learned speculations of mere closet theory are but "the baseless fabricks of a vision.[16]

Following a pattern set by Mark Catesby almost a century earlier, Wilson attempted to learn how to engrave in order to illustrate his own books. He gave this up, however, and instead worked in close cooperation with the engraver Alexander Lawson. In drawing birds he strove for accuracy and truth of color and form. It is difficult to know exactly how much of each of the figures appearing in Wilson's plates is a product of his own labor, and how much is due to the assistance and elaboration of the engraver, Lawson. The latter's daughter said:

> In the first place, Wilson never painted birds, he drew them in water colors, and more frequently in outline, either with pencil or pen, and my father finished them from the birds themselves.[17]

For his day, Wilson's work was most assuredly elegant and, of course, represented a giant step forward in the development of ornithological science in America. There was nothing to equal it in any other branch of American science, and the conception and completion of such a series testified to Wilson's outstanding ability. Published in the years 1808 to 1813, the volumes would have been known to Titian Peale in his youthful years, and their author was undoubtedly among his childhood heroes. The growing boy must have heard much talk about these books during his maturing years—praise of the persevering enterprise of its author and praise of the elegant, beautifully and accurately colored, figures shown in the plates. It did not occur to anyone to criticize the stiff profile views or the crowded compositions; their appreciation centered on the accuracy of details such as the beauty of the fine and precise plumage.

The Accession Book of Peale's Museum, now in the Historical Society of Pennsylvania, frequently records gifts from other interested friends of the family. The mineral collection was regularly augmented by items such as that presented by Reuben Haines, one of the early members of the Academy of Natural Sciences of Philadelphia, on May 22, 1808:

> Red Ochre from the Paint Spring on the Blue Mountain about five miles above the Delaware Gap, Walpae Township, Sussex County, New Jersey.

Or another item in the same year:

> Sept. 16, 1808. Native Sulphat of Magnesia from a cave in the State of Vermont.
>
> pr. by Mr. Joseph Cloud.

The mastodon, or "mammoth" as C. W. Peale preferred to call it, skeleton, first housed in Philosophical Hall, was one of the major attractions of the Museum throughout its existence. A few bones of a mastodon had been the initial inspiration for the Museum in 1784. Then in 1801, when Titian was but a baby, the elder Peale had heard of some skeletal remains of a prehistoric animal which had been found in upstate New York. He forthwith had gone to the site and after three months' excavating on that and several other nearby sites had succeeded in getting two nearly complete and one less complete set of bones. Out of these, and by using restoration techniques not too different from those of present-day museums, he put together two skeletons. One of these two of the older boys displayed in Europe in 1802 and 1803, and the other was put on display in Philadelphia. The latter was the first such skeleton assembled in America and the second in the world. It is a dominant object in Peale's well-known self-portrait, *The Artist in His Museum*, painted in 1822. Though little Titian did not share in the small but adventuresome excavating expedition, he must have heard the tale retold within the family many times. He could read about it, too, in the pamphlets his half-brother Rembrandt published in Eng-

[14] Wilson, Alexander, *American ornithology* 1: 71, Philadelphia, 1808.

[15] Wilson, 3: vi, Philadelphia, 1811.

[16] *Ibid.*, ix.

[17] As quoted by Frank L. Burns in *The Auk*, N.S., 34: 278, 1917.

land. In these Rembrandt discussed the geological formation of New York state, and told the story of the excavation and how "a swamp always noted as the solitary abode of snakes and frogs became the active scene of curiosity and bustle."[18] Rembrandt also marshalled opinions of European naturalists concerning prehistoric monsters and, at the same time, included notes on the North American Indian traditions which, he noted, echoed the lyrical phrases of Ossian.

It was natural for Charles Willson Peale to write to Jefferson on March 18, 1804, to express his enthusiasm over the Louisiana Purchase and the new areas it opened for physical and mental exploration:

With others I feel my obligations for your successful treaty which gives to my Country a new source of Wealth, and our Philosophers so extensive a range to acquire various knowledge.[19]

The very same week Peale acquired two baby grizzly bears from Lieutenant Zebulon Pike, who had transported them over sixteen hundred miles, which were kept for some time in a cage in the Museum yard. As they grew larger and larger, they became more dangerous and more ferocious, eventually had to be killed, and were mounted and installed in the Museum. Using these two specimens of the largest and fiercest of known bears, Thomas Say, another Philadelphia naturalist, wrote the first scientific description of this animal, *Ursus horribilis*, which has become a symbol of the American West. The name was suggested by still another Philadelphian who was a student of natural history, George Ord.[20] The bear cubs were among the pets of the Peale children, who played with these exotic animals, as well as North Carolinean alligators and African monkeys, as others played with dogs and cats.[21]

C. W. Peale and his philosophically minded friends in Philadelphia were excited about the achievements of Meriwether Lewis and William Clark in reaching the Pacific via an overland route, and it was with no small amount of pride that Peale recorded a long list of Indian artifacts and specimens of natural history which were given to the Museum on December 28, 1809. Peale's Musum was the nearest thing to a National Museum then in existence, so it was a logical repository; Jefferson, of course, had helped to steer the collections to Peale. Here visitors could see for themselves the Indian costumes, leggings, tobacco pouches, ornamental belts as well as the handsome

beaver mantle fringed with 140 ermine skins and studded with "prismatic coloured Shells" which Lewis had used on the journey. These objects made real to the merchants and farmers of the Philadelphia area, and to the Peale children, the stories of Western Indians as told by explorers and by occasional returning trappers. Several of the natural history specimens had been unknown to naturalists, and Peale eagerly mounted them for all to see the species of the New World.

Lewis' picture was painted by C. W. Peale in 1807 and, appropriately enough, was added to the row of portraits of national leaders and heroes which filled the upper ranges of the Long Room, where the ornithological and mineral collections of the Museum were kept.[22]

The Peale Museum was attempting to bring together a collection representative of the Old as well as the New World. Therefore, it was not unnatural for the father to describe himself as a "citizen of the world, who would go to that place which would give most incouragement to [his] favorite science."[23] Though the father did not travel outside his country in his mature years, his sons and his friends helped him to gather items for display from all parts of the world. For example, a gift of minerals from Abbé Haiiy of France resulted from Rembrandt's visit to France.[24] Exchanges with individuals and museums abroad, and gifts from American travelers, such as sea captains and merchants, all helped to provide objects and specimens for the Museum. Local residents gave such diverse objects as specimens of rock salt from Germany, a vase from Herculanium, and "a very handsome" vase of Derbyshire Spar.[25] Exotic items were brought by travelers in the Pacific. During the formative years of Titian Peale's life the Accession Book reveals all manner of objects from the other side of the world: a wooden pillow, a piece of sandalwood, cloth and thread from the Fiji Islands, a handsomely ornamented kreese or dagger from the East Indies, a wooden spear from islands in the South Seas, feathers of the Red-tail Tropic Bird from the Island of Tongataboo, and a paddle of wood beautifully carved from an island near New Zealand. The lure of far-away places and the excitement of gathering specimens and objects from all parts of the world, as well as the exacting problems of identifying, classifying, and understanding these objects, surrounded Titian Peale from his earliest childhood. It is not surprising that the conversations and activities of the people with whom the little boy associated as he played about the yard of the State House were important in forming his tastes and interests.

Though the Peale family may have been somewhat

[18] Peale, Rembrandt, *An historical disquisition on the mammoth, or great American incognitum, an extinct, immense, carnivorous animal whose fossil remains have been found in North America*, 25, London, 1803.

[19] CWP to Thomas Jefferson, March 18, 1804, CWP Letterbook 5: 32.

[20] Godman, John D., *American natural history* 1: 131–142, Philadelphia, 1826.

[21] Peale's Museum Record and Accession Book, MS, Historical Society of Pennsylvania, lists over a dozen entries of living animals which were acquired by the Museum at different times. This manuscript will henceforth be referred to as Accession Book. The Historical Society of Pennsylvania will be referred to as HSP.

[22] CWP to John Hawkins, May 5, 1807, CWP Letterbook 8: 30.

[23] CWP Diary 18, June 29, 1801, 41.

[24] Accession Book, MS, HSP, Dec. 1808 entries.

[25] Gift of Mr. Joseph Sansom, Feb. 26, 1808, Accession Book, MS, HSP.

more than ordinarily imbued with enthusiasm for the study of natural history, more closely associated with the events leading to the opening of the land to the West than many persons, and especially cosmopolitan in their scientific and artistic associations, there is no reason to believe they were a queer, odd family pursuing completely esoteric interests. The fact that C. W. Peale had so many friends who shared his enthusiasms, who also collected curiosities and objects of natural history, who were seeking after "useful knowledge," and who contributed to the Museum suggests that the interests of the father and of the family were those shared by many influential nineteenth-century men and women of the Enlightenment and of the Romantic Age.

However important the tastes and interests stimulated by life in Philosophical Hall were to the little Titian, a far more world-shattering event in the small, private world of the child must have been the death of his mother in childbirth on February 19, 1804.[26] In reconstructing a biography it is difficult to evaluate the importance of such an event upon the life of a person. However, modern psychiatric knowledge suggests that the loss of a mother in the first few years of life may have far-reaching effects on personality development. Suffice it to say that in Titian Peale's life there is a consistent thread of hypersensitive pride and imagined hurts that may have had deep roots in the bewilderment and insecurity that ensued after his mother's death.

The close-knit family remained together, with Sophonisba at eighteen, taking over many of the maternal duties. The father wrote reassuringly to his in-laws:

The pledges of her [his late wife, Elizabeth DePeyster Peale] love I will nurture with all that a fond Parent can give. . . . While I live they shall not be entrusted to the care of others to rear & to cultivate these tender endearing plants. Every kind of knowledge with the means I possess will be given to make them good and useful members of Society.[27]

For a year and a half the motherless family carried on at Philosophical Hall. Sophonisba found time to paint several fruit pieces and to classify some of the Museum collection—the pattern of life in the Peale household continued its old tenor. Rubens was his father's right-hand man at the Museum, and was entrusted with its guidance during the latter's brief trips to Washington and New York.

The companionship of women was essential to the old gentleman, and he began to turn his attentions toward a Quakeress, Hannah Moore, of Montgomery County. She was "as plain as any amongst Friends," but "uncommonly chearful for her time of life" and a

person "of suitable years."[28] Equally important, she was "very fond of Children, and mine are remarkably fond of her, it could not be otherwise, for she is indulgent, yet prudently so."[29] They were married on August 12, 1805.[30] A part of the bargain, about which Peale was reticent in his correspondence, but which was to become a major irritant to his children, was that Hannah Moore's sister, Rachel Morris, also became a part of the Peale household.

From the fond father's letters one receives the first impressions of the temperament or character of the child, Titian. In writing to Hannah before the marriage, he said:

Sophonisba and Rubins are much pleased with the account I gave them of Sibella's pleasing you so well. . . . They say Titian will be a specimen of the worst as Sibella is of the best of them, however, I know that he is very easily managed by some small attentions, and therefore I do not fear of making him also a favorite on a few days time of him.[31]

The boy Titian accompanied his father to Montgomery County for the wedding, and seems to have won the affection of his new relatives. A portent of the child's future interests was recorded in the father's comments:

Titian is astonishingly improved, he eats like a Plowman and behaves like a little man. The other day he brought home a ground Squirrel alive and the day before yesterday a field Mouse. He possesses no fear to take hold of such animals alive, and says that he won't let them bite him.[32]

During the early years of their marriage Hannah and Charles Willson Peale often visited the relatives in Montgomery County. It is probable that Titian attended school there for at least a short interval.[33] A few years later the father notes that "Titian already writes a fine round hand."[34]

---

[26] CWP to William DePeyster, Feb. 19, 1804, CWP Letterbook ✗ 5: 10–11.

[27] *Ibid*. In direct quotations a few changes in punctuation and capitalization have been made in the interests of greater clarity. The syntax remains unchanged.

[28] CWP to Raphaelle Peale, Sept. 7, 1805, CWP Letterbook ✗ 6: 127.

[29] CWP to Col. Nathaniel Ramsay, Oct. 30, 1805, CWP Letterbook ✗ 6: 166.

[30] CWP to Raphaelle Peale, Sept. 7, 1805, CWP Letterbook ✗ 6: 127.

[31] CWP to Hannah Moore, Aug. 2, 1805, CWP Letterbook ✗ 6: 119.

[32] CWP to Rubens Peale, Aug. 19, 1805, CWP Letterbook ✗ 6: 139.

[33] Peale, Albert C., Titian R. Peale 1800–1885, *Bull. Philos. Soc. Wash.* 14: 319, 1905, states, "He went to school in Germantown and in Montgomery County, Pennsylvania." Albert C. Peale was a nephew of T. R. Peale, and an eminent geologist who made family history a hobby. The majority of the facts he recorded in his short biographical study have been confirmed by my research. In the course of the present work I have several times come upon correspondence of A. C. Peale, in which he asked for documentation concerning T. R. Peale's life. There is thus reason to feel that his facts were accurate and based on documentation or family tradition not available to the present writer. No other references to Titian Peale's schooling in Montgomery County have been found, but he probably did attend school there either in these early years or during 1811–1812 when he again spent some time with relatives there.

[34] CWP to Rembrandt Peale, Nov. 1809, CWP Letterbook ✗ 10: 104.

For a time Thomas Jefferson's grandson, while study-ing in Philadelphia, lived with the family. Peale was busy with Museum affairs and with the founding of the new Academy of the Fine Arts. Sophonisba married an enterprising young businessman, Coleman Sellers. Rembrandt was off to Paris for further study of the Fine Arts. The household regime evolved into a regu-lar, well-disciplined pattern, with useful activities pre-scribed for the children, with no "vinous Liquors" ex-cept for guests, and the door of the house locked at 10 p.m.[35]

[35] CWP to Thomas Jefferson, Aug. 30, 1807, CWP Letterbook ⌥ 8: 59–61.

III

Youth In Germantown

AT A youthful sixty-nine years of age C. W. Peale decided to retire to a small country place. Rubens was placed in charge of the Museum. Though he had planned to buy only ten or twenty acres, a few weeks' search led spry Mr. Peale to decide in favor of a farm of 104½ acres, with a mansion house, tenant house, and a complete set of farm buildings. This he purchased in February, 1810. Located one-half mile outside Germantown, it was but six miles from Philadelphia.[1] Changes and improvements were made in the comfortable, rambling house, and within a month the family moved in. The father was full of plans for improving the grounds, building a spring house and a mill house, fitting out a painting room and making new labor-saving devices. Among the livestock a handsome antlered elk which the Peales kept was to become a Germantown legend. Many of these plans were fulfilled during the eleven years the family lived there, so that the farm and the gardens became a showplace, a veritable "Vauxhall of Germantown," and the Peales famous for their hospitality and generosity to guests.[2]

One of Peale's first projects was to be the building of a small bath house:

The House may be built of Stone by Franklin & the little Children, you may possibly laugh at this Idea, yet I think it will be a fine exercise for their talents and will certainly afford a fund of amusement for them, and learning to make a House will be as useful as going to School in the summer season—indeed it is not altogether what I can approve off, I mean that of huddling together with a great number in

one Room in hot weather, and a little relaxation from such studies is resumed again with more spirit & better effort.[3]

Such were the somewhat casual ideas of education held by the father. Whether or not the little children amused themselves with the rolling of stones for the bath house cannot now be known. It is doubtful whether much serious work was expected or achieved. By midsummer the old father was complaining that his high-spirited children were "running wild" about the place and eating too much green fruit. By August he had changed his mind about the virtues of allowing the children undisciplined freedom about the farm, and placed them in schools. The boys, Franklin and Titian, went to the Germantown Academy, and the two young girls to another local school. In good weather they trudged to and from school on foot, but in bad weather a light wagon or coach conveyed them.[4] One record at about this time notes, "Titian is a very good boy and goes to school constantly."[5]

The adolescent years were uneven ones for the growing Titian. The gulf of years between the adults and the young people of the household might have contributed to the atmosphere of disagreement that clouded the family life at times. During the father's brief absence from the farm in March, 1811, some childish hurt or quarrel prompted the boy to run away to his step-mother's relatives in Montgomery County, where he found a friendly refuge.[6] Later in the same month both boys were taken out of school for several weeks in order to help clear stones from the wheat

---

[1] CWP to Rembrandt Peale, Feb. 3, 1810, CWP Letterbook ✄ 11: 6.

[2] CWP Autobiography, Section 22; Deborah Logan's Journal **9,** 34. MS, HSP.

For paintings and drawings of the farm and neighborhood see: Jessie J. Poesch, Mr. Peale's 'Farm Persevere': some documentary views, *Proc. Amer. Philos. Soc.* **100:** 545–556, 1956, and Poesch, Some Germantown landscapes: a Peale family amusement, *Antiques* **72:** 34–39, Nov., 1957.

[3] CWP to Angelica Robinson, March 11, 1810, CWP Letterbook ✄ 11: 17.

[4] CWP to Angelica Robinson, Aug. 26, 1810, CWP Letterbook ✄ 11: 44.

[5] A. C. Peale, TRP, *Bull. Philos. Soc. Wash.* **14:** 319, 1905.

[6] CWP to Henry Moore, March 9, 1811, MS, Coleman Sellers Mills Collection.

FIG. 3. The "mansion house" on the Germantown farm where the Peales lived from 1810
until 1821. Drawing by C. W. Peale. When he purchased the farm, Peale named it
"Farm Persevere," but he later changed it to "Belfield," after the estate of the
painter, John Hesselius. Though modified, the house still stands. Unless otherwise
noted, all illustrations courtesy of American Philosophical Society.

field, labor for which their father paid them a small
sum.[7] Painting, affairs of the new Academy of the
Fine Arts, and a proper settlement for the Museum
preoccupied the father. In the spring Titian sat for a
portrait, which was exhibited at the Academy show in
May.[8]

The boy was having, or causing, trouble at school,
and in August the father communicated by letter with
the school master:

...I know my son Titian has talents for the fine Arts &
also for Mechanicks, but whether he has talents to acquire a
classical Education, a knowledge of languages, I know not.
Your superior judgment will best determine. If you think
he cannot learn the dead languages with facility, be so obliging as to inform me, in order that I may not suffer his
time to be lost in a fruitless course, and I may have other instructions suitable to his genius given him.

I shall be happy to make a suitable return for the trouble
you have had with him.[9]

[7] CWP Belfield Daybook, March 17, 1811.
[8] CWP Belfield Daybook, April, 1811.
[9] CWP to George Howell, Aug. 21, 1811, CWP Letterbook
⚹ 12: 19.

Languages were a stumbling block to the high-
spirited boy who preferred to work with his hands or
explore on his own in the out-of-doors. Though the
father was, in a sense, a learned man, his knowledge
was not the classical scholarship taught in the academies, but rather of science and art, useful and mechanical knowledge, and he did not place a premium
on classical learning. He had learned a fair amount of
scientific nomenclature through individual study and
he probably assumed that his son could do likewise
if he wished. The father's mind was quick and versa-
tile; he went from one enthusiasm to another, often
delving quite deeply into a subject. Enthusiasm rather
than strict discipline characterized his approach to
knowledge. Always indulgent, he did not demand
regular stints of work from his sons, but rather fired
their curiosity for knowledge and their enthusiasm for
activities of a somewhat practical sort by his own example.

A half-year later than the letter just quoted C. W.
Peale's Daybook records a payment on March 9, 1812,
"to Mr. Howell for Schooling of Franklin and Titian."
It would appear that Titian Peale's formal schooling

ended at this time, and that most of the next year was spent at home or in visits to his relatives in Montgomery County, for whom he showed a consistent fondness.[10] Again, it is hard to judge, but it appears that a lack of formal schooling and the lack of a sound knowledge of Latin grammar were to hinder Titian Peale's career in later life.

Of the older boys, only Rubens, in the Museum, was prospering. Raphaelle was spasmodically painting, including some still lifes which the father greatly admired but which did not sell, and regularly drew funds from his father to meet expenses. Rembrandt had some commissions, but the expenses of his Paris trip had come out of his father's pocket and had not been repaid. Linnaeus, who had shipped as a common sailor, returned from a voyage to Brazil and was undecided about his next step. None of the older boys had ever been formally apprenticed to a trade; instead they had shared the activities of their father, learned to paint from him, and helped in the Museum. Indeed, the father had been criticized by friends for his failure to find for his sons the more usual types of apprentice training which would have fitted them for a trade or a business.

The Germantown farm had several mill-sites; if the younger boys received training in the trades, then they could go into business together, and thus be adequately provided for in the future. So the father reasoned. He began to make inquiry "amongst the bustle of great works of manufacture on the Brandywine,"[11] for suitable openings for the boys. A year's training with one of the country's best machine makers would provide Franklin with enough skill to start out in his own business. For Titian there was to be a longer commitment:

Titian I shall bind untill he is 20 years of age, that is 6 years.[12]

The girls were sent to a boarding school run by the Quakers in Wilmington. The boys, according to the plans worked out, were placed nearby in a Mr. Hodgson's manufactory to learn spindle-making. Mr. du Pont, also of Wilmington and a friend of their father, had recommended the placement. Sundays the boys were invited to spend with the du Ponts. Their father had perhaps remembered his own unhappy apprenticeship days and by having family and friends of the family nearby he hoped the lot of the two boys would not be too difficult.

As soon as the boys were off and away, the father wrote long and rambling letters to them. The moralizing and the advice must have seemed tedious to the boys. Titian was urged to "make a friend of your

brother, and never be hasty to resent what may not please you at the time."[13] Franklin, though older, was of a softer and more pliable temperament. The father respected the minds of his sons, and shared fully with them ideas concerning new building projects at the farm, told them of the garden house he was building in the yard, and of other activities that absorbed his attention.

A clue to some problems of home life is suggested by a letter from Linnaeus to Franklin, suggesting that all the children sign a paper saying they would not enter their father's house as long as Rachel Morris, Mrs. Peale's sister, remained, "her stay being detrimental to the peace and quietness of the family."[14] There is no evidence to suggest that the other children complied, but deservedly or no, the children saw her as a source of friction in the household. Under the surface of life in the Peale family, as in every household, was the subtle, complex web of personal relationships which affected the development of each member of the family. The Peale family was not without its frictions, and Titian undoubtedly reacted and contributed to these.

Otherwise, things seemed to be going well. All the children came home for Christmas, and the boys appeared contented with their situation. They were growing up; they were good and talented boys; the father felt optimistic about their future. Of Titian, he could say:

. . . He promises well, and had I not placed him where he is, he would have been Idle and dissipated if kept at home; his disposition is firm and bold, and being lead to a good course will lead to greatness.[15]

By October, 1814, Titian was back with the family in Germantown.[16] Perhaps he had returned to help set up a manufactory with his brother Franklin, or perhaps he had found the work uncongenial and his father had granted, or given in to, his wish to return home.

In Wilmington, Franklin had been attracted to an overly-devout Quaker girl older than himself, a strange, odd girl given to startling bursts of religious expression. His mischievous and sharp-tongued brothers and sisters were not sympathetic. Sybilla wrote gleefully to Linnaeus, then in an army camp:

Oh! I only wish you could come home to see a fine job of a wedding here and some Quaker Preachers that are coming into the family. You can crack your sides laughing to know who it is. Try all your might to get a furlough, for besides the pleasure of seeing you, I would not that you should miss the pleasure of being groomsman and going into

[10] CWP Belfield Daybook, October 8, 1811; CWP to Henry Moore, Sept. 16, 1812, CWP Letterbook ⚹ 12: 71.

[11] CWP to John DePeyster, Aug. 8, 1813, CWP Letterbook ⚹ 12: 103.

[12] Ibid.

[13] CWP to Franklin and Titian Peale, Nov. 18, 1812, CWP Letterbook ⚹ 12: 117.

[14] C. Linnaeus Peale to Franklin Peale, Nov. 12, 1813, MS, Sellers Family Papers, 6: 44.

[15] CWP to John DePeyster, Feb. 6, 1814, CWP Letterbook ⚹ 13: 6.

[16] CWP Belfield Daybook, Oct. 14, 1814.

meeting with your great sword by your side and uniform on for the world.[17]

In April, 1815, Franklin married his Quakeress, somewhat against the better judgment of his father. Now the father was trying to work out satisfactory plans for the two boys, or all three if Linnaeus would but leave the Army, so that they might start a joint business enterprise. Titian was set to work putting the grindstones in order and making other tools. Franklin worked in another manufactory for several months to widen his experience.[18] But within a few months the plan, so assiduously fostered by the father, broke up.

I was much pleased when Franklin proposed to take Linneus into Partnerhsip with him, but he is now obstinately bent against having either him or Titian. However, my determination is to fit them to undertake the management of the Cotton business, and to divide the water powers between the three brothers, Linneus, Franklin and Titian allowing to each a Mill seat & about one acre of land—but I will not make over a right untill I see how they conduct themselves. I am not a little mortified at Franklin's conduct towards his brothers, yet I must say that they did not in every respect govern their tongues and gestures as they ought to have done. Franklin is young and I wish he may not be unfortunate, he has I am sure a difficult part to act.[19]

Franklin in truth had a hard role to play; he, too, was to realize what the others suspected, that his strange wife was clearly abnormal. A daughter was born in March, 1816, whom she threatened to kill. She was placed in a hospital in Philadelphia, and the marriage was eventually annulled in 1820. The burden of the young wife's support was to weigh upon the family for at least three more years, and was to involve much complex negotiation on the part of the father.[20]

The younger children of Charles Willson Peale often seemed the most troublesome and perplexing to him, but the older ones, too, contributed a share of worries to the parent. Rembrandt had launched a Museum in Baltimore; the father feared for its financial success.[21] Raphaelle was frequently ill, at one time quite seriously so, though his skill as a painter continued unabated. In the midst of his worries, painting, the gardens, and farm work were the joy and the possible solace of the aging Mr. Peale.

But the farm and the manufactory were not for Titian. He whose interests in later years were closely to parallel those of his father now clashed with his elderly parent; he had never quite respected his father's discipline, perhaps because his own wishes had been so

readily indulged. Rachel Morris probably contributed to the explosion, too. There was a quarrel; the father wrote in confusion and exasperation to his even-tempered son, Rubens:

Titian has so frequently treated his Mother with disrespect and usurpt too often authority by saying & doing such things as a Master of my House I cannot submit to—and as he says he will not live with me without I turn out one that has never done anything to injure him, & whom I know is a helpmate to your Mother & whose comfort I am bound by so many obligations to promote, therefore I do not wish to see him until a reformation takes place in his conduct. It is high time that he should apply himself to some business by which he may in future be able to support himself. His welfare is equally dear to me as any other of my children and it will make me happy to hear that he is like to do well—but to be short he must not expect to receive any favors from me untill I have evidence that he conducts himself with propriety, and is brought to a sense of his duty. Caution him about the company he should keep, he is young & thoughtless and has too long been indulged in all his fancies, and if he associates with those beneath him, no good will ever come of him. He must respect himself or he can never expect respect from others. He must not be Idle any longer. I will not support him in idleness, therefore urge him to engage in some active employment. It is of little consequence what kind of Business, so that it is honest. He possesses talents sufficient to acquire expertness in any difficult calling, where much learning is out of the question. He is equal to any Mechanic arts. . . .

His conduct has very much unhinged me. I am realy fearful that he will become dissipated and a disgrace to the family. And I am also fearful that he is so foolish as to wish to be engaged in matrimony with I don't know who—a young girl a daughter of a french man a ship builder in Kensington. He is a silly boy and may involve himself in difficulties that he will never be able to extricate himself—besides giving trouble to all his relations.[22]

And so the storm. Titian went into the city to join his brother Rubens at the Philosophical Hall, now jokingly called "Bachelor's Hall." The painter Thomas Sully had also rented rooms there. Sybilla kept house for her brothers. It was undoubtedly precisely what Titian wanted, to work in the Museum and to study natural history. Within a few months the worst wounds of the quarrel were healed, and the elder Peale wrote to a scientific friend in Paris:

My youngest boy Titian seems determined to pursue the study of Natural history, he says that he does not like making machinery nor spinning of cotton and he is now assisting his Brother Rubens at the Museum. He will preserve subjects for the Museum in a handsome manner, as he is a good Mechanick and takes pains to do what he undertakes with neatness—and at present he appears to be in his proper Element.[23]

It was indeed his proper element. The sins of the proud and sensitive boy probably had not been so great; he had wanted to shape his career to fit his own natural interests, and he had developed a deep affection for an attractive young woman, Eliza Laforgue,

[17] Sybilla Peale to C. Linnaeus Peale, Nov. 29, 1814, MS, Sellers Family Papers 6: 55.
[18] CWP to Franklin Peale, Oct. 23, 1814, CWP Letterbook 13: 55; CWP to Rembrandt Peale, March 12, 1815, CWP Letterbook 13: 95.
[19] CWP to Rembrandt Peale, July 16, 1815, CWP Letterbook 13: 132–134.
[20] References to the Eliza Greatlake episode occur in CWP's Letterbooks throughout the 1815–1824 period. It is summed up in Sellers, CWP 2: 295–296.
[21] CWP to Rembrandt Peale, July 22, 1812, CWP Letterbook 12: 59–61.
[22] CWP to Rubens Peale, Aug. 24, 1816, CWP Letterbook 14: 76–77.
[23] CWP to Mongʳ P. de Beauvoir, Oct. 13, 1816, CWP Letterbook 14: 91.

a girl of French origin and daughter of a ship builder. He had struggled to assert his own authority and own personality against those of a father and other adults more than twice his age.

A tiny sketchbook from his Germantown and Philadelphia days, marked "TRP 1817, Philadelphia and Germantown," testifies to the fact that his hours on the farm had not been wholly idle. It contains a series of delicately executed water colors of butterflies and insects, with brief notes of observation on their development.[24] If he had not mastered the classical languages at school, he had mastered some of the Latin names of the creatures of nature which so interested him.

It was at the Museum that Titian wished to work and to associate with the kind of men who had been the heroes of his childhood. It was at the Museum that Alexander Wilson, author of the first attempt at a comprehensive description of American birds, had spent many hours sketching specimens. It was here that the boy must have heard and shared in the excitement of the current scientific discussions. Here he must have listened to the reports of ardent naturalists upon their return from collecting expeditions. Here, too, were the Indian artifacts from the Lewis and Clark and other Western expeditions, which the archaeologically minded men of science examined with interest and excitement. Here it was that he had seen some of the Indian chiefs who had been invited by the U. S. Government to visit the white men's centers of learning in the East.

During these years a number of pioneer works on American natural history were being written and published, several from the pens of men in and around Philadelphia. After Alexander Wilson's death, George Ord and the engraver Alexander Lawson had undertaken the completion of Wilson's nine-volume work on American birds. Ord was also at work on an account of American zoology which was published anonymously in 1815.[25] Thomas Nuttall was studying the botanical collections of the Academy of Natural Sciences in Philadelphia and in 1818 published his book on the genera of North American plants, for which he set most of the type himself.[26] William P. C. Barton, a professor of botany at the University of Pennsylvania, was probably already at work on his study of the flora of North America,[27] while the experienced and well-traveled artist-naturalist Charles Alexandre Lesueur had begun work on a study of American fishes, for

FIG. 4. A page from Titian Peale's Germantown sketchbook. The caption reads, "Argus Comyntas/found about the last of July/ another specimen on the 29th of August."

which he planned to draw all the figures himself, as Wilson had done and as Audubon was to do. Competent talent was being developed in the new country; America no longer had to rely entirely on the authority of visitors from Europe.

Among these men Titian readily found acceptance. One of his acquaintances, Thomas Say, was preparing the first important and pioneer book on American entomology, and Titian apparently was making sketches for this as early as July, 1816. At that time Say sent the first two experimental plate proofs of the proposed book to his friend J. V. Melsheimer, in York County, Pennsylvania:

On the lid of the box within you will find two plates of Insects intended for my American Entomology. They are all to be coloured. I send you the Plate of *Tityus* as the first one that I have had coloured. You will therefore not criticize it with too much severity as the artist is young and will improve. I have the satisfaction to see in this his first attempt that the thing is practicable in this country, which has heretofore been much doubted.[28]

The descriptions were to be brief; correct drawings were all-important if the work was to be acceptable in scientific circles.

Charles Willson Peale was now proud of his son: "Titian is improving in various studies—Doctor Wistar has politely invited him to attend his lectures on anatomy, and he regularly attends at the University— I mean at the Doctors lectures."[29] A sketch of a human skull and other anatomical drawings preserved among Titian's papers now at the American Philosophical So-

---

[24] The sketchbook, 5″ × 8″, had 13 pages and was tied with ribbon; it was formerly in the Jacqueline Hoffmire Collection. It is now at the APS where the individual pages have been separated, and a record kept of their original order.

[25] In William Guthrie's *New geographical and commercial grammar*, second American edition, Philadelphia, 1815. His descriptions included some of the Lewis and Clark specimens at Peale's Museum.

[26] Nuttall, Thomas, *The genera of North American plants, and a catalogue of the species, to the year 1817*, Philadelphia, 1818.

[27] Barton, William P. C., *A flora of North America*, 3 v., Philadelphia, 1821–1823.

[28] Thomas Say to J. V. Melsheimer, July 30, 1816, MS, Academy of Natural Sciences of Philadelphia. This institution will hereafter be cited as ANSP.

[29] CWP to Angelica Robinson, Nov. 24, 1817, CWP Letterbook 14: 200.

FIG. 5. Plate I, *Papilio philenor*, Lepidoptera, from the Prospectus for Thomas Say's *Entomology*, Philadelphia, 1817. Drawn by Titian R. Peale, engraved by Cornelius Tiebout. This was hand-colored in brilliant blue, tans, oranges, and black.

ciety and at the Academy of Natural Sciences in Philadelphia may date from this period.

On November 16, 1817, the prospectus of Say's *American Entomology* came off the presses; the first volume did not come out until 1824. The six colored plates in the prospectus were by Titian Peale—fine, delicately executed drawings, his first published works.

Like many of the Peale children, he seems to have played with painting materials from his early childhood. The first reference to Titian's artistic skill occurs in the father's letter to the schoolmaster, already quoted, in which he said, "I know my son Titian has talents for fine arts." The thirteen minute pen and pencil or water color sketches of butterflies, moths, and insects in the Germantown sketchbook indicate the

particular direction in which the young man's skill and tastes were taking him. All appear to be precise in detail with the lines and colors clear and sharp. The notes which accompany some of the sketches suggest that all were drawn from life—"caught on the 21st of August." Several are placed on branches or a leaf, but in most cases no setting is provided; accuracy of the figure was of first importance. Knowledge of these early sketches may have led Say to ask the young Peale to do the figures for his book.

Butterflies, multi-colored denizens of the air, and other insects, unattractive in many ways but often possessing jewel-like qualities of decorative detail if observed objectively, were among the first things Titian Peale delineated, and they were also among the last. He was interested in these insects from a scientific point of view, but his prose descriptions in his unpublished "The Butterflies of North America," written in his old age, indicate that throughout his life he was not unmindful of their aesthetic qualities, and that he shared with his father and other scientific men of his age a kind of loving awe for these small creatures of God's universe.

Scientists were soberly and carefully attempting to identify each species and to fill in the interstices in the scheme of classification first proposed by the Swedish naturalist, Linnaeus, but this did not prevent them from being awed and delighted by their subject matter. There was not the sharp demarcation between the arts and sciences we often assume exists today. A man with the imaginative and poetic bent of William Bartram had written a widely popular book, read and respected by scientific and literary people alike. Alexander Wilson had been a poet before be became an ornithologist. George Ord was not only devoted to the study of natural history, but was a lexicographer of some note. The combination of painting exhibitions with exhibits of natural history in a museum such as Peale's seemed a logical juxtaposition. Cabinets and collections of learned gentlemen often contained both. Botanizing was a fashionable pastime, and the more expert amateurs among the people—for the study of natural science was taken seriously by only a small portion of the people and the word "scientist" had not yet been coined—enjoyed a certain amount of prestige.

On November 26, 1817, when he was just eighteen, the name of Titian R. Peale was proposed for membership in the Academy of Natural Sciences of Philadelphia. A friend of the family from Germantown, Reuben Haines, put forth the motion.[30] Although the Academy of Natural Sciences was still a youthful organization, having been formed in 1812, membership was something of an honor, and his election indicates how quickly the youngest Peale found acceptance among those interested in natural science in Philadelphia. Most of the members were older than he. William Maclure, who became the president in December,

[30] Minutes of the Academy of Natural Sciences of Philadelphia 2, Nov. 26, 1817, MS, ANSP.

was a wealthy Scottish merchant and philanthropist who was to do much to foster scientific work in the new country. His *Observations on the Geology of the United States,* first published in 1809 and issued in a second and improved edition in 1817 made his name secure as that of the first prominent American geologist.

Charles Alexandre Lesueur, another member, then thirty-nine, had behind him a long record of accomplishment in the study of natural history. In 1800 he and his close friend, François Péron, had survived an extremely difficult French scientific expedition exploring the coasts of Australia. They brought back over 100,000 zoological specimens, and were credited with discovering more new species than all the other naturalists up to their time. Later Lesueur had joined Maclure in a survey of the West Indies and on a tour of the interior of northeastern America. He was a skilled draughtsman and made sketches and paintings of the area they traversed. In his notebooks Lesueur frequently made detailed notes of the time of day a sketch was made; usually he noted the condition of the sky, and made records of the colors of particular details within the sketch, and at times he even recorded the temperature of the day when the sketch was made. This was in keeping with the scientist's concern to record the scene as accurately as possible.[31] So fine and precise was his work that tradition has it that he usually offered a magnifying lens to the viewer in order that all the details could be seen.[32]

Lesueur made his home in Philadelphia from 1817 until 1825, earning his living by engraving and printing his own plates and by teaching painting and drawing. During these years he participated in a number of short surveying expeditions, and is generally considered one of the most active zoologists in America during the early part of the nineteenth century. In 1819, 1820, 1821, and 1836 Lesueur displayed paintings at the exhibits of the Academy of the Fine Arts in Philadelphia and at several other exhibits in the city. The union of artist and naturalist in one profession was a logical one for the time, and simultaneous participation in the activities of both the Academy of the Fine Arts and the Academy of Natural Sciences did not seem unusual.

George Ord was thirty-six in 1817. He had completed Wilson's *Ornithology* after the latter's death and had prepared an anonymous account of the zoology of North America for the second edition (1815) of William Guthrie's *New Geographical and Commercial Grammar,* as well as a number of articles for the journals of various societies. In addition to pursuing actively his scientific interests in the fields of ornithology and zoology he devoted much time to research in philology, compiling many of the data subsequently used in the first edition of Webster's dictionary. A quiet, cultured man with wide-ranging interests and fierce loyalties, Ord, except for the 1817–1818 journey to Florida to be described shortly, seems to have preferred the life of the scholar, researcher, and writer to that of the active field man. He was to become one of Titian Peale's most trusted friends and advisers.

Young Peale's work for Thomas Say's entomological prospectus certainly contributed to the former's election to the Academy of Natural Sciences. Say at this time was proving himself as an outstanding taxonomist; his future researches were to earn him the accolade of being called the father of American conchology.

Among these scientifically minded men young Peale had happily found his element; he was pleased and proud to be included among this alert and creative group. He was to be one of the minor officers of the Academy off and on during the next fifteen years, and, many years later, would spend his days of retirement quietly working in their building.

---

[31] Lesueur, Charles Alexandre, Photographs of Sketches, APS; Gilbert Chinard, The American sketchbooks of Charles Alexandre Lesueur, *Proc. Amer. Philos. Soc.* **93**(2): 114–118, 1949 (*Lib. Bull.* for 1949).

[32] Jordan, David Starr, Charles Alexandre Lesueur, *Dict. Amer. Biog.*

IV

Widening Horizons, Florida and the West

CHRISTMAS Day, 1817, saw the departure of George Ord and T. R. Peale from Philadelphia. They boarded the regular sailing vessel for Savannah, Georgia. Here they were to meet Thomas Say and William Maclure. The four were about to embark on a scientific collecting expedition in Georgia and Florida, which Mr. Maclure was financing. Their plan was to follow somewhat the route of William Bartram,[1] described in his *Travels through North and South Carolina,* etc., first published in 1791. Though they knew this was not a "land of milk and honey," they knew it abounded with undescribed insects, birds, and animals and was therefore a naturalist's "promised land."[2]

The story of the expedition in brief, as it is generally known to historians of the natural sciences, is drawn largely from Thomas Say's letters to his close friend, J. V. Melsheimer.[3]

In Savannah they chartered a sloop and laid in supplies. So eager were they to begin that Ord and Peale went hunting and collecting there, leaving their specimens with an acquaintance. The group visited the Sea Islands, took in more provisions at St. Mary's, and then began their voyage up the St. John River. They went as far as an old Spanish fort, Picolata, and then the three younger men sloshed through the swamps to the Spanish Governor's palace at St. Augustine; Florida was still a possession of Spain at this time. Here they learned that, because of the hostility of the Indians, it would be imprudent to venture further. Disappointed in not being able to carry out their original plans, they backtracked, with the idea of exploring the Mosquito

River area, and possibly going as far as Cape Florida. Again they were warned of Indians, and again they turned back. They decided to make another attempt at getting into the upper reaches of the St. John, but near Picolata they met a plantation owner who had narrowly escaped death and whose son had been killed by the Indians. The party retreated, very probably just escaping an Indian attack upon themselves.

They collected specimens at the mouth of the St. John and tarried at several of the Sea Islands off the coast of Georgia. The sloop was disposed of when they reached Charleston, and they made their way back to Philadelphia, arriving near the end of April. They had succeeded in collecting some specimens, many of which were turned over to the Peale Museum. However, they were not completely satisfied with the results of their expedition. Most dissatisfied was Thomas Say, who had hoped to stay longer into the spring, so that it might have been possible to collect a much wider variety of specimens.

A hitherto unnoticed manuscript, possibly written by Titian Peale's grandson from an account told him by his grandfather and now found among Peale's papers at the American Museum of Natural History in New York, provides more graphic details concerning the experiences of the foursome, and of their adventures, social and scientific:

...On leaving the city [Savannah] the Merchants and Planters sent them letters to every Island along the Coast of Georgia. Having learned their route, they also sent word to their friends, to offer every facility to the party. This intended kindness proved a great annoyance, for at every place they approached, invitations were sent to them to come and visit. Mr. MaClure invariably answered that they were on a trip that did not admit of visiting and that they were only equipped for what they had to do....

They landed at Great Warsaw island, and began shooting, to the great alarm of the inhabitants, who armed themselves with all possible speed, thinking they were outlawed negroes shooting their cattle. Mr. Peale shot here among other things, a large Baldhead Eagle. At Ossabon island, he got the large Crow-blackbird (Greakle) [sic] for the first time, shortly after Mr. Ord shot another.

---

[1] CWP to Thomas Jefferson, Jan. 15, 1818, CWP Letterbook 🗶 14: 213.

[2] Thomas Say to J. V. Melsheimer, Dec. 12, 1817, and June 10, 1818, MS, ANSP. It is interesting to note that the Portuguese diplomat-scholar, Correa da Serra felt slighted because the group did not stop to call on him in Washington. Davis, R. B., The Abbé Correa in America, *Trans. Amer. Philos. Soc.* 45(2): 159, 1955.

[3] *Ibid.*; also CWP Letterbook 🗶 14: 210–213; CWP Letterbook 🗶 15: 27, 29–31, 38–39.

They were charmed with Blackbend island, on which they landed. The interior was covered with beautiful groves of live Oak, and abounded with Deer that fed on the acorns.

Collecting specimens of natural history was their major preoccupation, but the son of Charles Willson Peale made notes concerning architecture and paintings as well:

[At Cumberland island they went] to visit Mr. and Mrs. Shaw at the celebrated Mansion built by Gen. Greene of Revolutionary fame—a perfect castle in dimensions—but most singular in effect being built of concrete made of oyster shells put into a box of the intended thickness of the walls, with plaster poured in and let stand until hard. The house thus gradually made, forming a substantial dwelling. The walls being very thick, took a long while to make, especially with the slow slave labour, and getting impatient, they used it without plastering the interior. The effect, of course, was incongruous, almost ludicrous. Sitting in the vast Hall in which they dined—on elegant imported furniture, at a most sumptuous table, they saw when they looked up, oyster shells sticking out of the walls in every direction, in strange contrast to the elegant hospitality below. The garden and the grounds seemed quite a paradise with hedges formed of lemon, groves of Orange trees, roses and other flowers in full bloom, though it was January.... Mr. Peale saw here a painting of Sully's, a copy of the likeness of Gen. Greene by his father, Chas. W. Peale, who was the only one who painted the General from life....

Interestingly enough, this manuscript makes no mention of the near encounters with Indians, but makes a lively story of the visit to the Governor:

The next day having a fair wind that blew almost a gale, they reached fort Picolata, which they found in ruins. They hunted all day without seeing anyone, until near night when two countrymen came along; hearing the guns they came to see who fired them. From them they learned that that was the nearest point to St. Augustine—whither it was determined to go next day to report themselves and present their Passport....

Mr. McClure ... had doubted whether he would be allowed to go [to Florida] on account of constant inroads from the north, and on applying to the Spanish Consul in Philadelphia for a passport, was told that he had no authority, but would write to Spain about it. The answer was a royal passport for Mr. McClure and party. Armed with this, he had organized his small expedition—but now shrank from presenting it, on account of the twenty-three miles it was necessary to go, through a country entirely unprovided with accommodations of any kind. The rest of the gentlemen, however, undertook to do it, starting immediately after breakfast, Mr. McClure remaining in the sloop.

They passed through Pine barrens and swamps, frequently up to their middle in water, the whole twenty-three miles, and saw no vestige of habitation, nor a single inhabitant. They arrived at the gates of the city about sundown and were obliged to enter in this soiled condition, to the Governor's house, which consisted of two stories, the first containing the offices and the Guard house, into which they were shown. In the second were the private apartments of the Governor, who chanced to be entertaining two British Officers that day, and the attendant no doubt when he announced that some strangers sought audience, represented that they were travellers of little consideration judging from their appearance—as he continued at dinner, leaving the gentlemen in the guard room, where their impatience was not lessened by the sound of enjoyment reaching them from above.

After a while Gov. Coppinger (afterwards Gov. Gen. of

Cuba) sent for them, and they were ushered, in their soiled travel garments, into the convivial hall, where the guests were still seated. The Governor, probably annoyed by the interruption, from such unattractive visitors, haughtily demanded their business, while his guests looked patronizingly on them as they stood there. When the passport was handed him, the effect was magical. As soon as he saw the royal seal and signature, he exclaimed, "from the King," and was completely astounded, rising immediately and bowing low, with many apologies for the detention. He urged them to sit at dinner which they declined—but as he insisted on their taking wine with him, they consented. He was profuse in his offers to serve them, bowing low all the time, as did everyone—following his example, guests and all.

They told him all they wanted was to find lodgings that they might retire to, and get rid of the load of soil the unusual travel had laden them with and make themselves comfortable for the night. Immediately persons were sent in different directions, but no quarters could be found—until the British officer said, at their boarding house they might possibly be accommodated and sending, they got rooms for the party.

After calling next day on the Governor—who they found was much beloved by the people—they returned to the vessel, and sailing on, anchored in an eastern branch of St. John's river and landed on a plantation just deserted, where they hunted some time with very great success. Landing again the next morning they shot as many Partridges as they wanted before breakfast.

They then went ashore to dig at an Indian mound in the middle of a neighbouring plain. It was 90 ft. in circumference and 9 or 10 ft. high. They dug about 7 ft. in the centre of it—found three flint spear heads, a stone hatchet, a copper rod sharp at both ends, and a large Conch shell of a species that is not found on the coast of America and is probably extinct, and some lumps of red paint....

[They coasted several days to Ft. Picolata.] Mr. Peale made a drawing of the fort....

The trip, as recalled by Peale, provided some very exciting collecting adventures:

After coming to anchor at the mouth of Pottsburgh Creek, Mr. Ord and Mr. Peale ascended in the canoe several miles, stopping at a plantation and dining on Parakeets—which they saw in great numbers. Going up the creek Mr. Peale shot an alligator in the head with a ball, cut its throat and laid it on its back on the bank—coming back in the evening it had so far recovered life as to turn itself, and run in the marsh some distance. He fired another long ball into its head, and took it on board the vessel alive! It was 8 ft., 4½ inches long.

At night they harpooned fish by firelight. At St. John's Bluff they heard the roar of Alligators for the first time, and near the mouth of the river, Mr. Ord and Mr. Peale spent the day in the canoe hunting Pelicans. The next day going off again at day break they were surprised at the great quantity of Medusae cast on the shore. It was indeed immense. They estimated that in one place for half a mile the ground was completely hidden by them.

Mr. McClure not wishing to go to sea again, concluded to go to Amelia island, in a boat that was ready to go, & Mr. Say accompanied him.

Mr. Peale sank a barrel in the sand to shoot Pelicans from, Mr. Ord in the meantime was fishing, and caught sixteen Sheeps Head of from seven to eight pounds each. The equinoctial storm coming, they were obliged to run up the river several miles for a harbor. When the storm was abated they sailed down the Beach, saw but few marine animals and went in among the ponds in the interior of the sand hill hunting ducks. They amused themselves for some time with the Porpoises, their young at this season being about a foot and a half long, they carry them on their pectoral fins and are sometimes seen with them in their mouths.... After cruising about for several days, with great success, they crossed the bar, and in a short time bade adieu to St. John's river.

All suffered from seasickness on their return voyage to Savannah. The narrative continues:

On arriving at Savannah they found a great change, whole rows of stores and houses were going up—some of the latter were built of "Tabby," a composition of oyster shells, lime and sand, cast in mould—the same as "Dunginner," the residence of the Shaws on Cumberland island. They tried to get a pilot for the islands between Savannah and Charleston, but failed. Mr. McClure decided to go in the steamboat, and the two other gentlemen by sea, in the Rambler, a sailing vessel. Both left early next morning and reached Charleston in the afternoon of the second day. They left Charleston 16 of April....
[They] arrived safely at home, enriched with abundant collections in their several departments and having enjoyed immensely their winter trip to Florida.[4]

Dining on parakeets, shooting alligators, and sharing the company of prominent scientific men and royal governors, the young man had had a taste of high adventure and had experienced both the excitements and the frustrations of collecting "useful knowledge." The Peale Museum Accession book shows that Titian and his associates contributed a number of articles to the collection. Artifacts dug up from an Indian mound on St. John's River included a stone hatchet, two stone spear points, a copper rod pointed at each end, and fragments of earthen pots. Specimens of birds and quadrupeds collected by Titian as well as the skins of several South American birds given by the manager of the Charleston Museum enlarged the natural history collections, while shell specimens increased the conchology holdings.

Titian's father was now properly proud, and wrote of him in one of his letters to Jefferson, "My young son is a very industrious collector."[5] To his daughter, Angelica, he commented, "Titian not only preserves Animals with neatness but is also clever in drawing and is a most indefatigible collector.... It is an important tour for Titian."[6] The young man had further warmed his father's heart by writing letters to the family while

away. The father in turn encouraged his son to make careful notes of his observations and to appreciate the opportunity of associating with such important company.[7]

Upon his return to Philadelphia, Titian again took up his work at the Museum. He was now given the responsibility of preparing specimens to be exchanged with foreign museums, and wrote some of the correspondence in this connection.[8] The father privately admired his son:

He has grown so tall that you would scarcely know him, and promises to be a distinguished man, studious and discrete for his years.[9]

The remainder of the year seems to have passed smoothly, with Titian and Rubens working at the Museum, and with the younger generation of Peales—sons and daughters of James, Raphaelle, and Rembrandt—enjoying a busy social life. Titian's attentions and devotion to the girl of French descent, Eliza Laforgue, continued unabated.

The West was creeping deeper into the consciousness of the people of America. Fur traders and fur-trading companies were pushing westward. More and more settlers were following in their footsteps, and border relations with Indian tribes demanded the attention of the government. The conflicting claims of the United States, England, and Spain were being discussed. Eastern merchants were interested in the profits to be gained in trading furs from the Pacific Coast for desirable Oriental goods. Much of the vast territory acquired by the United States in the Louisiana Territory was unknown and unmapped. In the circles in which young Mr. Peale moved, expeditions were the order of the day. Practically every expedition of any size that journeyed to the West included a naturalist; "botanizing" and collecting enjoyed a sufficiently wide popularity so that these men were accepted and understood in part by colleagues more devoted to conquest and profits. Thomas Nuttall, the botanist, had journeyed up the Missouri River with John Bradbury, a Scottish naturalist, and had accompanied the famous Astoria expedition in 1811.[10] Other naturalists made collecting trips in the Great Lakes region and along the Mississippi.

It is not unnatural that Thomas Say and Titian Peale, both of whom had tasted the challenge and adventure of a short expedition, should have become interested in a proposed government expedition to the West. A capable army topographical engineer, Stephen Harriman Long, was to head a specialized scientific

---

[4] A signature, "L. Peale," appears on the last page of this manuscript. There are corrections in pencil on the manuscript, and the number of words has been calculated in the margin of the first page. Titian Peale's second wife was Lucy MacMullen Peale. His grandson, Louis T. Peale, visited them in Washington in the 1860's, and lived with his grandfather in Philadelphia from 1875 to 1879. The grandson was a printer at that time, and later became an editor. The style and appearance of the manuscript suggest that it was prepared as a schoolboy's essay, or as a rough draft for an article. So far as is known to me, it has never been published. MS, TRP Sketches, Notes & Photographs, American Museum of Natural History in New York. This institution will hereafter be cited as AMNH.

[5] CWP to Thomas Jefferson, Jan. 15, 1818, CWP Letterbook ✳ 14: 213.

[6] CWP to Angelica Robinson, March 2, 1818, CWP Letterbook ✳ 15: 27.

[7] CWP to TRP, March 7, 1818, CWP Letterbook ✳ 15: 29–31.

[8] CWP to Dr. Bradford, Jan. 17, 1818, CWP Letterbook ✳ 15: 7.

[9] CWP to Angelica Robinson, July 24, 1818, CWP Letterbook ✳ 15: 51.

[10] See Jeannette A. Graustein, (ed.), *Nuttall's travels into the old northwest*, Waltham, Mass., in *Chronica botanica* **14**, 1950/51.

corps. His skill and leadership had been tested and proven in an 1817 expedition, which had explored the Fox, Wisconsin, and upper Mississippi waterways.

The new venture had its genesis in an ambitious project known as the Yellowstone Expedition. The original plans called for wide territorial explorations and the establishment of a series of military posts on the upper Missouri. The posts were to provide protection to the expanding fur trade and to exert control over the Indian tribes of the area, thus weakening the strong influence of the British fur-trading companies.[11]

As subsequent events were to show, the larger scheme was not to be carried out in its entirety. Long was named as head of the scientific part of the enterprise; the military part was to be directed by Colonel Henry Atkinson. Troop movements were begun in the fall of 1818. Unfortunate mistakes in trying to use the new steam navigation for river travel, complicated by the employment of an apparently incompetent contractor, delayed the military part of the expedition and caused far greater expenditures than had been anticipated by Congress. In September of 1819 some troops finally reached Council Bluffs, on the Missouri, where a halt was made for the winter. Long's group of specialists was organized during the winter of 1818–1819, and assembled at Pittsburgh in May, 1819. They traveled on an especially designed steamer to St. Louis, and then up the Missouri to Council Bluffs, where the group set up a winter camp near the military establishment. As will be seen, the orders were changed in 1820 and the broad scope of the initial plan was curtailed. Ultimately the most valuable results of the project were those obtained by the specialized group under Long, and the expedition has appropriately become known as Long's Expedition.

The arrangements for Titian Peale to join Long's group of specialists were worked out in December, 1818. In that month Charles Willson Peale, accompanied by his wife and his two nieces, Sarah and Anna Peale, made a leisurely visit to the nation's capital. The spry old man had several reasons for making the trip. He wanted to paint the President and other prominent members of the government, thus enlarging and enriching the collection of American military and civil heroes hanging in the Museum gallery. He hoped also to forward his scheme of making the Museum a National Museum; he had not forgotten his dream of having it a part of a new national university. Since his young son had set his heart upon participation in the expedition of Major Long, the father would use what contacts he had to work out the necessary arrangements. It would, furthermore, be an advantage to the nation and to the Museum if appropriate arrangements were made to care for and house the collections to be brought back from this new expedition, arrangements

similar to those which had been carried out upon the return of the Lewis and Clark Expedition. A land bounty and back pay were due Linnaeus, and James Peale's right to receive a pension resulting from his services in the Revolutionary War had to be worked out. Working alongside her uncle, Anna, a skilled miniaturist, would have a good opportunity to establish her artistic reputation by painting prominent Washingtonians. All these missions—except for the cherished dream of founding a National Museum—were accomplished with little difficulty. Moreover, the feminine Peales enjoyed the social season in Washington.[12]

Colonel Johnson of Kentucky was one of the sitters whom C. W. Peale painted; Johnson, in turn, seems to have carried a petition to the President, suggesting that Say and Titian Peale be employed on the Long Expedition, at modest salaries.[13] When C. W. Peale called on Secretary of War Calhoun a few days later, he was told that Thomas Say, who was an obvious choice as zoologist for the expedition, had already been appointed, and that a letter had been written to Major Long concerning Titian's application.[14] Within three weeks Titian's appointment came through.[15] It was also agreed that the articles collected would belong to the Museum.[16] The father was fearful that the expedition would be long and hazardous and would involve much suffering. Still, it was an excellent opportunity for the young man to make a name for himself, and the youth was determined to go.

Say and Peale were not the only Philadelphians selected for the specialized corps. Augustus Edward Jessup was named geologist and mineralogist; Major John Biddle was to be the journalist for the party. William Baldwin, from Wilmington, was named physician and botanist. Among the latter's earlier travels had been visits to the Southern river ways Say and Peale had visited. Before the departure from Philadelphia, C. W. Peale painted portraits of Major Long, Dr. Baldwin, Say, Jessup, and his own son, Titian.[17] Jessup and Biddle accompanied the expedition only during the first season, and were replaced by other men during the second year. Baldwin, suffering from tuberculosis, died en route.

Titian was to be assistant naturalist and painter of natural history. At the time of the group's departure from Philadelphia, a landscape artist had not yet been found. The risks were great and the rate of compensation low. There was a possibility that Titian would be

---

[11] The objectives of the expedition were set out in a statement by Calhoun, see Military affairs, *American state papers* 2: 33, as cited in R. G. Thwaites, ed., *Early western travels* 14: 9, Cleveland, Arthur H. Clark Co., 1905.

[12] CWP Diary ⚮ 23; CWP Letterbook ⚮ 15; CWP Letterbook ⚮ 16.

[13] CWP to Rembrandt Peale, Dec. 5, 1818, CWP Letterbook ⚮ 15: 89.

[14] CWP to Coleman Sellers, Dec. 15, 1818, CWP Letterbook ⚮ 15: 99.

[15] CWP to Rubens Peale, Jan. 7, 1819, CWP Letterbook ⚮ 16: 9.

[16] CWP to Rubens Peale, Jan. 29, 1819, CWP Letterbook ⚮ 16: 22.

[17] CWP to Mr. Fitzhugh, April 1, 1819, CWP Letterbook ⚮ 16: 37.

the only artist. Rembrandt contributed advice to his younger half-brother in a letter which tells something of Titian Peale's artistic abilities at that time:

I suspect you will be the only Draughtsman. I therefore recommend you to practise immediately sketching from nature. I know how well you draw when you have the object placed quietly before you, but if you practice sketching from human figures as well as animals and trees, hills, cataracts, etc., you will be able to present us with many a curious and interesting representation. I hope your company will harmonize in all things and not unnecessarily risk safety from the love of doing anything singular. Get into the habit of making notes of everything as it occurs, no matter how short. Memoranda written at the time has always an interest and accuracy that distant recollections never have. Make drawings of the Indians in their warrior dresses; these will be infinitely more interesting than if made from the dresses put on white men afterwards. Give us some accurate drawings of their habitations. I have never seen one that was decently finished.[18]

An artist and engraver of whom little is known, Samuel Seymour, was employed in Pittsburgh before the departure of the expedition. Titian Peale's duties were outlined by Major Long as follows:

Mr. Peale will officiate as assistant naturalist. In the several departments above enumerated his services will be required in collecting specimens suitable to be preserved, in drafting and delineating them, in preserving the skins, &c. of animals, and in sketching the stratifications of rocks, earths, &c. as presented on the declivities of precipices.[19]

Seymour, now the official painter for the expedition, was to

. . . furnish sketches of landscapes, whenever we meet with any distinguished for their beauty and grandeur. He will also paint miniature likenesses, or portraits if required, of distinguished Indians, and exhibit groups of savages engaged in celebrating their festivals, or sitting in council, and in general illustrate any subject, that may be deemed appropriate in his art.[20]

The few known water colors and the engraved drawings which were used in the published report of the expedition, by Seymour, are generally regarded as the first depictions of the Rocky Mountains and the surrounding Plains country. Two engravings after Peale were included in the first report. A scrapbook and a collection of drawings by Peale, recently acquired by the American Philosophical Society, bring to light a number of sketches and water colors made by him on this expedition. Thus, however ephemeral a distinction it may be, Peale's name should be placed alongside that of Seymour as one of the initial delineators of the American landscape west of the Mississippi.

The little group of nine specialists was thus organized and ready to depart from Pittsburgh at the end of April, 1819. The country entertained great expectations concerning the venture, and newspapers carried articles about their proposed departure:

We anticipate much useful information from the result of this voyage; it appears to have been arranged by the government with a great conviction of its importance, and the design bears a strong resemblance to the French expedition into Egypt, in which the cause of science was not lost sight of during their military operations. Although the Missouri is not embellished by such stupendous monuments of art as is the Nile, her Indian mounds afford matter for much interesting disquisition; and although no Thebes, nor mutilated statues of Memnon may be found, yet some clue may yet be discovered to assist our historical researches into the ancient manners of the Aborigines. At all events, the field of science may be much extended by the party. To this object government has been particular in its attention; and it is a matter of no little pride that such gentlemen as Drs. Baldwin and Say, and Messrs. Jessup, Peale, and Seymour, have embarked in the enterprise. Philosophy will undoubtedly be aided, and geology, botany, and mineralogy, will more than probably receive a powerful accession from the researches of some of these learned men; from the pencils of Messrs. Seymour and Peale we expect much pleasure: no important specimen will be lost, and no striking view omitted.

Undertakings of this kind do honor to a government; at the same time that they extend her own influence, the cause of universal science is advanced. . . . The defects of the plan so boldly executed by Lewis and Clarke, will now be remedied: they were the pioneers to establish the practicability of a safe journey; their journal is the outline of a scheme to be yet filled up; the present expedition bids fair to add some splendid touches, if not to complete the work.[21]

The men of the new republic thought in bold, grand terms—the ancient cultures of the American aborigines were to be for the New World what the tombs of Egypt were for the Old.

Major Long's assignment was to "assume the command of the Expedition to explore the country between the Mississippi and the Rocky Mountains." The orders elaborated further:

The object of the Expedition, is to acquire as thorough and accurate knowledge as may be practicable, of a portion of our country, which is daily becoming more interesting, but which is as yet imperfectly known. With this view, you will permit nothing worthy of notice, to escape your attention. . . .

You will enter in your journal, every thing interesting in relation to soil, face of the country, water courses and productions, whether animal, vegetable, or mineral.

You will conciliate the Indians by kindness and presents, and will ascertain, as far as practicable, the number and character of the various tribes, with the extent of the country claimed by each. . . .

The Instructions of Mr. Jefferson to Capt. Lewis, which are printed in his travels, will afford you many valuable suggestions, of which as far as applicable, you will avail yourself.[22]

Titian Peale's own journal kept during the first three months of the trip survives. It covers their travels from

[18] March 26, 1819, MS copy in Coleman Sellers Mills Collection with a notation, "copied from letter from Cousin Anna Peale, June 12, 1897."

[19] James, Edwin, *Account of an expedition from Pittsburgh to the Rocky Mountains* 1: 3, Philadelphia, 1823. Hereafter cited as James, *Long expedition.*

[20] *Ibid.*

[21] Dispatch from Pittsburgh, dated April 23, in Washington *Daily National Intelligencer,* May 10, 1819.

[22] Thwaites, ed., *Early western travels* 14: 37–38.

Pittsburgh to Fort Osage, Missouri. Whether he failed to keep a journal beyond that time, or whether other journals have been lost, is not known. The journal has been published elsewhere.[23] Peale was observant and discerning, and his work makes good reading.

The group started off in high spirits, pleased with their unusually decorated vessel. This belching serpent boat was especially designed to draw no more than two and one-half feet of water. Sand bars and frequent engine trouble were to slow their progress, but nevertheless it was to be the first steamboat to voyage in the upper waters of the Missouri.

Titian Peale's journal begins with a description of the boat and their final preparations:

May 3, 1819. Left the garrison 2 miles from Pittsb[g] on the Aleghany River at 4 o clock in the afternoon after firing a salute of 22 guns which were answered with as many from the arsenal. We steered for Pittsb[g]; our appearance attracted great numbers of spectators to the banks of the River. We fired a few guns and were cheered in return from the shore. Our boat appears to answer very well, but being quite new, the machinery is rather stiff. Our party are all in excelent spirits, but Dr. Baldwin who is rather unwell.... Our boat is built in the most convenient manner for the purpose. She draws about two feet and a half water, the wheels placed in the stern in order to avoid trees, snags and sawyers, etc. On the quarter deck there is a bullet proof house for the steersmen. On the right hand wheel is *James Monroe* in capitals, and on the left, *J. C. Calhoun*, they being the two propelling powers of the Expedition. She has a mast to ship and unship at pleasure, which carries a square and topsail, on the bow is carved the figure of a large serpent, through the gapping mouth of which the waste steam issues. It will give, no doubt, to the Indians an idea that the boat is pulled along by this monster. Our arms consist of one brass four pounder mounted in the bow, four brass 2 7/8 inch howitzers, two on swivels, and two on field carriages, two wall pieces carrying four ounce balls; twelve muskets, six rifles, and several fowling pieces, besides an air gun, twelve sabres, pistols and a quantity of private arms of various sorts and a great sufficiency of ammunition of all kinds wanted for our purposes. This evening, we sent up a few rockets....

They made a short run on the river the following day. Several visitors came aboard and suggested some alterations to be made in the engine. They were visited also "by a commissioner of the Bible Society who left [them] two bibles and one or two other books for the good of [their] souls."

The next day they were off:

5th. Wedn[y]. Having completed all alterations and taken all stores aboard at 1/2 past 4 in the afternoon we bid adieu to Pittsb[g] and descended rapidly down the Ohio. At about fourteen miles below the town we saw a steam boat aground. We received and returned her salute as we passed by. In the evening we heard the first cry of the Whipoorwill (Caprimulgus vocifterus). Vegetation is progressing very rapidly. Most of the forrest trees are already clothed. In coming down the river saw a Cormorant (Pelicanus carbo) and two Turkey Vultures. We saw some bird that I took to be the Teltale Sandpiper (Tringa –––). Our boat seems to attract universal attention, the people stopping all along the shore to gaze at us as we pass by.

[23] Weese, Asa Orrin, ed., The journal of Titian Ramsay Peale, pioneer naturalist, *Missouri Hist. Rev.* **41**: 147–163, 266–284, 1947.

The next few days saw them passing by Steubenville, Ohio, and Wheeling, Virginia. "The country we are passing through is grand and beautiful in the extreme." They explored an Indian mound near Marietta, Ohio, and then started down the river again. On Sunday, May 9, they arrived late in the evening at Cincinnati:

Cincinnati, like some other towns in the western country, has risen like a mushroom from the wilderness. It is laid out at right angles. The buildings are exceedingly neat and many handsome. There are some country seats in the neighborhood that vie in beauty [with] any that I have ever seen. The present population is said to exceed 2500. Immigrants are every day arriving from all parts of the world. The inhabitants have already founded a college and subscribed eight or ten thousand dollars for a museum. They have a few articles collected for that purpose, mostly fossils and animal remains.

They stayed here several days to make repairs on the boat and to give Dr. Baldwin a chance to rest more comfortably. On the eighteenth they were off again, and the following day passed the falls at Louisville, Kentucky. Peale immediately saw the potentials of this vast new country:

After taking in wood and procuring a pilot, we crossed the falls. They are not so difficult to navigate as expected. What are called the falls are two miles in length and in that distance the water falls 22 feet over flat rocks of limestone which are filed with organic remains. The water boils and splashes about in a most violent manner, and in one place resembles exactly the surf of the sea. The town of Shipping Port stands directly at the foot of the falls. At this place most of the steam and other boats load and unload their cargos, for unless the water is in the highest stage large boats cannot ascend. It is in contemplation to make a canal around the falls, which I think is of the first rate importance to the vast extent of country about. Steam boat navigation from here is progressing in a most astonishing manner. A few days ago, there was no less than twenty steamboats unloading here, most of them in the New Orleans trade; the facilities of the W. India trade will at no distant period be superior to that east of the mountains. When the obstructions are removed from the rivers and canals made in some places, the interior navigation of this extensive country will be superior to any in the world. There will be an easy and safe communication for thousands of miles through as fine a country as was ever known. Near the falls we found a specimen of the Lake Erie Tortoise. (Testudo geographica of La Sueur).

Their journey continued with minor mishaps, and with Peale faithfully recording his observations on natural history. By the thirtieth of May they reached the mighty Mississippi. On the first of June they had their first encounter with some Indians. Troubles with the steamboat engine detained them from time to time. On the ninth of June they arrived in St. Louis, where Titian was disappointed to find but one letter from a cousin waiting for him. Here they were entertained by army officers and steamboat captains.

There are several Osage Indians in town, among them an old chief whose portrait Remb[t] painted in Phil[a] some years since. Mr. Choteau, an experienced French trader of this place recommends our paying particular attention to great numbers of large bones found at some salt licks up the Osage River.[24]

Peale and Say, with one man-servant, spent the next few days making a detailed study of some Indian mounds, measuring them and taking voluminous notes. The comments recorded in the published record of the expedition, probably taken from Say's notes, show the reflective and romantic mood of the two explorers:

The survey of these productions of human industry, these monuments without inscription, commemorating the existence of a people once numerous and powerful, but no longer known or remembered, never fails, though often repeated, to produce an impression of sadness. As we stand upon these mouldering piles, many of them now nearly obliterated, we cannot but compare their aspect of decay with the freshness of the wide field of nature, which we see reviving around us; their insignificance, with the majestic and imperishable features of the landscape. We feel the insignificance and the want of permanence in every thing human; we are reminded of what has been so often said of the pyramids of Egypt, and may with equal propriety be applied to all the works of men, "these monuments must perish, but the grass that grows between their disjointed fragments shall be renewed from year to year."[25]

They left St. Louis on the twenty-first of June, and the following day started up the muddy Missouri. Peale's duties sometimes included helping with the astronomical observations as well as preserving and drawing the specimens collected. Near St. Charles, Major Long proposed that a party go by land. Peale, Say, Seymour, Jessup and one other man, Kenna, made up the party. Their short overland expedition was not without its hardships:

June 26th.... [We] set out at 8 o clock as the boat left the town to proceed up the river. After a march of 18 miles, 8 of them without any water, and mostly through prairie with scarcely a bush to shade us from the scorching rays of the sun, we stopped at the edge of a large prairie to hunt for water. Our horse here took fright, threw his pack, and made off full speed towards St. C[harles]. Jessup and Kenna pursued her and found her stopped by some travelers 4 miles back on the road. Her recovery saved our backs from a heavy burthen which could not be very agreeable in crossing these extensive prairies. Secured our mare and pitched our tent in the borders of a wood, but had to go half a mile for water to the house of a person by the name of Nailor, who never can boast of hospitality. He would neither sell nor give us anything, and granted us even water with a bad grace. We were dressed in the fatigue jackets of common soldiers, but even if we had been such, we would have been entitled to some respect. We roasted and made a supper of a hawk that Mr. Jessup shot with his rifle in the day's march. It furnished us (5) with a slight but good supper.

27th. Slept comfortably last night; rose early and had our horse packed ready to march at sunrise. Our course lay almost wholly through prairies 9 miles of which we had to go

through without water, for 2 canteens held but a scanty supply for 5 persons. At 11 o clock came to a house where we had plenty of water, some milk and corn bread. Mr. Say became quite sick, from long fasting, having eaten nothing since last night's scanty supper. Marched at 5 p.m. up a valey 4 miles to Kenedy's fort, where we found an excelent place to encamp for the night on the banks of a small creek, cooked, and made a supper on some squirrels and larks, to which we added some corn bread and butter milk that we purchased of Kenedy.

28th. Purchased a ham and a loaf of cornbread of Kenedy. For the ham we paid 10 cents per pound, and 25¢ for all the bread, milk, and corn for our horses since last night. At ½ past 9 o clock a.m. halted having come 8 miles. Procured some milk, made a fire, and cooked some ham on which we breakfasted. In what few bottoms we have come through we saw turkeys and heard the screeching of parakeets. Partridges and larks are very abundant in all the prairies, and some few of Bartram's Sandpiper (Tringa Bartramia) are to be seen. An hour after halting, missed our horse. All started out on the pursuit leaving one to guard the camp. Hunted untill we tired ourselves in vain, having seen nothing of our mare. At sundown hired a horse from the house near which we were encamped, and dispatched Kenna back on the road we had come to look for the horse. Some travelers coming past say they have seen a horse resembling ours at a house 6 miles back.

29th. Kenna returned at sunrise without the horse or having seen anything of her. On the prairies there is a species of green headed fly which torments horses and cattle so much that crossing the prairies in the day is next to impossible. This, I believe, was the cause of our horse running away. It is said that these flies will sometimes kill a horse, therefore in crossing prairies travelers mostly turn night into day and day into night.

No alternative was left us but to divide the pack and turn pack horses ourselves, then to make to the nearest point on the river, and meet the boat. By taking the inner bark of hicory saplings, we were able to make our pack into tolerable knapsacks. At 8 o clock a.m. marched 6 miles to the edge of Loutre prairie. This prairie is 20 miles across, and in this season is remarkably dry. The sun very powerful, and no possibility of any shade or water, we concluded to make to the nearest part of the river. We received directions and crossed part of the prairie, and proceeded along a ridge of hills for 12 miles without any water excepting what we had in our two canteens. The sun was extremely warm, and we were obliged to measure our water out a mouthful at a time. Arrived at Loutre Island just at dark. Here we found water [in] plenty, and it seemed as though it was impossible for us to satisfy our thirst. Not having any milk or bread at the first house we arrived at, we crossed onto the island ½ mile further, and were directed to a good camping ground where we soon cooked our supper and retired to rest, much fatigued and our feet very sore. Distance 21 miles, but rough roads, a hot sun, and heavy loads, made it the longest 21 miles ever I traveled.

After breakfasting, struck our tent, and marched up the river 2 miles. Came to another house on the island and encamped on the banks of the river. On the march I killed 4 turkeys, two of them at one shot. They are more numerous here than ever I saw them. Procured a kettle at the house, cooked, and feasted on our turkey.

July 1st. We went out to hunt, killed a turkey, a rabbit, and some squirrels which are extremely numerous. A person walking through the woods is scarsly ever out of sight of them. Parrakeets abound; deer are numerous. The land is very rich, and covered with remarkably fine timber. Buttonwood is the most prevalent. There are some black walnut trees, it is said will make 200 fence rails. Some not of the largest have made 150. Loutre Island is 8 or 9 miles long, and has several settlements on it. Waited impatiently

[24] Journal of T. R. Peale, kept by Titian R. Peale, as Assistant Naturalist of Long's Expedition West of Rocky Mountains, May 3 to Aug. 1, 1819. Film 694, APS; original in Library of Congress. Hereafter cited as TRP Journal, Long expedition.

[25] James, *Long expedition* 1: 66; quotation from Maturin.

but nothing of the boat. The evenings are now disagreeably cold and the days warm.

July 2nd. Went out to hunt, killed 2 rabbits, a polecat, and wounded a fine buck. Mr. Jessup killed a turkey. In the evening we were gratified by the approach of our boat. She passed us and came to a mile above where all went on board.[26]

The six-day struggle across the prairies was a good test for the more difficult experiences they were to undergo during the forthcoming year. The up-river journey was slow, and the naturalists, confined to the ship, accomplished little. Baldwin, a gentle and usually optimistic person, wrote of his discouragement to friends; because their orders demanded that they push forward so steadily he questioned the possibility of the naturalists being able to accomplish much on an expedition of this sort.[27] By August, Baldwin was too ill to continue, and left the party at Franklin, Missouri. He died August 31, at the age of forty-one. All knew they had lost an able botanist.[28]

Peale had been ill for a few days after the six-day march, but soon recovered and attended to his duties. In one of the towns these Eastern men of scholarly bent outfitted themselves with the garb of the Western trapper and frontiersman:

Here we all purchased moccasins and skins to make leggings. I purchased a leather hunting shirt for 4 dollars and a pair of leggings for $2.50.[29]

The party reached the military encampment at Council Bluffs, on the Missouri, on September 17, 1819. Beyond Charaton, Missouri, theirs was the first steamboat to have traversed the river, and great numbers of settlers came to the banks of the river to witness their progress. To the uninitiated it must have seemed a strange apparition. The St. Louis *Enquirer* described the boat dramatically:

The bow of the vessel exhibits the form of a huge serpent, black and scaley, rising out of the water from under the boat, his head as high as the deck, darted forward, his mouth open, vomiting smoke, and apparently carrying the boat on his back. . . . To the eye of ignorance the illusion is complete, that a monster of the deep carries her on his back smoking with fatigue, and lashing the waves with violent exertion.[30]

Settlers told of Indians who, upon seeing the strange vessel, had said, "White man bad man, keep a great spirit chained and build fire under it to make it work a boat." [31]

Near Council Bluffs, in the present Blair County, Nebraska, Long's party prepared their winter encampment, called "Engineer Cantonment." Here they were

to stay, pursuing various studies, through the long winter and spring until June 6, 1820.[32]

Long and Jessup returned to the East for the winter. In Long's absence Mr. Say was to

have every facility afforded him that circumstances will admit, to examine the country, visit the neighbouring Indians, procure animals, &c. for the attainment of which, he will call on Lt. Graham, who is authorized to make any expenditures in behalf of the expedition that may be deemed reasonable and necessary, and afford any aid in his power, consistent with the performance of other duties. Mr. Seymour, or Mr. Peale will accompany him, whenever their services are deemed requisite.[33]

The Indian agent and the interpreter were to help to arrange visits to the Indians and to aid the work of the expedition in whatever ways necessary. The two army lieutenants were to make barometric and meteorological observations. The party was encouraged to consult their original orders and, again, to refer to the orders of Mr. Jefferson to Captain Lewis for additional guidance concerning the broad outlines of their duties.

The record of the winter activities, apparently taken largely from the notes of Say and of Dougherty, the interpreter, is an extraordinary ethnological and anthropological document. These two areas of study had not yet developed into the specialized disciplines they are today. These pioneer scientists did not have a disciplinary framework within which to organize their evidence, nor did they try to arrive at many generalized conclusions. Hence much of their material seems diffuse and occasionally meaningless to the reader. They did, however, assemble an amazing number of facts.

Say and his associates visited the tribes of the Pawnee, Otto, Iowa, Missouri, and Omaha Indians. They took detailed and voluminous notes about the habits and appearances of the tribes. In the published report of the expedition there are detailed descriptions of Indian dress, of their eating habits, their hunting methods, attitudes toward and methods of childbirth and child-rearing, of Indian dances and ceremonials, of authority patterns—who the chiefs are and how they maintain their status, the kinds of habitations in which they live, the modes and patterns of travel and tribal movement—all the material they could collect these men recorded.

They did not often succeed in securing information about the abstract and metaphysical concepts of the Indians. To the scientific men of this group, the Indians they so carefully scrutinized were not always noble savages. In Long's final report, in which he draws from Say's work for comments about the Indians of the western country, one finds the terse comment:

The delicate trains of thought and reflection, attributed to them by writers, who have attempted to enlarge our acquaintance with the Indian character, usually have their origin in the ingenuity of the writers themselves.[34]

[26] TRP Journal, Long expedition.
[27] Darlington, William (ed.), *Reliquiae Baldwinianae*, 320, Philadelphia, 1843.
[28] *Ibid.*, 321–322.
[29] TRP Journal, Long expedition.
[30] St. Louis *Enquirer*, June 19, 1819, as quoted in Thwaites, 14: 178n.
[31] *Ibid.*

[32] James, *Long expedition* 1: 427.
[33] *Ibid.* 1: 165.
[34] *Ibid.* 2: 369.

These men, applying the principles of accurate scholarship discussed in the Eastern intellectual circles, tried to present a factual picture of what they saw and experienced. If they found little evidence for the high antiquity of Indian religious tradition, they reported this.[35] Likewise, if they found little evidence that all Indians were naturally possessed of strong appetites for hard drink, they reported this.[36] They succeeded to a large degree in coming to know the Indian "ideas of decorum."[37]

In these winter months they assiduously collected specimens of natural history. Their descriptive notes are careful and detailed, and suggest a diligent use of a small library of books they appear to have carried with them. (Some of the bibliographical references may have been added after the return of the expedition.) Throughout the published report one finds an almost equal number of references to Peale's hunting prowess as to his drawing activities. Often at points of extreme need Peale could be counted upon to bring down necessary game.

The official journal describing the long, gray weeks of February records:

> 19th. The sand is blown by the violence of the wind from the sand bars of the river, so as to resemble a dense fog. We have been hitherto very well supplied with fresh meat, from game killed principally by Mr. Peale, who, on one occasion, killed two deer at a single shot and with one ball, but we are now reduced again to salt pork of a very inferior quality. . . .
>
> 22d. Messrs. Dougherty and Peale returned from a hunt, having killed twelve bisons, out of a herd of several hundreds they met with near Sioux river, and brought us a seasonable supply of meat. They saw several herds of elk, and yesterday they saw swans, geese, and ducks, flying up the river. . . .

This provided an excuse for one of the few social events of the winter:

> 25th. Cooked for dinner the entire hump of a bison, after the manner of the Indians. . . . Mr. Lisa and family dined with us by invitation. That we have sometimes food in great sufficiency, the provision upon our table this day will sufficiently attest. It consisted of the entire bison hump, above mentioned; the rump of a bison roasted, boiled bison meat, two boiled bison tongues. . . . It is true that we have no vegetables whatever, but having been so long estranged from them, we scarcely regret their absence. Their place is supplied by excellent wheat flour, of which our cook prepares us bread fully equal, in point of excellence, to any that we have ever eaten. The above repast was prepared for eleven persons, of whom two were ladies. The collation was succeeded by coffee as a desert.

The guests were from a nearby trading post and the two ladies are believed to have been the first white women to ascend the Missouri River this far.[38]

Peale's duties included the illustration of natural history subjects. In his journal one finds him noting that he or Mr. Seymour "took a view" of some of the sights they beheld, as, for instance, those on June 6, 1819, when they "passed some of the most Sublime cliffs of Limestone rocks that I ever beheld."[39]

All of Peale's Long Expedition studies appear to have been made on small sheets of drawing paper or in a small sketchbook which could have been carried easily. Many of these are in a scrapbook which has only recently come to light, and is now at the Library of the American Philosophical Society. Of these drawings located to date, none measures more than 8″ × 10″ in size. They are executed in pen and ink or in water color with a very fine brush, and include carefully executed figures of insects, butterflies, and birds as well as a few Indian scenes and landscapes (figs. 6, 7). A view of the steamboat *Western Engineer* (fig. 8) shows a far more docile-looking craft than the fiery smoke-eating serpent conjured up by the newspaper articles concerning this, the first steamboat to travel the upper reaches of the Missouri River. The water color betrays a rigid quality in the young artist, who had concentrated thus far on work requiring meticulous close-up detail.

A young buffalo bull, the kill of the first day's hunt (fig. 9), is shown in another of these small sketches. The excitement of the buffalo hunt, and the beast itself, interested Peale the sportsman and Peale the naturalist. He did several sketches in ink which, as will be seen, were later to be incorporated into lithographs and paintings (figs. 10–11).

Long returned to the Engineer Cantonment from the East on the twenty-seventh of May. He was accompanied by Captain J. R. Bell, who was to take over some of the duties previously performed by Major Biddle, and by Dr. Edwin James, who was to carry on some of Dr. Baldwin's former work as a botanist and surgeon. James was later to become the author of the two-volume published report on the expedition.

Bell's journal records the arrival of Long's party:

> Saturday, May 27th [1820]. . . . The Major crossed over [the river Boyer] with his baggage, his horse swam over, and he set out for the Engineer Cantonment distant about 2 miles, leaving us to wait until some men arrived to assist us in crossing—presently we heard the discharge of ordnance announcing the Majors arrival—the report of the guns produced in us very pleasing sensations—it reminded us that we were yet in the land of civilization, and for a moment we forgot our fatigues and privations. I was particularly gratified on an other account, it demonstrated the attachment, the members of the expedition had for their commander, it was a proof of their respect and esteem after having served with him one season. We soon had the pleasure to see arrive on the opposite bank, Lieut. Swift and Mr. Peale with three men, they set to work and soon completed a raft, which took us and our baggage over perfectly safe and dry—our horses swam across. We then travelled about two miles, much of the distance thro' willows or a young growth of cotton wood, and arrived on the bank of the Missouri river opposite to the Engineer Cantonment, here a boat was waiting to take us and our baggage across—our horses swam along side of the stern of the boat by our holding their heads above water by the bridles. . . .

[35] *Ibid.* **2**: 371.
[36] *Ibid.* **2**: 374.
[37] *Ibid.* **2**: 376.
[38] *Ibid.* **1**: 191–193.

[39] TRP Journal, Long expedition, 11.

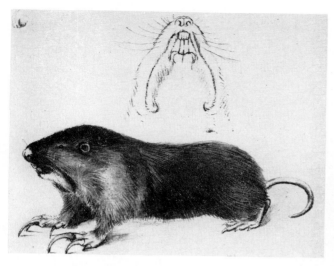

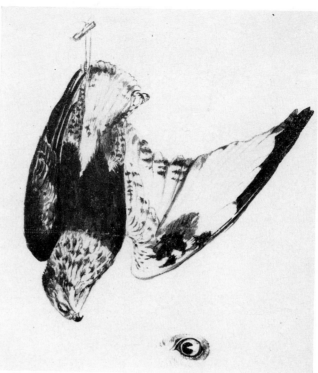

FIG. 6. Sketch by Titian R. Peale made while on the Long Expedition. Caption reads, "No 18/ Arrow Rock/ July 21, 1819."

FIG. 7. Sketch by Titian R. Peale made while on the Long Expedition. Caption reads, "birds/ No. 1/ Engineer Cant^t/ Feby 1820."

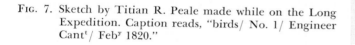

FIG. 8. Water color sketch by Titian R. Peale made while on the Long Expedition. The steamboat, the *Western Engineer*, was the first to ascend the Missouri in 1819. It is shown in the left foreground. Caption reads, "Engineer Cantonment/ Feb 1820/ TRP." "(Council Bluffs)" written on margin of paper on lower right.

FIG. 9. Water color sketch by Titian R. Peale made while on the Long Expedition. The caption reads, "Young Buffalo bull/ The 1st days hunt for Buffalo. by TRP, Feb 1820."

FIG. 10. Pen and ink sketch by Titian R. Peale probably made while on the Long Expedition.

FIG. 11. Pen and ink sketch by Titian R. Peale probably made while on the Long Expedition.

Opposite to us is the Engineer Cantonment consisting of log buildings, handsomely situated on the bank of the river, over which a flag hoisted. The steam boat "Western Engineer" was lying in the stream in front of the quarters decorated with all her colors set, in honor of the arrival of the commanding officer—the day was fine, the young foliage of the trees in rear of the cantonment, to the sumit of the hills was beautiful—the waters of the Missouri seemed charged with less sediment than usual—the small cotton woods bent gently to the breeze—all nature appeared to harmonize with our feelings—may it augur well for the success of the expedition. We landed and was met on the bank by Doctor Say, Lieut. Graham and Mr. Seymour, to welcome our arrival, these gentlement with Lieut. Swift & Mr. Peale had been here 8 months, secluded from the world —they were dressed in leather hunting shirt & leggens— which appeared to me, as if they had assumed the dress and appearance of the hunter from choice or singularity.[40]

The arrival of the new men meant a slight shifting about of duties. More significant, Long brought back new orders from Washington which curtailed the original purposes of the expedition. The *North American Review* was later to call this action of Congress "ill-judged, narrow, and preposterous."[41] The legislative body had been disappointed in the results of the first year (in truth, most of the time was occupied in reaching the field) and had decided to economize. An economic depression that occurred at the time no doubt influenced Congress to greater penury. At any rate, the original and more elaborate plan was abandoned. As the *Review* pointed out, their resources were curtailed at the very point when they had developed enough experience to be able to accomplish the original purposes of the expedition with real hope of success. However, the "further progress of the Exploring Expedition up the Missouri [was] arrested during the present season. By the same authority, an excursion, by land, to the source of the river Platte, and thence by way of the Arkansa and Red rivers to the Mississippi [was] ordered."[42] Lieutenant Graham was ordered to take charge of the steamboat and to proceed down the Missouri to the Mississippi. The rest of the group, plus a few additional guides, interpreters, and hunters were to proceed as soon as practicable. For their route see map 1 on front end leaves.

A small, poorly equipped party under Major Long began the next phase of the expedition on June 6, 1819. The party included Major Long, Captain Bell, Lieutenant Swift, Corporal Parish and six privates as the military contingent. Say, James, Peale, and Seymour made up the scientific corps. Two interpreters, Dougherty as hunter, a baggage master and two additional men completed the party. Two Frenchmen to serve as guides and interpreters were to join the party

at the first Pawnee village.[43] They had twenty-eight horses and mules, one for each member of the party, and the rest for carrying packs. An eloquent testimony to the inadequacy of their equipment is the fact that only six of the horses had been provided by the government. The rest were supplied by members of the party. Their saddles and other equipment were rude and makeshift, some purchased from the Indians and the rest constructed by the men themselves.[44] They carried a supply of food with them, a few instruments for making topographical measurements, some small articles and tools for trade with the Indians, and a supply of ammunition.

The Indians were frankly skeptical of the success of the expedition, warning of the possibilities of attack by strong and warring Indian tribes, and of the dangers of traveling across a land where little water and game were to be had. The explorers recognized that the Indian warnings were not without design; the Indians quite consistently tried to prevent the white men from encroaching on their territory and from usurping their role as middlemen in the trading chain that stretched across the Plains between the various Indian tribes. Even so, it was not cheering to be told by the Chief of the Pawnees:

> You must have long hearts, to undertake such a journey with so weak a force; hearts that would reach from the earth to the heavens.[45]

Captain Bell and a guide led the line of march. The squads of soldiers and attendants who managed the pack horses followed in single file. The scientific gentlemen were allowed to travel in the line wherever it was most convenient for their purposes. Major Long followed in the rear, to care for stragglers and to act as a kind of rear guard.[46] At night they pitched their three tents in a straight line, with the baggage piled to the left and right of each entrance. This arrangement was designed for convenience and so that, in case of an Indian attack, the baggage might serve as a kind of breastwork.[47]

They stopped for several days among the Pawnees, and then continued their steady march to the west, following the valley of the Platte River. They diligently took their topographic measurements, made astronomic observations, described the soil, the plants, the animals, and the landscape of the prairies. They saw herds of bison grazing on the broad expanses of the countryside, "blackening the whole surface of the coun-

[40] Fuller, Harlan M., and LeRoy R. Hafen, *The journal of Captain R. Bell, official journalist for the Stephen H. Long expedition to the Rocky Mountains, 1820,* 85–88, Glendale, California, Arthur H. Clark Co., 1957.

[41] James, *Long expedition* 1: 423; Keating, William H., Major Long's second expedition, *North Amer. Review* 21: 179, July, 1825.

[42] James, *Long expedition* 1: 423.

[43] *Ibid.* 1: 425–426.

[44] *Ibid.*

[45] This rather poetic quotation is given only in the London edition of James's account of the Long expedition, *viz.,* James, Edwin, *Account of an expedition from Pittsburgh to the Rocky Mountains* 2: 126, London, 1823. The Philadelphia edition gives a more prosaic phrasing: "Your heart must be strong to go upon so hazardous a journey. May the Master of Life be your protector." James, *Long expedition* 1: 442.

[46] James, *Long expedition* 1: 431.

[47] *Ibid.* 1: 430.

FIG. 12. Water color sketch by Titian R. Peale made while on the Long Expedition. The
caption reads, "Indian 'breast work' &c on the river Platte. Longs Exped 1820."
Detailed notes about the scene are recorded in the upper right-hand corner.

try" through which they passed.[48] They weathered several storms; on one or two occasions they saw signs of
Indian war parties, but escaped any encounters.

On the thirtieth of June, at eight o'clock in the morning, they had their first distant view of the Rocky
Mountains. It took several more days than they had
anticipated to reach the mountain ranges. On the sixth
of July they reached the chasm through which issues
the South Platte River, not far beyond the present site
of Denver. A fairly finished sketch of a scene of Indian
"breastworks" on the river Platte is among the Peale
sketches (fig. 12). A small herd of the still-plentiful buffalo is seen off to the left. As with so many of Peale's
field studies, and in the manner of Lesueur and others,
detailed notes about the scene are recorded, this time
in the upper right-hand corner.

Peale and James, with two men, were sent out to cross

the first range of the mountains and to gain the valley
of the Platte beyond, an initial step in the exploration
of the sources of the Platte, which was one of the defined purposes of the expedition. The climbing was
difficult and hazardous. Each time they reached a summit, they discovered there were still higher and more
difficult ridges beyond. They were forced to give up
their attempt to cross. They could see the two branches
of the Platte beyond, but these mountains were not to
be penetrated, except possibly by an occasional hunter,
for another twenty years.[49] Poor equipment, short provisions, and the tight time schedule of the expedition
are certainly among the reasons for their failure to
achieve their goal. A few days later, on the twelfth of
July, James and two other members of the expedition,
Wilson and Verplank, climbed Pike's Peak; so far as is
known, they were the first white men to accomplish

this feat.[50] The peak was named James Peak, but local usage has long since caused it to be renamed Pike's Peak.

From Pike's Peak they moved southwestward, traveling steadily across the monotonous landscape under temperatures between 90° and 100° F. They suffered from heat, thirst, and fatigue, and were reduced to a gill of maize per day for each man. Survival had become a major problem.[51] Again, seemingly impassable barriers caused them to abandon further exploration of the headwaters of the Arkansas River.[52] Want was stalking their steps; their scant provisions were all but exhausted, and they were dependent upon the sparse game of the area as their chief source of food. On the nineteenth they turned their backs on the mountains and began the slow descent of the Arkansas River.[53] They continued to fill their notebooks with detailed notes on the flora and fauna of the region: the published account of the expedition includes many lengthy discussions of the various species encountered. A mention of Peale's brief encounter with a grizzly bear later called forth a seven-page digression, including notes from the Lewis and Clark expedition, Pike's experiences, and notes on the behavior of the two young animals kept at Peale's Museum in Philadelphia.

In keeping with their orders to explore the courses of the Arkansas and the Red Rivers, the party was divided in two groups on the twenty-fourth of July. James and Peale, and seven of the men, were to accompany Major Long in the exploration of the Red River, one of the major objects of the expedition. The other party, which included Say and Seymour, was to explore more carefully the already known route of the Arkansas.[54]

Long's party traveled across country for eleven days; food supplies were low, and rain added to the discomfort of several days' travel. Peale was violently ill one night and unwell for several days following. Their horses were becoming lame and weary, but drawings, measurements, and detailed notes on natural history were not neglected. On the fourth of August they reached a tributary of what they believed to be the Red River,[55] which they began to follow. The ensuing days were painful and occasionally harrowing. They gladly ate horsemeat to assuage their hunger.[56] When this was exhausted, James recorded:

Our sufferings from want of provisions, and from the apprehension of still more distressing extremities, were now

so considerable that we gave little attention to anything except hunting.[57]

An Indian party they encountered assured them, in the bland manner of the savages, that they were of course on the Red River, though their own maps and instruments suggested that they had made an error and were (as was true) following a tributary of the Canadian instead.[58]

The silent and orderly way in which these Indians organized their camp, their conic lodges rising "like an exhalation" did not go unnoticed and unrecorded.[59] An engraving, entitled "The Moveable Skin Lodges of the Kaskias,"[60] after one of Peale's sketches was used in the Philadelphia edition of the official report. This is quite similar to a sketch, marked "Sioux Lodge" (fig. 13); as the explorers noted, the "conical lodges" of the different tribes of Plains Indians were very much alike. The engraving is one of the earliest published representations of the Indian tepee, the tepee which has since become a symbol of the life of the Plains Indians. The sketches of Peale and Seymour, cramped and tiny as they are, represent some of the first visual reports we have of the American prairies.

The Kaskia Indians were not overly friendly. They were, however, unarmed except for bows and arrows, a situation seldom encountered as late as 1819–1820, and they seemed to respect or fear the firearms of the obviously weak and hungry members of the exploring party.[61] Departing from the Indians, the small band continued onward, plodding through the monotonous country, occasionally reveling in extra supplies of game, but for the most part traveling on meager rations. Ticks and dirty clothes added to their discomfort.[62]

For some time they had sensed that they were on the wrong route, but this was not confirmed until they reached the confluence of the Canadian River with that of the Arkansas on September 10:

Our disappointment and chagrin, at discovering the mistake we had so long laboured under, was little alleviated by the consciousness that the season was so far advanced, our horses and our means so far exhausted, as to place it beyond our power to return and attempt the discovery of the sources of the Red river.[63]

In seven weeks they had slowly and often painfully covered a distance of somewhere between six and seven hundred miles. They had made some useful collections and valuable notes and measurements, but they had not accomplished their mission.[64]

---

[50] According to Bell's diary the two men were Wilson and Verplanck; see Fuller, Harlan M., and LeRoy R. Hafen, *op. cit.*, 167. Several short biographical notices, including that of A. C. Peale, are apparently incorrect in stating that Titian R. Peale was one of the party.

[51] James, *Long expedition* **2**: 39.

[52] *Ibid.* **2**: 44.

[53] *Ibid.* **2**: 50.

[54] *Ibid.* **2**: 63–67.

[55] *Ibid.* **2**: 94.

[56] *Ibid.* **2**: 98.

[57] *Ibid.* **2**: 101.

[58] *Ibid.* **2**: 104.

[59] Thwaites, **16**: 106.

[60] Maps and plates. *Long expedition*. The engraving of "Movable skin lodges of the Kaskaias" is also reproduced in *PortFolio* **14**: opposite 517, 1822.

[61] James, *Long expedition* **2**: 108.

[62] *Ibid.* **2**: 142–143.

[63] *Ibid.* **2**: 167.

[64] *Ibid.*

Fig. 13. Sketch by Titian R. Peale made while on the Long Expedition. "Sioux Lodge/
TRP/ 1819." Courtesy of Miss Ida Edelson.

Fig. 14. Sketch made by Titian R. Peale while on the Long
Expedition. "No. 80/ on a branch of the 1st fork of
the Arkansas July 26th 1820 female / Length from
nose to tail 11½ inches. Tail 9 inches. Iris burnt
Umber, pupil black."

The two parties of the Long Expedition joined at
Fort Smith. The other group had had similar experiences, though, on the whole, less difficult. Most serious
had been the desertion of three soldiers who wantonly
took several of the notebooks of Say and Swift, thus destroying some of the valuable records of the expedition.

The feather beds of civilization, which they were given
at Fort Smith, gave only a restless and unquiet sleep to
the hardy travelers.[65] During the interval when they
were preparing for their return to the East, all but
Peale suffered from intermittent fevers. On the first of
November, then, Peale, Say, Seymour, and Graham departed, taking first a small boat from Cape Giradeau,
and changing to a larger steamboat for the downstream
trip to New Orleans.

Negative research and negative results, even when
they provide some necessary and useful information,
are seldom greeted with the kind of enthusiasm positive findings produce. Neither Congress nor the nation,
experiencing a minor economic recession, had cause to
greet Long's official report with enthusiasm. The expedition had not accomplished certain specific objectives. The lands it had traversed were reported as barren and uninhabitable—hardly the news an expanding
young nation wished to learn. The Long Expedition
is generally remembered for having reported the existence of a "great American desert." Long and his colleagues could not know the effects future developments
in irrigation and railroading were to have in trans-

————————
[65] Ibid. 2: 265.

forming these "thirsty regions." At best, Long reported, this sparse area would provide a suitable frontier barrier:

In regard to this extensive section of country, we do not hesitate in giving the opinion, that it is almost wholly unfit for cultivation, and of course uninhabitable by a people depending upon agriculture for their subsistence.... The whole of this region seems peculiarly adapted as a range for buffaloes, wild goats, and other wild game, incalculable multitudes of which, find ample pasturage and subsistence upon it.

This region, however, viewed as a frontier, may prove of infinite importance to the United States, inasmuch as it is calculated to serve as a barrier to prevent too great an extension of our population westward, and secure us against the machinations or incursions of an enemy that might otherwise be disposed to annoy us in that quarter.[66]

[66] *Ibid.* **2**: 361.

In several of its major objectives the expedition failed to fulfill the original purposes for which it had been sent. In the long view, the achievements in added knowledge of natural history and ethnology were the most valuable fruits of the journey. Many new specimens of plants, insects, birds, and shells were to be described in subsequent publications. Many of these were to enhance the collections of the Peale Museum. During the journey Peale had executed one hundred and twenty-two sketches and drawings, of which only twenty-two were considered as finished. Seymour made one hundred and fifty landscape views, of which sixty were completed.[67] Many of the superb data collected by the naturalists, probably chiefly the work of Say, concerning the Indian cultures were perhaps too esoteric to have attracted wide public attention.

[67] *Ibid.* **2**: 330n.

V

Finding A Place In Life

TITIAN returned to Philadelphia at the beginning of 1821, tall and straight as an Indian, the hero of his family and numerous female relatives.[1] His father was pleased that he had achieved a record of good conduct and persevering industry throughout the trip, and that the young man had been well liked by all members of the party. The new collection was perhaps not quite as much as had been hoped for, but was more than satisfactory considering the perils to which the group had been exposed. It was good to have Titian back from the dangerous and savage-inhabited lands to the West. All of them had worried and fretted about him while he was gone, the father writing long letters about "family particulars intermixed with moral instruction and pious reflections that follow from a study of Natural History."[2]

They must have gathered around to hear Titian's stories of the experiences and hardships of the two-year expedition. Like any family, they might have been even more eager to regale him with details of events that had taken place in his absence. They had some rollicking stories to tell of the first velocipede, or "fast walking machine," in Philadelphia, which they, of course, had built, after an English print. Father, daughters, and sons had mastered this predecessor of the bicycle. Since there were no pedals, one pushed with one's feet and could get up a vigorous speed. There was Ruben's marriage in March to Eliza Patterson to report. It was a suitable marriage and in truth it had been the first time C. W. Peale had honestly approved a choice of one of his sons. In November, Titian's sister Elizabeth had married the brother of Rubens' wife, making a double tie with the substantial Patterson family. Sybilla and her new baby

were living at the farm because her husband had lost his job when the bank in which he worked had closed. Franklin's unfortunate marriage had been annulled, though the Peales were still paying for his former wife's care at the hospital. Franklin was working at the Museum, setting up a display of electrical apparatus. Linnaeus was involved in a not-too-successful razor strap manufactory. Raphaelle was suffering more than ever from gout and trying to eke out an income from painting in Annapolis. Rembrandt's huge history painting, *The Court of Death*, was being exhibited and attracting much notice; Rembrandt's zeal for painting was glowing anew. The younger members of the family took Titian aside and reassured him that his favorite, Eliza Laforgue, had been faithful to him in his absence—the hot-blooded youth had written once saying he'd never return if she married another. Further, his young relatives assured him that while he was gone they had learned to love her as he did.[3]

A big piece of news, and one which probably most interested Titian, who cared so much for the Museum, was the plan of incorporation just presented to the Select and Common Councils of Philadelphia.[4] The Museum was to be under the direction of a Board of Trustees and to remain permanently and entirely in the city of Philadelphia, and it was to be known as the Philadelphia Museum. As expected, the act was passed by the legislature, and in the forthcoming months several articles about the Museum and its new status appeared in Philadelphia newspapers.[5] Though Charles Willson Peale had been unsuccessful in getting his institution to be a National Museum, he be-

---

[1] Rosa [Iba] Peale to TRP, Jan., 1821, MS, Sellers Family Papers 6: 95.

[2] CWP to Angelica Robinson, Feb. 22, 1820, CWP Letterbook ✳ 16: 142.

[3] Sophonisba Peale to TRP, April 6, 1819, MS, Sellers Family Papers 6: 84.

[4] CWP to John C. Calhoun, Dec. 24, 1820, CWP Letterbook ✳ 16: 219–20; Sellers, *CWP* 2: 334.

[5] To cite two articles: *The National Gazette and Literary Register*, Mar. 16, 1821; *Poulson's American Daily Advertiser*, May 16, 1821.

36

lieved he had now provided a framework that would guarantee the Museum's place as a permanent institution of the city. The trustees appointed by C. W. Peale, who was the sole stockholder, were drawn from among his acquaintances in the American Philosophical Society and at the Academy of Natural Sciences. Rubens and Sophonisba's husband, Coleman Sellers, represented family connections.

The Museum collections were becoming crowded in the upper halls of the State House. Still worse, the city fathers had demanded the removal of the workshop over the tower stairs, thus limiting even more the Museum space. Plans were afoot to find or to build new accommodations where the collections could be displayed more effectively and where space for lectures could be provided. Museum income had declined, probably because people had less money in the depression years of 1819–1820, and probably also because the Museum and its collections were well known; other, more garish competitors could provide more exciting displays of waxworks figures and menageries. Philadelphia was one of the cities most affected by the economic crises of 1819–1820,[6] and the drop in Museum income and more than usual number of family financial problems were but indices of similar difficulties occurring on a wider scale.

After his arrival home, Titian began working in the Museum, mounting and arranging the subjects he had collected on the tour, and working over his drawings. The list of Titian's drawings received by the Peale Museum in March, 1821, included seven finished and forty-four drawings or paintings of birds as well as seventy-three sketches of plants, insects, fishes, shells, snakes and lizards.[7] He seems to have been a slow and meticulous artist, making small sketches in the field and then slowly and carefully developing a finished composition. Later, he was to record that it took him at least two weeks to complete a painting for the plates to be used in the Wilkes Expedition publication.[8]

A part of the scheme for the new Museum was to be a series of lectures. A staff of "professors" was named, including Thomas Say, Drs. Godman and Troost, and Titian as zoologist. Godman was a talented young doctor, anatomist and naturalist who had recently married Rembrandt Peale's daughter; Troost was a cosmopolitan European geologist who had established a pharmaceutical and chemical laboratory in Philadelphia and in 1812 had been one of the seven founders of the Academy of Natural Sciences in Philadelphia. There is no evidence to suggest that the lecture program ever got very much beyond plans on

paper. The father was pleased that his sons were associating with these men and wrote hopefully of Titian's future:

I am inclined to think that Titian may become an expert Surgeon if he applies himself to that branch of Science, he possesses strong nerves and is an expert disector of anatomy, and has talents of macanism.[9]

But soon there was to be tension and friction between them again. Titian was not the only one of Elizabeth DePeyster's children to clash with their father. Yet this father and son, who shared common interests in nature, the arts, and in experimenting with mechanical devices, who both cared very much for the Museum and dreamed of a national institution, these two who must have shared a deep mutual respect and affection —between these two there was frequently tension. One feels that often each had consciously or unconsciously hurt the other. Now Titian wanted more responsibility in the Museum; he wanted his old place which he felt had now been usurped by Franklin. Titian also wanted to make plans for marriage, plans which only angered the older man, both because he deemed the girl unsuitable and because he feared further economic burdens.[10]

Rembrandt, his interest in painting welling up anew, seems to have suggested a partnership arrangement with Titian in Baltimore. Until things could be worked out at the Museum, Titian went to Baltimore, where he spent most of June and July. A pained and formal letter from Titian to his father bares the tensions and conflicts at issue:

It is with sincere regret I hear that I am not likely to get the situation at the Museum to which I think myself justly entitled, having laboured so long to make myself competent & worthy of it. You know yourself that it will not do for me to stay long with Rembrandt. He can't give me anything like a salary but proposes to pay me by an increasing share in his museum, this will [be] involving me in his debts and thereby preventing my doing anything for my own benefit.

Thus sir you see I have no prospects of getting a living excepting what I may get by your aid in Philadelphia. Franklin has been proposed to take my place there merely because he is not provided for. Am I not in the same situation. You have already set him up in business, me you have not. I have been a long time learning to prepare and arrange animals. He has neither the taste nor experience. I only ask you to look for yourself if you think me unworthy the situation, let me know it for suspence and dependance are worse than beggary.

You expressed a fear that I would become involved with a woman, I am already and have for some time been so. I see nothing unnatural in it, but never suppose sir that I am going to become a dependent on you. I have too many examples before me. I would rather starve than ask a cent that I do not earn of anybody in the world.

If you attend yourself sir to making an arrangement in the affairs of the Museum you may see and keep clear of the interested views of others, and to prevent any jealousy I wish you to establish a salary for me on which I may live with-

[6] Taylor, George Rogers, *The transportation revolution 1815–1860*, 337, New York, Rinehart, 1951.
[7] Accession Book, March 20 and 23, 1821, MS, HSP.
[8] TRP, The South Sea Surveying and Exploring Expedition, MS, Smithsonian Institution. Hereafter referred to as TRP, Surveying. This was published as an article in 1874 in the *American Historical Record* 3: 244–307. However, the manuscript was used as a basis of reference for this study.

[9] CWP to Angelica Robinson, April 2, 1821, CWP Letterbook ℀ 17: 22–23.
[10] CWP to TRP, June 14, 1821, CWP Letterbook ℀ 17: 44–45.

out interruption from the interests of others. Rubens and I have always lived in the greatest harmony and can still when this little jealousy is removed. I shall be glad to hear your views and advice as soon as you can make it convenient.

Your affect Son[11]

Titian's letter makes clear that he did not want to associate himself with his half-brother's Baltimore Museum. The finances of the Museum, as Rubens Peale was later to discover, were hopelessly entangled, and the young man chose not to become involved in that enterprise.

During this same period Titian may have made some attempts at portrait painting under the tutelage of his brother. When Titian returned to Philadelphia, Rembrandt wrote to him:

As to your painting Portraits, I believe your talent in drawing would enable you to succeed, provided you would devote your whole soul immediately to it and entirely abstract all your thoughts from Natural History. The two are entirely incompatible with each other—as soon as my father commenced Naturalist he lost all enjoyment in painting. And I know by my own experience that when I attend to Mechanics, or for a few days occupy myself with the Museum, it indisposes me to painting. If you can devote your eyes and your mind to the study of colour, countenance, character—the general instead of the minute of anatomical details you may succeed in Portrait painting after a year's preparatory study & practice.[12]

At this point in his youthful career Titian already had a strongly developed interest in natural history, and had two collecting trips to his credit. He was accepted as an equal among the men at the Academy of Natural Sciences and he aspired to make his mark in this field. The Museum in Philadelphia probably seemed a far more attractive prospect than any attempts at developing his skill as a portrait painter in the manner of his brother Rembrandt. The latter was wrong in stating that their father had not been able to combine painting with an interest in natural history, as some of the best works of the older man were painted after he had begun the Museum. Rembrandt was probably right, however, and Titian probably accepted his judgment, in stating that Titian's experience in painting natural history figures had caused him to focus too much on minute details, and that he had failed to comprehend the techniques necessary for achieving a more general organic unity in his work.

One painting, an engraving, and several sketches are among the evidence suggesting that Titian Peale experimented with portrait painting at this time in his life or a little later; the scanty evidence seems to indicate that he soon gave it up.

In the collection of the Museum of Natural History in New York there is a portrait of Titian Peale in an oval frame (fig. 1). On the back is a paper with the following notation:

T. R. Peale—by himself with a little help from his brother Rembrandt. Mrs. T. R. Peale to John M. Hoffmire, Red Bank, 1886.

This note was written by his second wife after Peale's death. The painting hung for some time in the home of Titian and Lucy Peale in Washington.[13] The painting has been executed with competence. Indeed, the painting appears to bear many of the characteristics of Rembrandt Peale's painting style. How much did Rembrandt paint, and how much did he supervise his brother's hand? The painting is undated; in it Titian Peale is seen as a good-looking young man, possibly in his twenties or thirties.[14] Might this be a painting of Titian in 1821, when he had returned from the Long Expedition and had spent a month or two with his brother Rembrandt? Or is it a painting of him made before his departure for South America in 1830?

In *A Memoir of the Public Services of William Henry Harrison of Ohio*, written by James Hall and published in 1836, there is a frontispiece engraving (fig. 15) of Harrison in a civilian suit with the caption, "Engraved by T. B. Welch from the Original Portrait by T. Peale." The dress, with a wide black throat band, is similar in style to that seen in the Titian Peale portrait. There is also a lithograph in existence showing Harrison in a very similar pose but in a uniform, with the caption, "By A. Newsam, from a painting by R. Peale," and a portrait of Harrison by Rembrandt Peale was described in 1929 by Mantle Fielding.[15]

In the case of the engraving "from the Original Portrait by T. Peale," one is faced with the perplexing problem of attempting to interpret the artist's style from its reproduction in an engraving. A stiff, straight, slightly wooden figure is posed against a plain background. The three-fourths profile view is at an angle almost identical with that in the portrait showing Harrison in military garb. Until further evidence is discovered, it is impossible to know whether Titian Peale painted a portrait of Harrison. The stiffness of the engraving labeled as being by T. Peale, however,

---

[11] TRP to CWP, June 21, 1821, MS, Sellers Family Papers 7: 25.

[12] Rembrandt Peale to TRP, Aug. 4, 1821, MS, Sellers Family Papers 7: 33.

[13] A photograph of the interior of their Washington home shows this. Jacqueline Hoffmire Collection.

[14] I have consulted a number of books on American costume, and studied some of the portraits by Sully and other early nineteenth-century American painters, but so far I have felt unable to date the painting more precisely by the costume detail.

[15] The photostat of the engraving after the portrait by T. Peale is from the copy of the book belonging to the William Henry Smith Memorial Library of the Indiana Historical Society, in Indianapolis, Indiana. The information concerning the other Peale painting and engraving is from the Arthur G. Mitten materials in that Library; Caroline Dunne, Librarian, has provided this information. A portrait of Harrison, with the sort of glowing background typical of Rembrandt Peale is reproduced in a booklet describing Berkeley, the James River home of the Harrisons.

suggests the hand of a somewhat inexperienced artist; moreover, the costume suggests the same period as when Titian probably was experimenting with an attempt at self-portraiture. One can simply say that *if* Titian Peale did paint any portraits, the Harrison portrait may reflect one example of his work.

A sketch of a Penobscot Indian done around 1829, when Titian Peale made a collecting trip to Maine (fig. 16), and a sketch of a Tahitian made in 1839 show that Peale did make portrait sketches at other periods in his life. But Titian Peale, over-sensitive and proud, often had difficulties in personal relationships. Maintaining a friendly and sociable relationship with a fashionable sitter would not have appealed to him, and his studies with Rembrandt seem to have come to naught.

A quarterly settlement of Museum affairs was to take place on July 1, 1821, and Coleman Sellers, now on the Museum Board, undertook to pour oil on troubled waters.[16] By early August, Titian was again in Philadelphia, not without having hurt Rembrandt's feelings through tactless criticism. The latter, after Titian's departure, wrote his younger half-brother that his Baltimore offer had been made with good feelings, and that Titian's severe comments were unwarranted. He advised the younger man not to be selfish and self-centered, and not to suppose himself to be "the only correct man in the world."[17]

Still somewhat at loose ends, Titian decided to apply for duty on another exploring expedition, but nothing seems to have come of this.[18] Long lists of new additions to the Museum collections, appearing in the columns of the Philadelphia newspapers, suggest that a temporary truce was worked out, and that Titian was busily occupied in the Museum.[19]

Illness and tragedy struck at the family in October when Charles Willson Peale, and then his wife, Hannah, were stricken with fever. Both lay ill in adjacent bedrooms, and on October 10, 1821, Hannah Moore Peale, the Quakeress, died. She was buried in Germantown in the Friends Burying Grounds. The ailing father was taken into the city and nursed back to health by Sybilla and by James's daughters. As soon as he recovered, the elderly man, who had always felt so healthy, whose youthful vigor had astounded and delighted his friends, felt that he too must prepare for his end. He no longer desired to live at the farm, with no one to replace the capable Hannah, so it was soon offered for sale. He began to make plans for the division of his property, and to dispose of some of his

Fig. 15. Engraving of William Henry Harrison. "Engraved by T. B. Welch from the Original Portrait by T. Peale," from James Hall, *A Memoir of the Public Services of William Henry Harrison of Ohio*, Philadelphia, 1836. Courtesy of the Indiana Historical Society Library, Indianapolis, Indiana.

Fig. 16. Drawing by Titian R. Peale. "Penobscot Indian TRP. 1829?"

---

[16] Sellers to TRP, June 21, 1821, MS, APS.

[17] Rembrandt Peale to TRP, Aug. 4, 1821, MS, Sellers Family Papers 7: 33.

[18] CWP to Commodore Steward, Aug. 30, 1821, CWP Letterbook ⚹ 17: 64; CWP to Pierce Butler, Aug. 7, 1821, CWP Letterbook ⚹ 17: 131.

[19] *Poulson's American Daily Advertiser*, Aug. 30, 1821.

portraits and personal effects. For the time being, it was decided he would live with Rubens and his wife.[20]

It was probably Rubens—peaceable, dependable Rubens whose very personality seemed to have healing qualities—who helped the family to work out a series of changes that provided a solution to the conflicting claims of Franklin and Titian. After their marriage Rubens and his wife had thought of purchasing the pictures in Delaplaine's Gallery and starting a museum of their own in Washington.[21] Instead, Rubens now decided to buy out Rembrandt's museum in Baltimore—some of Rubens' money was already invested in this. Rembrandt, in turn, wished to devote all his energies to painting; he felt his *Court of Death* had introduced a new concept of allegorical painting, and he hoped to go on to greater successes in this line. Thus, he now made arrangements to live in New York, renting a house on Broadway. The two younger boys, Franklin and Titian, were to be employed at the Museum in Philadelphia with salaries of $600 per year; the father was to supervise both boys.[22] These changes took place in March and April. Titian had achieved his wish to be at the Museum.

In his marriage plans the strong-willed young man continued to be frustrated. In May his father flatly refused to approve of the match. The girl and her mother were "bigoted low-bred Catholicks," and thus not, thought the elderly and usually more democratic Mr. Peale, a fit connection for anyone in his family. The Peales were never one of the first families of Philadelphia, but they did enjoy a local and even national celebrity. They were of that gifted, intelligent, cosmopolitan class who often move freely between classes. In more courteous terms, the old gentleman penned a letter to the mother saying the marriage seemed inappropriate.[23] And so the discord continued.

In their work they must have found comfort and distraction. Titian was arranging the new exhibits in an attractive and scholarly manner. Franklin was helping with labels for these, and also developing as a popular speaker at the evening chemical display lectures. Franklin, always interested in ancient and archaeological artifacts, was arranging a new display of coins, while Titian catalogued and arranged the shell collection in classical order.[24]

It was at this time that C. W. Peale began his now famous self-portrait with a view of the Museum in the background. As a preliminary study for the view of the Long Room in the background, C. W. Peale drew perspective lines and Titian meticulously painted with water colors the minutiae of the Museum displays—so precise were the details that one needed a magnifying glass to see them all. Coleman Sellers was so deceived and delighted by it, thinking it a view of the Museum, that he suggested they include it as a deception piece in the Museum display.[25] Titian was drawing with taste and dispatch, and he undertook a similar painting for Rubens' museum in Baltimore.[26]

Though somewhat ruefully, the father began to give in on the marriage issue. In September, Charles Willson Peale had discouraged his son from joining a Missouri fur company as a trapper.

> In short, it was not only an expensive but a dangerous undertaking, and what is more, not in the least likely to enable him to get married.[27]

Instead, the father agreed to pay board and to live with Titian and his wife if the latter married. Whether or not it was because the family needed a new housekeeper, or whether he realized it was a losing battle, the father finally approved. It had been a kind of war of attrition between the two men and, interestingly enough, Titian had not gone forward with his plans until he had his father's permission. Franklin was angered, but what right, argued the basically indulgent father, has a parent to attempt to control a child arrived at full age?[28]

On the evening of October 10, 1822, Eliza Laforgue and Titian Ramsay Peale were married. After the simple rites were read, a gay reception was held at the Peale home. The father, in a magnanimous gesture, gallantly told the new bride she *"was welcome here,"* as she crossed the threshold. The elaborately decorated cake was cut, and later all gathered round the piano as the new bride played and then sang. Franklin harmonized with her in his fine tenor voice.

The next day the father came round to call on the new couple and to wish them happiness and a long life of enjoyment. He was able to have a private moment with the bride and to plead with her to use her abilities to produce harmony in the relationships between the two brothers. He knew that the children of his second wife were, as she had been, often hasty and passionate, but then soon forgiving.[29]

A kind of harmony did descend over the Peale ménage after Titian's marriage. Titian patched up a minor quarrel with Rubens almost immediately, and the father noticed that the tension between the two youngest sons had decreased noticeably.

[20] CWP to Angelica Robinson, Nov. 1, 1821, CWP Letterbook ✗ 17: 67.

[21] CWP to John C. Calhoun, CWP Letterbook ✗ 17: 156.

[22] CWP to Angelica Robinson, Mar. 10, 1822, CWP Letterbook ✗ 17: 85.

[23] CWP to Rubens Peale, May 5, 1822, CWP Letterbook ✗ 17: 95–96.

[24] CWP to Dr. Godman, Dec. 2, 1821, CWP Letterbook ✗ 17: 73–74; CWP to Rubens Peale, June 9, 1822, CWP Letterbook ✗ 17: 117.

[25] CWP to Rubens Peale, Aug. 4, 1822, CWP Letterbook ✗ 17: 147–48.

[26] CWP to Rubens Peale, Oct. 4, 1822, CWP Letterbook ✗ 17: 160.

[27] CWP to Rubens Peale, Sept. 10, 1822, CWP Letterbook ✗ 17: 154.

[28] CWP to Rubens Peale, Oct. 4, 1822, CWP Letterbook ✗ 17: 162.

[29] CWP to Rembrandt Peale, Oct. 11, 1822, CWP Letterbook ✗ 17: 163–65; CWP to Rubens Peale, Oct. 14, 1822, CWP Letterbook ✗ 17: 169.

Franklin boarded with the James Peale family, and old Charles Willson lived with the young couple. He was gratified to be able to report that Eliza, as well as Titian, was attentive to his wants.[30] In fact, two years later when he was going through his letterbooks he added a marginal note to his earlier unkind comments about Eliza's background. He did not destroy the offending document since he felt it only honest for all to be made known to his posterity, but annotated it as follows:

[I] will say that Eliza has been a faithful, affectionate wife, and a patient nurse to my Son Titian, also has been kind and attentive to all my wants; having done everything in her power to make me comfortable since I have lived here —(I have boarded with them ever since their marriage and have paid 5 dollars per week having my washing done in the House, and Eliza has mended my clothes when [they] were wanting.)[31]

---

[30] CWP to Rubens Peale, Nov. 4, 1822, and Nov. 8, 1822, CWP Letterbook ⚹17: 176 and 178.

[31] CWP Letterbook ⚹ 17: 97.

VI

Philadelphia Years: 1822–1838

BY 1822 Titian R. Peale had established himself in the Philadelphia Museum, which was one of the few situations where one could practice the relatively new profession of naturalist. (Until 1837 the city directories always listed him as an artist.[1]) He had a circle of friends with whom he shared common interests; most of them were members of the Academy of Natural Sciences. He had married the woman he loved, and they had established a household of their own. In Philadelphia, his home community, he was surrounded by friends and family.

The field of natural history absorbed Titian's interests, and he hoped to devote his life to work connected with this study. He had already proven himself as a good field man. In the new biological sciences the most important task seen by the students of the subject was to find, describe, name, and publish new species to fill the interstices of the classical systems of classification worked out by Carolus Linnaeus and others. Titian knew his subject matter, the existing collections, and the few available publications well enough to recognize readily new species probably undescribed. He knew what to look for and what to collect. He had the technical skills necessary for a field man: he was exceedingly able with a gun; he knew and understood anatomy, and was a capable dissector and preserver. He could draw with competence and accuracy, and was thus able to record certain details on the spot. His associations with other scientific men had taught him to be accurate in making measurements and in immediately recording his observations. Peale also had the courage and physical hardihood to undertake and enjoy field work.

In the Museum, as a conservator and as an organizer of displays, he had accumulated some sound experience. The fact that he had literally grown up in the Museum meant that he had broad familiarity with all types of natural history subjects. He could arrange a collection of shells, or of birds, and was interested in artfully arranging habitat groups that illustrated the interrelationships between different types of living creatures. There is evidence to suggest that he called upon one or two close friends to help him on the fine points of precise classification.

Franklin dealt more with the public in the Museum. His charming, gentle manners and his love of puns must have made his lectures on mechanics and chemical demonstrations attractive and interesting to the public. Titian was more the technical man behind the scenes, preparing and arranging the displays, and performing other related duties.

Within the wide range of natural history subjects, Lepidoptera, butterflies, were of most interest to Titian Peale. Specialization was only beginning to develop in the natural sciences, and young Peale's broad, rather diffuse interest in all phases of the subject was typical, and especially suitable for his museum work. Peale was less of a book scholar than some of his associates. One cannot detect in his remaining letters and manuscripts the single-minded devotion to ideas and facts that one finds, for example, in the correspondence of Thomas Say or Charles Lucien Bonaparte. Though few of the men of Peale's acquaintance had had a great deal of advanced training, he was more handicapped than some in dealing with complex questions of classification, on taxonomy, by his limited formal education.

Titian's artistic training and skill were particular assets. It is as an illustrator of natural history books that Titian Peale is best known today, and it was in this field that he was perhaps most recognized in his own day, though his accomplishments as a collector, museum administrator, and scholar should not be discounted. His was the combined profession of the artist and naturalist. Others of similar caste include Mark

---

[1] *DeSilver's [Philadelphia] Directory*, 1825, 1828, 1829, 1830, 1831, 1833, 1835, 1837.

Catesby, William Bartram, Alexander Wilson, Charles Alexandre Lesueur, and John James Audubon. In the process of identification, description, and publication of natural history subjects the figure, or drawing, was all important because in it details could often be shown which the verbal descriptions failed to convey.

By 1822 several of Peale's drawings had been used to illustrate articles appearing in the *Journal of the Academy of Natural Sciences* of Philadelphia.[2] Two engravings after his drawings were used in the Philadelphia edition of James' account of the Long Expedition, published in 1823.[3] During 1823 and 1824 Titian would have been busy drawing the plates to be used in Thomas Say's pioneer publication, *American Entomology*, the first volume of which was finally published on November 3, 1824.[4] The problem of obtaining funds, time spent on the Long Expedition and a shorter expedition in 1823, and work in helping James with the account of the Long Expedition had served to interrupt Say's work, for which the prospectus had been published in 1817. All eighteen of the colored plates of the first volume were drawn by Titian Peale and engraved by the skillful hand of Cornelius Tiebout. They are delicately patterned, fine and precisely delineated plates, and, appropriately, have long since become collectors' items.[5] One of the original sets of drawings, depicting *Hymenoptera*, is now owned by the Academy of Natural Sciences of Philadelphia. This reveals the meticulous care, skill, and artistry with which Peale executed his work. The book received acclaim at the time of publication. The influential *North American Review,* for example, eulogized it:

For beauty and elegance of execution, this work surpasses any other that has been printed in this country. The letter-press of Wilson's *Ornithology,* and of the famous edition of the *Columbiad,* is executed in a more finished style; but in the exquisite delicacy of the drawings and beauty of the engravings, as well as in the marks of taste indicated in the external attractions of the volume, the *American Entomology* is much superior to either of them. The fanciful and highly emblematical frontispiece was delineated by C. A. LeSueur; the figures of the insects were drawn from nature by T. R. Peale, and engraved by C. Tiebout. The specimens of their labours here furnished are in the highest degree creditable to these artists. The work, as it has come from their hands, affords a most encouraging testimony of the state of the arts in this country, and as such deserves the patronage not more of lovers of science, than of all persons who are disposed to advance the progress of liberal pursuits by rewarding the successful efforts of genius and skill.[6]

The plan of the book was patterned after Donovan's *British Insects.*[7] The title page and cover design were

Fig. 17. Engraving. *Smerinthus*. Plate 12 from Thomas Say's *American Entomology* 1, Philadelphia, 1824. Drawn by T. R. Peale, engraved by Cornelius Tiebout.

executed by Lesueur. Romantic in spirit, they represent the mood of the study of natural history at the time—a kind of joyful excitement about the world and God's creatures, great and small. On the cover two playful cupids are shown in the pursuit of insects. The title page shows an idyllic and rustic scene with a delicate spider web across one corner and harmless-looking insects creeping about in a wooded glade below. Stillingfleet's lines aptly expressed the mood:

Each moss,
Each shell, each crawling insect, holds a rank
Important in the plan of Him who fram'd
This scale of beings.[8]

The sentiments inscribed by C. W. Peale on the garden seat at the Germantown farm had expressed a very similar mood:

Meditate on the Creation of worlds, which perform their evolutions in prescribed periods! on the changes and revolutions of the *Globe* which we inhabit: on the wonderful vari-

[2] For example, in 2(II): 243; and 4: pl. 1, opp. p. 14.

[3] See maps and plates for *Account of an expedition from Pittsburgh to the Rocky Mountains,* Philadelphia, 1823.

[4] *The National Gazette and Literary Register,* Nov. 3, 1824.

[5] Bennett, Whitman, *A practical guide to American nineteenth century color plate books,* 94, New York, Bennett Book Studios, 1949.

[6] Say's American entomology, *North American Review* 21: 251, 1825.

[7] Thomas Say to J. V. Melsheimer, Nov. 6, 1817, MS, ANSP.

[8] Thomas Say, Prospectus, *American entomology,* Philadelphia, 1817.

Fig. 18. Water color by Titian R. Peale. Probably one of the "finished" water colors made after sketches and specimens collected while on the Long Expedition. Printed caption reads, "TRPeale delin:" Longhand caption reads, "Sc quadravittatus / Natural size/ Specimen obtained at the Rocky mountains/ by TRP." This may be the water color, "Striped Squirrels," which Titian Peale exhibited at the Annual Exhibition of the Academy of the Fine Arts in Philadelphia in 1822.

Fig. 19. Water color by Titian R. Peale. Probably one of the "finished" water colors made after sketches and specimens collected while on the Long Expedition. Caption reads, "American Antelope. Antilocapra Americana Ord." The plants shown in the foreground, the beard-tongue and the prickly pear cactus are appropriate and typical of the locale.

FIG. 20. Water color by Titian R. Peale. Probably one of the "finished" water colors made after sketches and specimens collected while on the Long Expedition. Caption reads, "Bulls Feb[y] 1820." This is probably the water color entitled "Buffaloes" exhibited in the 1822 exhibition of the Academy of the Fine Arts in Philadelphia.

ety of animals inhabiting the earth, the air and the waters: their immense number and diversity: their beauty and delicacy of structure: some immensely large, and others gradually descending into a minuteness almost eluding our sight, even when aided by the Microscope![9]

In May, 1822, Titian exhibited four water colors at the Annual Exhibit of the Academy of the Fine Arts in Pennsylvania. Three were of western subjects—Buffaloes, Striped Squirrels, Missouri Bears—and the fourth, a study of Peale's beloved butterflies.[10] This appears to have been the only time he exhibited at the Academy, and suggests that he was not interested in painting as such, but rather that his skill served as a tool for him.

A natural history painting, a study of a Suffolk Boar by C. A. Lesueur, was shown at the same exhibit,[11] as were four paintings of Indian subjects by John Neagle.[12] George Catlin, who was then studying portrait painting in Philadelphia, was another artist who exhibited at this time; within not too many years he was to become well known in Europe and in America for his now well-known series of Indian portraits and scenes. Perhaps these early studies of Peale and Neagle, and the talk of the West which Catlin heard in Philadelphia circles of artists and scientists served to stimulate his interest in things Western, and inspired him to go West himself in the 1830's.[13]

[9] Sellers, CWP 2: 284.
[10] Catalogue, Eleventh annual exhibition of the Pennsylvania Academy of Fine Arts, May, 1822, 7 and 13, Philadelphia, 1822.

[11] Ibid., 9.
[12] Ibid., 18.
[13] Sully, Neagle, and Rembrandt Peale are said to be among the artists who encouraged Catlin. McCracken, Harold, Portrait

Artistic efforts such as those just mentioned, museum duties, family affairs, and social and professional meetings with his scientifically inclined friends would have kept the young man busy. Titian's museum duties included preparing subjects for exchange with foreign collections and handling the correspondence from abroad.[14]

Like most of his colleagues in the group, Titian was a faithful attender at the weekly meetings of the Academy of Natural Sciences of Philadelphia. In December, 1821, he was appointed a member of the Zoological Committee, and continued as a member for several years. From time to time he served on small special committees; often such three-men committees were asked to read a draft of a paper before it was presented to the larger group.[15] A New Jersey man, a Dr. Porter, visiting Philadelphia in 1825, gives us a vivid picture of this group as seen by an outsider. He had attended one of the meetings, and wrote of it to a personal friend:

> ...I sometimes indulge myself in contemplating great minds, who have not had the advantages of either an Academic or Collegiate education.... LeSuer [sic], with a countenance weather-beaten and worn, looked on, for the muscles of his iron-bound visage seemed as incapable of motion, as those on the medals, struck in the age of Julius Caesar.... Peale is the son of the original proprietor of the Philadelphia Museum, and one who visited the Rocky Mountains with Major Long; he is a young man, and has no remarkable indications of countenance to distinguish him. Say, who was his companion in the same expedition, is an extremely interesting man; to him I am particularly obligated for showing me their Museum and extensive Library.... Bonaparte is the son of Lucien Bonaparte and nephew to the Emperor Napoleon; he is a little set, blackeyed fellow, quite talkative and withal an interesting and companionable fellow. He devotes his attention to ornithology, and has published a continuation of Wilson's work on the above subject....
> To a novice it seem curious, that men of the first intellect should pay so much attention to web-footed gentry with wings.[16]

In July, 1823, a son was born to the Titian Peales; both mother and child were sickly for weeks afterwards. The child continued to suffer pain; it was a "poor affected being," and died after three months of life.[17]

In November of the same year Titian himself became seriously ill with pleurisy, probably the most serious illness of his life. After seeming to recover somewhat he suffered another attack, and for a time the family feared for his life. In February the father tried to arrange a collecting trip to the South for Titian, thinking the warmer climate would do him good, but Titian was too weak for this. They feared he was a victim of consumption. It was not until April, 1824, that Titian was able to go outdoors in good weather, and he does not seem to have been fully recovered until midsummer. The long siege of illness must have taken a toll on his wife as well. She, too, was "thin and little as ever" during the summer.[18]

While recuperating he worked at drawings for Charles Lucien Bonaparte's proposed extension to Wilson's nine-volume *American Ornithology*. The collections from the Long Expedition had brought to light many new species, and the Philadelphia naturalists were eager to see them published and recognized. Charles Lucien Bonaparte, the highly intelligent nephew of Napoleon, undertook to write several supplementary volumes to Wilson's work. All but one of the plates in the first new volume, published on July 21, 1825, were drawn by Titian Peale. Witmer Stone has pointed out that many of the subjects described by Bonaparte were first noticed and collected by Peale, and should, in a sense, be credited to Peale. The latter did not attempt, however, to describe and to classify the new subjects himself, probably because he felt that the European-trained Bonaparte was far better equipped to do so. In a field where publishing new species was increasingly the mark of accomplishment and skill, Peale's failure to take full advantage of his own field work was missing an opportunity.[19]

Most of Peale's plates followed in the Wilson-Lawson tradition, with birds in profile perched in life-like poses on small branches or clumps of grass existing in an undefined space. Most of the plates are less crowded than Wilson's plates, and the spacing seems somewhat more subtle. There is little animation in most of them, however, and the chief aesthetic satisfaction derives from a feeling of quiet, cool clarity which they convey. There is an economy of line and a simplicity of arrangement that helps to create a clear and uncluttered picture.

The most elaborate of the compositions is that shown in Plate IX, Volume I, of the Wild Turkeys, illustrated here in figure 22. The coloring is rich and applied with genuine skill. The original specimen from which this bird was probably drawn is now in the collection of the

---

of the old west, 47, New York, McGraw-Hill, 1952. Sully was a close friend of the Peales and rented rooms at Philosophical Hall from 1812 to 1822. Thomas Sully's Journal, 14, 19, 21 and 26. Typescript copy, New York Public Library.

[14] CWP to Thomas Jefferson, Feb. 8, 1823, CWP Letterbook ✕ 17: 203; Catalogue of "Duplicate Specimens in Natural History belonging to the Philadelphia Museum Company," May, 1822, Peale-Sellers Papers, in Museum Material box. This latter is a neat and carefully drawn up catalogue, apparently in TRP's handwriting.

[15] Minutes of the Academy of Natural Sciences of Philadelphia 3 and 4, MSS, ANSP.

[16] Dr. Edmund Porter to Dr. Thomas Miner, Oct. 25, 1825, in *Penna. Mag. Hist. and Biog.* 16: 249, 1892.

[17] CWP to Rubens Peale, Aug. 5, 1823 and Sept. 29, 1823, CWP Letterbook ✕ 17: 276 and 298. See also Sellers, *CWP* 2: 421.

---

[18] CWP to Rubens Peale, Nov. 23, Dec. 18, 1823, Feb. 11, 1824, CWP Letterbook ✕ 17: 315 and 327; CWP Letterbook ✕ 18: 20. CWP to Commodore Porter, Feb. 5, 1824, CWP Letterbook ✕ 18: 4. CWP to Eliza, April 18, 1824, CWP Letterbook ✕ 18: 43. Sybilla P. Summers to Elizabeth P. Patterson, Oct. 6, 1824, MS, Sellers Family Papers 7: 44.

[19] Stone, Witmer, Titian Ramsey Peale, *Cassinia*, Proc. Delaware Valley Ornithol. Club 19: 1–13, Philadelphia, 1915.

FIG. 21. Engraving. Wild Turkeys. Plate 9 from C. L. Bonaparte's *American Ornithology* **1**, Philadelphia, 1825. Drawn by T. R. Peale, engraved by Alexander Lawson.

FIG. 22. Specimen of Wild Turkey from Peale's Philadelphia Museum, *Meleagris gallopavo sylvestris* (Vieill.), now at the Museum of Comparative Zoology at Harvard University (MCZ 67842). This is probably the specimen from which T. R. Peale made the drawing for the engraving in figure 21. Frank White photograph, courtesy of Museum of Comparative Zoology at Harvard University.

Museum of Comparative Zoology at Harvard University (fig. 22). Comparison with the plate from Bonaparte's book shows how carefully and exactly Titian Peale and Alexander Lawson recorded the figure. Incidentally, this same Wild Turkey appears in a different pose in the lower left foreground of Charles Willson Peale's *The Artist in his Museum.*

The one plate in Volume I of Bonaparte's *Ornithology* not by Titian Peale was drawn by Alexander Rider and John James Audubon. Audubon had recently come to Philadelphia, and his drawings had attracted the admiration of Bonaparte, if not that of some of the other of the coterie of Philadelphia naturalists. George Ord, friend and traveling companion of Peale, was to become one of the leading critics of Audubon. He apparently felt the latter's romantically posed compositions a travesty on the pure profile-study drawings of his former friend, Alexander Wilson. Peale, whose drawings followed in the tradition of Wilson's style, shared these views, and is said to have felt himself to be the better artist. Peale apparently contributed to some of the hurts received by Audubon in Philadelphia by refusing to show the latter a rare bird specimen in their collection. "This little incident filled me with grief at the narrow spirit of humanity and makes me

wish for the solitude of the woods," Audubon wrote in his journal. So far as can be discerned, however, Peale and Audubon maintained a polite, if not warm, friendship with each other. In 1825 Audubon wrote to Bonaparte in admiration of Peale; there is also a record of their having gone birding together in 1829, when Audubon returned from a visit to England, and an October, 1836, record of Peale's having given a number of natural history subjects to Audubon.[20]

Another of Titian's distinguished acquaintances during these Philadelphia years was Charles Waterton, the English naturalist, who had penetrated into the wilds of South America in search of additions for his collection. In 1824 he came to the United States. One of his chief purposes in coming was to study taxidermy methods and to see the Philadelphia Museum. The frequent references to its collections in Wilson's *Ornithology* had made him feel a visit was imperative. Wilson's book had been an inspiration to him, and had served to renew his enthusiasm for ornithology, a subject he

---

[20] J. J. Audubon to C. L. Bonaparte, April 14, 1825, Film 542, APS; original in Bibliothèque Nationale, Paris. Ford, Alice, *Audubon's butterflies, moths and other studies*, 77, New York, 1952. [Kelso, Leon], The six journals of Mr. Peale, naturalist, *Biological leaflet*, No. 55, 1, 1951.

had neglected for some time. Strangely enough, Waterton, a well-informed English naturalist, did not become aware of Wilson's work until ten years after the author's death. This suggests not only the frequent sluggishness in the flow of an international exchange of knowledge among even the most informed scholars during the early nineteenth century, but that English and European students often paid little attention to American publications at this time.

Waterton, an eccentric, had not bothered with letters of introduction for his visit to the United States. His acquaintance with the Peales was begun when Titian came upon him while the former was looking about the Museum. Their first conversation began with Waterton's diatribe against the impossible tea served in Philadelphia. Titian forthwith refuted the point by inviting the English visitor to the Peale home where, agreed Waterton, the best was to be had. Waterton was delighted with the entire Museum—to him the mammoth was "the most magnificent skeleton in the world." Such was the beginning of a warm friendship between Waterton and the Peales, father and son.

One of Waterton's best-known exploits had been a heroic and victorious barehanded battle with an alligator; it was the only way he could obtain an untorn skin as a specimen. The Englishman might well have delighted in Titian's tale of putting a live alligator on the boat when he was in Florida. Another kindred note must have been struck if Titian recounted how uncomfortable feather beds had seemed when he first returned from the Rockies; Waterton, a hardy traveler who must have had similar experiences, had long since taken to sleeping regularly on the floor with a wooden block as his pillow. A more serious mutual interest was the whole problem of preparing and preserving specimens. Like the Peales, Waterton had experimented with new techniques, and, like the Peales, he had worked out a method of modeling the muscular form before mounting the skin.[21] They argued and discussed their methods, and in July, Titian, his health recovered, took Waterton on a birding trip to Salem, New Jersey. Waterton was to remember the trip as one of the high points of his American experience; the only untoward incident was when he found live mice in his bed. They used Waterton's new method to preserve their specimens and Titian found it "beautiful in practice."[22] Henceforth Titian used Waterton's methods in his work. In 1831 Titian published a small pamphlet describing and illustrating methods of preparing subjects for museum displays.[23] In it he credits Waterton

for the suggestions concerning preservation of birds and mammals. Peale also worked out his own unique system for the preservation of butterflies. The many subjects prepared by T. R. Peale, still in an excellent state of preservation in the collections of the Academy of Natural Sciences of Philadelphia and the Museum of Comparative Zoology at Harvard are mute testimony to Peale's superior skills in these somewhat humbler fields. These collections, containing type specimens described by men such as Say and Bonaparte, are of unique historical value.

Through the Peales, Waterton came to know George Ord, the prominent naturalist, who was described by an acquaintance as "a very singular person, very excitable, almost of pure nervous temperament. Proud, shy and reserved towards strangers; but expansive and brilliant with his friends."[24] Ord and Waterton became life-long friends and correspondents, and it is through their correspondence that one learns many details of Titian Peale's later life. If Titian Peale was a common friend of these two men, Audubon was to become a common enemy. Critical of Audubon because, by not preserving his specimens or the "vouchers" of his observations, he seemed to them to be unscientific, and doubtful of some of Audubon's theories and facts, the two men helped to make life unhappy on both sides of the ocean for the great artist-naturalist. Ord's overzealous admiration of Wilson, and the desire to defend the reputation of his dead friend, seem to have been among the bases of this famous feud. There must have been temperamental differences too which aggravated the quarrel.

In his preface to Volume I of his *Ornithology,* Bonaparte had written:

He [the author] had been equally solicitous to procure the best representations of his birds; in which he hopes he has succeeded, through the happy pencil of Mr. Titian Peale, who has invariably drawn from the recent bird, and not from the preserved specimen; this being the principal advantage of works on Natural History, published in the country where the animals figured are found. The want of such opportunities of making drawings, causes the chief defect of various magnificent European works, in which beauty and brilliance of colouring scarcely compensate for the unnatural stiffness, faithfully copied from stuffed skins. . . .

As the birds of Florida were principally wanting, and it is even supposed that several of those belonging to Cuba, and other West India Islands, may occasionally resort to the southern part of Florida and thus be entitled to a place in our work, a painter-naturalist was selected to visit that part of the union which Wilson had been so desirous of exploring. A better choice could not have been made than that of Mr. Titian Peale, whose zeal in the cause of natural history had previously induced him to join those useful citizens, who, under the command of that excellent officer Major Long, explored the western wilds as far as the Rocky Mountains. Mr. Peale's success in that expedition, where he procured and drew on the spot almost all the new birds contained in this

[21] Waterton, Charles, *Wanderings in South America, the northwest of the United States, and the Antilles in the years 1812, 1816, 1820, and 1824,* 245 and 264, London, 1825. Aldington, Richard, *The strange life of Charles Waterton, 1782–1865,* 114–121, New York, Duell, Sloan and Pearce, 1949. Sellers, *CWP* 2: 369–371.
[22] CWP to Thomas Jefferson, July 2, 1824, CWP Letterbook ℀ 18: 63–65. Aldington, *Waterton,* 121.
[23] Peale, Titian R., *Circular of the Philadelphia Museum containing directions for the preparation and preservation of objects of natural history,* Philadelphia, 1831.

[24] Description by Malvina Lawson in letters written from June 21, 1879, to February 20, 1883, quoted by Frank L. Burns, Miss Lawson's recollections of ornithologists, *The Auk,* n.s., 34: 279, 1917.

volume, will warrant us in anticipating much from his exertions in Florida.[25]

If Titian Peale was not the most brilliant of painters, as Bonaparte subtly suggests, he was nonetheless to be admired for the accuracy and precision of his drawings.

It was, then, as a painter-naturalist that Titian was employed by Bonaparte to make a collecting trip to Florida in the winter of 1824–1825. He probably left in October, for on November 20, 1824, the newspapers of Charleston, South Carolina, reported that Mr. Titian Peale, "Superintendent of the Museum of Philadelphia . . . has been some days inspecting the Museum of South Carolina and making drawings there."[26] He sailed for Florida on the same day. In mid-December he was not far outside St. Augustine.[27] A sketchbook, with a series of perspective views, testifies to his presence in Georgia and North Carolina.[28]

It will be remembered that Titian helped his father in the painting of the well-known self-portrait in the Museum by drawing a preliminary sketch of the background view. At that time the elderly painter wrote to Rubens:

To make tryal of the effect in the perspective of the long room, I drew the lines with my machine, I set Titian at work to fill it up with his Water Colours, and he has nearly finished an admirable representation of the long room, the minutia of objects makes it a laborious work. It looks beautiful through the magnifiers.[29]

It was, and is, of course, not uncommon for an artist to sketch out the perspective lines before executing his work. In many of Titian Peale's landscapes one is conscious of the precise lines he laid out, and it is not surprising that the Peales, always interested in mechanical gadgets, should have used an instrument to help them do this. There is a sketch of Titian Peale, possibly made on the Florida trip, which especially emphasizes his draughtsman-like approach. It is shown

in figure 23, and appears to be a view of Key West; it is dated 1826. Here, as in Lesueur's work, is the precision of the scientific record-taker. The view is looking north. Notes were recorded concerning details of the landscape which were to be filled in later: "houses white washed shutters green," "palings white wood & green tops," "boxes around young trees." Accuracy, honesty, and visual verisimilitude were his aims.

At a meeting of the Academy of Natural Sciences of Philadelphia on May 10, 1825, C. L. Bonaparte read a paper reporting upon several new species which had been found by Mr. Titian Peale. Though not drawn by Peale, these birds were included in later editions of Bonaparte's work, and the author credits Peale with discovering them in the field.[30] A year later the erudite Bonaparte paid effective tribute to Peale in his 1826 *Observations on the Nomenclature of Wilson's Ornithology*, where he wrote in connection with a specific problem:

We should have been obliged to have left the matter unsettled, had it not been for the successful zeal of Mr. Titian Peale, whose practical knowledge (the most important) of North American birds, is equalled by none.[31]

During 1824 and 1825 many of Philadelphia's important and promising naturalists became deeply interested in Robert Owen's scheme for a new utopian community at New Harmony, Indiana. William Maclure, geologist, wealthy patron of the Academy of Natural Sciences, and Peale's traveling companion in Florida, invested $150,000 in the project, and soon thereafter left Philadelphia for Indiana. In December, 1825, members of a "boatload of knowledge" departed from Pittsburgh for New Harmony. The party included several of Philadelphia's most outstanding students of nature and Titian Peale's friends: Thomas Say, Charles Alexandre Lesueur, and Dr. Gerard Troost. Though Philadelphia was to continue as one of the important intellectual centers of the country, this departure removed several of the leaders in the active circle of naturalists who had gathered in Philadelphia during the first quarter of the nineteenth century and whose shared enthusiasms had led to an important series of pioneering works on American natural history. Preeminent leadership in the natural sciences was soon to shift to the academic communities of New Haven and Cambridge.

As has been indicated, Titian Peale during these years was occupied with Museum and family affairs, with the collecting trip to Florida for Bonaparte, and with doing illustrations for the latter's work.

Another of those interested in natural science who stayed in Philadelphia at this time was the gifted and brilliant young doctor, John D. Godman, whose short

[25] Bonaparte, Charles Lucien, *American ornithology* 1: iv–v, Philadelphia, 1825.

[26] *Charleston Mercury*, Nov. 20, 1824, as quoted by Anna Wells Rutledge, in Artists in the life of Charleston, *Trans. Amer. Philos. Soc.* 39: 215, 1949.

[27] TRP, Dated observational note in Sketches, Miscellaneous Notes and Photographs, MS, AMNH.

It is impossible to trace the details of his journey since the journal has not yet been located. In 1913 it was listed in the privately printed (Boston) *Catalogue of a collection of books on ornithology in the library of John E. Thayer*, by Evelyn and Virginia Keyes. The item, on p. 139, read as follows: "Peale, Titian R. Original Mss. journal of the expedition to the south to collect birds for the continuation of American Ornithology, for which Prince Charles Bonaparte advanced the money to defray expenses. Complete journal from Nov., 1824, to April, 1825. 71 pp. 16 cm." This writer has traced the journal from the Thayer family to a dealer who handled the Thayer collection, but has not yet been able to locate the present owner despite a series of most helpful suggestions from the people who have handled it. Hopefully, the manuscript will eventually be located and published.

[28] In Peale Papers, HSP.

[29] CWP to Rubens Peale, Aug. 4, 1820, CWP Letterbook ≹ 17: 147–148.

[30] See C. L. Bonaparte MSS, ANSP; Charles Lucien Bonaparte, *American ornithology* 2: 25–27; 4: 109 and 114, Philadelphia, 1833.

[31] Bonaparte, C. L., *Observations on the nomenclature of Wilson's ornithology*, under "243 *Sterna aranea*" (no pagination in book), Philadelphia, 1826.

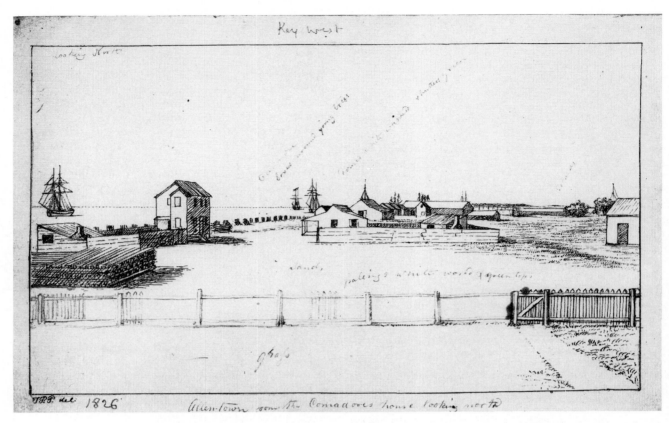

FIG. 23. Drawing by Titian R. Peale. Key West, 1826. Detailed notes are written upon
various parts of the drawing.

career was ended by tuberculosis in 1830. In the years
1826 to 1828 Godman published his ambitious three-
volume work, *American Natural History,* a work he
had begun in 1823 and the first original treatise on the
subject. An engraving after Titian Peale's drawing of
a mastodon is included in the first volume. As in virtually every Philadelphia-published natural history
volume of the period, one finds mention of Titian
Peale. In his preface, for example, Godman thanks
Bonaparte for the use of the latter's library, George
Ord for the occasional use of his notebooks, and Titian
Peale, "who in practical acquaintance with the natural
history of his country has few equals," for frequent aid
and suggestions.

Titian Peale, who grew up with grizzly bears in the
yard of the Philosophical Hall and with an elk at the
Germantown farm, was at home in the world of beasts
and birds. Godman's notes throughout the book help
to make this clear. For example, in writing about the
Shrew-Mole, Godman comments:

That an animal of this kind should be domesticated with
facility would seem hardly possible, yet our friend TITIAN
PEALE tamed a very fine one, which he caught while we
were together examining their modes of burrowing.[32]

An 1826 article by Godman on "Natural History"
and appearing in the newly-founded *Journal of the
Franklin Institute* is illuminating as a contemporary
comment on this field of study which so absorbed Peale
and his friends—it was widely popular, yet not always
taken seriously. The popularity of the subject was at-
tested to by the fact that when the Institute made it
known that members might bring ladies to a lecture
series on the subject, nearly a hundred appeared.[33]
Pleased by the general interest, Godman nonetheless
wanted to make it clear that this was not a field for
idlers and children:

Few departments of knowledge, have been more injured
by incorrect or prejudiced views of their real character, than
Natural History; which some regard as mere collection of
tales for the amusement of children, or idlers; and others as
an aggregation of learned lumber, too heavy for use, and too
harsh to be interesting. That such notions are not altogether
unwarranted by those who have been called Naturalists, is
too true; many of their books being filled with the most incredible nonsense, while a very large number of those claiming to rank as purely scientific, are little better than Dic-
tionaries, in which the authors have tasked their ingenuity,
to accumulate all the harsh and barbarous terms they could
compound from various living and dead languages. . . .

At the same time, he stressed the fact that the natural

[32] Godman, *Natural history* 1: 90.

[33] Godman, Natural history, *Jour. Franklin Inst.* 1: 16–19, 1826.

sciences were not an esoteric field limited only to the most highly educated, though he did not deny the advantages of a classical education:

Another prejudice which has tended to retard the diffusion of a proper knowledge of Natural History, is the idea that a great deal of *learning* is necessary to beginners of this study. Hence, many excellent opportunities have been entirely lost of observing and establishing facts, concerning which the world may long remain in doubt; those who have enjoyed such opportunities have supposed it necessary that they should be very learned, before they would have a right to announce what they had seen. It is most true that preliminary education is of great advantage in all Sciences and Arts; but in Natural History, which is almost exclusively a science of observation, a close attention to facts seen, and an accurate relation of them as they occur, are of more value than the most learned discussion. . . .

Like Wilson before him, Godman stressed the importance of *observation* of the living creatures, and, like Wilson, inveighed those who placed too much stress on arriving at appropriate nomenclature:

To study Natural History, it is only necessary for us to use our eyesight—to look upon the multitudes of living beings by which we are surrounded, observe their peculiar construction and adaptation to the places they occupy, their modes of living, and the relations they bear to other animals, and to man himself; this is the study of *Natural History*. The fruitless and wearying discussion of technical phrases, or the propriety of various classico-barbarous appellations, with hair-splitting distinctions of genera, sub-genera, species and varieties, is NOT Natural History, but the study of *Nomenclature*; a dry and barren waste! tenanted only by fierce and fruitless jealousies, recriminations and disquiets of every degree!

It seems clear that Peale, whose talents were for the more practical aspects of his chosen field, would have wholeheartedly shared Godman's dictum.

In honor of the Florida trip just completed, and in honor of the earlier Florida expedition of fond memory, Titian and Eliza named their daughter, born July 23, 1825, Mary Florida.[34] The responsibility of a growing family, museum duties, working on plans for moving the Museum to the proposed new Arcade Building, social life among the younger Peales, attending Academy meetings—all these activities absorbed the attention of Titian and his wife, Eliza. They were attentive to the specific needs of the venerable old father, but in their absorption in their own affairs they failed to provide any real companionship for him. He had outfitted a room for himself in their house, where he had a lathe, carpenter bench, a printing press, and a furnace. Of late he had been experimenting with new kinds of false teeth. He often occupied himself with his tools, or with his brush. In 1824 he painted a portrait of Titian's Eliza. Deafness plagued him and cut off still further his contact with others. He tried to shrug off his unhappiness and distract himself by activity. To Rubens he could confide his loneliness:

For I often feel uncomfortable that I cannot with perfect freedom ask my friends to take a meal with me. But Titian and Eliza are very attentive to all my wants when they know them. Still I am like a fish out of water and nothing but my constant employment would make me bear it.[35]

There were some misunderstandings as well. The sons did not seem to believe in or appreciate the financial problems of the Museum, and kept demanding higher salaries. They had known the Museum during its days of greatest prosperity, and couldn't quite realize it was declining in popularity and in income. They were embarrassed and annoyed by their father's advertising that he would make porcelain teeth. There exists an unhappy memorandum of the old painter to his two youngest sons. In it was a series of queries which were in apparent reply to charges made by them in a family quarrel. In addition to commenting on the Museum salaries, the father defended his wish to practice dentistry as honorable work "in order to clear myself of debt," and not "to serve a number of old maids." However right the boys were about the father's craving for companionship, one can only hope they were quick to forgive and make amends. On the other hand, however genial and spry Charles Willson Peale must have seemed to Philadelphians, he occasionally must have been a trial to his family and friends. Again one senses that on both sides there were conscious and unconscious hurts that neither was able to control.[36]

The beautiful but rather pathetic story of the old gentleman's last courtship, a search for a new life partner at the age of eighty-six, is well known. He failed to win the lady's hand and caught a cold from walking in a storm while trying to catch the stagecoach to Trenton. He was taken ill, and though he seemed to rally for a time, the end was near. He died on February 22, 1827, at the age of eighty-six. His had been a rich and creative life. He had delineated the features of many leaders of American life; the stamp of his own life and the enthusiasms which he shared with and generated in others were perhaps even more indelible. These interests were to be carried on through his children and his children's children.[37]

After his death there were the usual family settlements. Titian's share of personal property included such mundane items as a feather bed and bolsters, sofa, carpet, and razor.[38] The Germantown farm had been sold a year before so that the family was clear of debts.

The Museum continued as a joint-stock corporation, with the children now holding shares. As planned, they moved to the new Arcade Building on Chestnut Street above Sixth in the fall of 1827.[39] The new, spacious rooms on the third floor of this structure, probably the

---

[34] Sellers, *CWP* 2: 421.

[35] CWP to Rubens Peale, March 26, 1826, CWP Letterbook 20: 21.

[36] CWP to TRP and Franklin Peale, 1826, MS, Sellers Family Papers 7: 51.

[37] Among living descendants one finds artists, architects, scholars, engineers, and scientists.

[38] Account of Coleman Sellers, Admin., Jan. 1, 1828, in CWP Belfield Daybook.

[39] *The United States Gazette,* Sept. 8, 1827.

FIG. 24. Lithograph by Titian R. Peale for his Prospectus of *American Lepidoptera,* Philadelphia, 1833. Courtesy of Academy of Natural Sciences of Philadelphia.

cluded a huge magnet and, in 1832, an English model of a railroad, that iron horse that in a few short years was to transform the nation. A monotonous number of firsts are associated with the Peales, and it is not surprising to learn that in 1833 Franklin aided in the construction of "Old Ironsides," one of the earliest locomotives to be built in the United States.[43] Further, he was now lecturing at both the Franklin Institute and at the Museum.

The young men had absorbed their father's enthusiasms for the promotion of the study of the arts, nature, and mechanics. It was natural for them to share in the logical expansion of these ideas through active participation in institutions such as the Franklin Institute and the Academy of Natural Sciences, both of which had taken on and elaborated upon some of the serious functions which Peale's Museum had fulfilled in Philadelphia, yet by this very token these newer institutions indirectly contributed to the later failure of the Museum. At the same time their own high standards hampered them from effectively competing with some of the flashier galleries of curiosities and waxworks that competed with the entertainment aspects of their own institution.

In the early thirties Titian enjoyed a reputation as one of the local authorities on natural history and as a seasoned traveler in the wilder parts of the country. In the latter part of 1829 he made a collecting trip to Maine, one of his many efforts to add to the natural history collections.[44] With a friend he had published one article in the Academy's *Journal,* was planning a book on American butterflies, and with Franklin and several of their friends was planning a more popular natural history publication.[45] In 1831 the Philadelphia Museum (the official title, though popularly it was still "Peale's Museum") issued a circular written by Titian *Containing Directions for Preparation and Preservation of Objects of Natural History.* This is a competently written little pamphlet in which Peale described the methods he had developed, and in which he gives due credit to those he had learned from Waterton. This was one of several aspects of natural history in which Titian R. Peale knew few, if any, peers. Two letters from the former diplomat and amateur naturalist, Benjamin Vaughan, from his home in Hallowell, Maine, to a friend in Brunswick, Maine, indicate that Peale's pamphlet was well known among amateur naturalists

first office building in this country, provided plenty of space for the collections. Franklin was named Manager,[40] and Titian was "Professor of Zoology in, and Curator of the Museum."[41] There were family rumblings about the "two youngest" and the high expenses and low dividends of the Museum,[42] and it is probably true that the two Peales now in charge of the Museum worried less about cash dividends than did some of the more prudent trustees. But both worked to improve the Museum's value and importance in a manner they deemed appropriate.

Franklin was becoming more expert in things relating to engineering and mechanics. His displays in-

[40] Franklin Peale to Trustees of Philadelphia Museum Company, April 30, 1833, in box of Museum Material, MS.

[41] TRP, *Circular of the Philadelphia Museum.* Title page.

[42] James Peale, Jr., to C. Linnaeus Peale, July 12, 1828, in box of Museum Material, MS.

[43] Patterson, Robert, An obituary notice of Franklin Peale, read before the American Philosophical Society, Dec. 16, 1870, *Proc. Amer. Philos. Soc.* 11: 597–604, 1871. See also Sellers, *CWP* 2: 382.

[44] In the short-lived magazine, *The Cabinet of Natural History and American Rural Sports,* published between 1830 and 1833, one finds numerous references to Mr. T. R. Peale. George Ord, Paris, to TRP, Jan. 8, 1830, MS, indicates TRP was in Bangor [Maine] on Oct. 4, 1829.

[45] TRP and Jacob Green, Description of two new species of the Linnaean Genus Lacerta, *Jour. Acad. Nat. Sc.* 6: 231–234, 1829; also TRP, *Circular of the Philadelphia Museum.* See also Reuben Haines to C. L. Bonaparte, March 6, 1830, Film 542, APS—original in Bibliothèque Nationale, Paris.

in various parts of the country. On December 16, 1832, he wrote:

By this day's post I have recᵈ everything you asked for from my brother John, who always exerts himself for science & for his friends. I will send you the documents by the next traveller; consisting of a circular pamphlet on the part of the Philᵃ Museum, a letter from Titian R Peale himself, & another from my brother. In the pamphlet, I observe that your arrangement governs their mineralogy at the Museum.⁴⁶

Early in January, 1833, Vaughan again wrote to his friend. He, for one, was doing all he could to distribute Peale's work so that the study of natural history could be more effectively carried out in corners of the world remote from Philadelphia, be they Maine, Rio de Janeiro, or the Sandwich Islands:

I hope you have recᵈ from Mʳ R H Sanderson *Peale's Circular* to preserve articles for the Peale Museum, with directions how to prepare them....
I have a letter from Mr. W Ladd, who has just gone for the Sandwich islands, & promises that he will send with much pleasure to B[runswick] College "any collection of Natural or Artificial curiosities." He is to study on his Voyage Mr. Peale's Circular; as I hope will Dr. Hill, who stops at Rio Janeiro, & will have the perusal of the Circular on board the vessel.⁴⁷

Sometime in 1830 plans seem to have been worked out for Titian to make a collecting trip to South America. It has been difficult to piece together the story of the events or the precise nature of this expedition. Just as the earlier Maclure-Say-Ord-Peale Florida expedition had been inspired in part by William Bartram's reports of his travels in that area, one wonders whether Charles Waterton's reports on his travels in South America might not have spurred Peale to undertake this South American venture. Mr. Silas E. Burrows, a merchant, was the patron,⁴⁸ and Titian seems

to have been gone from Philadelphia from the fall of 1830 to the spring of 1832.⁴⁹ By June, 1831, he had already sent boxes of bird, shell, and fish specimens from the port city of Cartagena,⁵⁰ and he was at the mountain city of Bogotá, at least a day's hard climb from the Magdalena River, on August 19, 1831.⁵¹ Peale traveled four hundred miles up the Magdalena. During his stay in South America he also visited Surinam and Brazil.⁵² One of the glowing memories of the expedition for the lepidopterist Peale was recorded by him years later:

Near Buena vista, below the first falls of the river, our boat grounded, the water fell, and we remained "high & dry" on a sandbar for several weeks, until a canal could be dug. In the shallow cavities on the bar, where moisture remained, numerous butterflies assembled every day, to bask in the sun rays, and imbibe the moisture around the puddles.... That sandbar on the Magdalena river was a glorious field for the Lepidopterist....
They [*Urania fulgens*] congregated on the sand-bars in societies of hundreds—sitting with expanded wings in clusters on the moist earth, rising in such confusion when dis-

⁴⁶ Benjamin Vaughan to Parker Cleaveland, Dec. 16, 1832, MS, Benjamin Vaughan Papers.
⁴⁷ *Ibid.*, January 8, 1833.
⁴⁸ The *National Gazette and Literary Register*, June 26, 1832: 1, as well as a letter, probably written by TRP and dated May 3, 1833, names Mr. Silas E. Burrows as the patron, and this is no doubt correct. This Mr. Burrows can only be found listed once in a Philadelphia Directory during the late 1820's and 1830's; he is listed in *DeSilver's Philadelphia directory and stranger's guide for 1835 and 1836* as a merchant, with a dwelling house at 110 N. Front St. Among the James Buchanan papers at the HSP a number of letters from a Silas E. Burrows are to be found, all indicating him to be a New York merchant with wide commercial contacts. A pamphlet, *Important trial for seduction, in the Superior Court of N. York, before Justice Oakley, Nancy van Haun vs. Silas E. Burrows, on Wednesday 27th and Thursday 28th November, 1833*, in the Free Library of Philadelphia, describes the defendant as "being well known in New York as an eminent and wealthy merchant." (The hearings drew large crowds; no conviction resulted as the jury could not agree upon a decision.) Though one cannot be sure, it seems probable that the Silas E. Burrows referred to in each of the above-mentioned references is he who was the patron of Peale's expedition.
A. C. Peale in TRP, *Bull. Philos. Soc. Washington* 14: 322, 1905, states that the trip was sponsored by Dr. Marmaduke Burrows. R. Tucker Abbott in The Titian R. Peale shell collection, *The Nautilus* 68: 123, 1955, states, "Seven years later Titian ac-

companied the Dr. M. Burrough's expedition to the Magdalena River in Colombia, South America. The land and freshwater mollusks were described by Isaac Lea, and some of the figured types were retained in Titian's private collection." Lea's article, Description of new freshwater and land shells, *Trans. Amer. Philos. Soc.* n.s. 6: 1–109, 1839, mentions shells collected by Peale in South America as well as from the collection of Dr. Marmaduke Burroughs, but does not make any specific or direct connection between the two men and makes no mention of a shared expedition. Robert Cushman Murphy in The sketches of Titian Ramsay Peale (1799–1885), *Proc. Amer. Philos. Soc.* 101: 526, 1957, also states that the expedition was sponsored by Dr. Marmaduke Burroughs.
Dr. Marmaduke Burroughs was a member of both the American Philosophical Society and the Academy of Natural Sciences of Philadelphia. For a time he was resident consul in Vera Cruz, Mexico. During the years 1830 to 1832 he made a number of gifts of specimens to the ANSP from such widely diverse places as the East Indies, Bengal, Calcutta, etc., as well as from some locations in South America. He attended meetings of the ANSP during the period Peale was away, but there is no mention in the Academy's minutes connecting the two men in any way. Moreover, while Peale was away there is no mention of him or his South American expedition in the Academy minutes. After his return from South America, Peale was less active in Academy affairs than he had been earlier.
I believe that Silas E. Burrows, the merchant, was the sponsor of the expedition—an expedition especially designed to increase and to improve the collection of the Philadelphia Museum, and that there was no direct connection between this expedition and Dr. Marmaduke Burroughs or the ANSP. The substitution of the name of Marmaduke Burroughs for Silas Burrows probably began with A. C. Peale's error when he cited Dr. M. Burrows. Possibly he remembered T. R. Peale telling him a Mr. Burrows had sponsored the trip and later, when he checked contemporary records, he came upon the name of Dr. Marmaduke Burroughs. Others possibly "corrected" A. C. Peale's spelling of Burrows to Burroughs.
⁴⁹ Target Book, 1828–1840, MS, United Bowmen Collection, HSP.
⁵⁰ Peale Museum Record and Accession Book, June 28, 1831, MS, HSP.
⁵¹ Franklin Peale to TRP, May 5, 1831, marked "received Bogota, Aug. 19th," MS.
⁵² TRP, Butterflies of North America, comments about Plate CLII, Plate XLVIII, Plate CXL, and Plate XXIX, MS, AMNH.

FIG. 25. Drawing. "Steamer Libertador/ Stranded near Buenavista/ Below Houda, the
head of Navigation/ of the Magdelena river New Grenada/ T R Peale 1830."
Courtesy of the American Museum of Natural History.

turbed that numbers were caught at a single sweep of a collector's net.[53]

A freely drawn sketch of the steamer *Libertador* (fig. 25), dated 1830, commemorates the time of which Peale writes. It is a pleasing, attractive sketch that informs one in direct terms about the boat, the landscape, and the activities of the men involved. A brilliantly colored water color of the head of a King vulture, taken from life in 1830 at Turbaco, New Grenada, as well as several other small sketches are further pieces of visual evidence left from this expedition.

A bone-handled, steel-bladed machete of Titian Peale, now in the Jacqueline Hoffmire collection, bears a label in Peale's hand which reads:

This "Machette de Ceimino" I obtained at Baranka on the Magdalena river, New Grenada, S.A. It was used day after day for many months, to cut my way through the cane brakes and tangled forrests of that noble river, while I was collecting specimens in natural history for the Philadelphia Museum in 1830–1; and has been my bedside companion almost constantly ever since—it has done [torn off] if for me. T. R. Peale.

Each person fulfills himself in a particular way, and to Peale the challenge and excitement of the often hard and lonely life of the natural history collector in the field seem to have provided some of the happiest moments of his life. He may have been listed as a professional artist in the Philadelphia city directories, and he had executed drawings with skill and taste, but the record of his life suggests that he was probably most

proud of his abilities as a collector and observer in the field. George Ord's fierce loyalties probably made him a biased judge, but there was certainly a good bit of truth in his generous statement to Titian:

Without any design to flatter you, I can say, that I do not believe our country can produce a better [collector].[54]

Titian Peale returned to Philadelphia in the spring of 1832, with a rich collection of new specimens. There were over five hundred new birds, and work was already underway for the arrangements to be "in appropriate and characteristic groups, illustrative of their habits." The realistic habitat group was but one of the many modern museum techniques the Peales had introduced. In the close and cosmopolitan world of the natural scientists, from England to China, Peale's friends learned his trip had been successful and congratulated him. George Ord wrote with enthusiasm to Waterton on April 23, 1832:

I am not sure that I informed you in my last letter of the safe arrival of Mr. Titian Peale, with a rich cargo of the natural productions of the South. His collections are in fine order; and he is up to his eyes in business, mounting and arranging upon your plan. Before his departure for South America, he mounted an Elephant, which contains nothing within it but seats for the accommodation of those whose curiosity leads them to inspect the interior of the Monarch of the East.[55]

[54] George Ord to TRP, Jan. 8, 1830, MS, HSP.
[55] *National Gazette and Literary Register*, June 26, 1832; George Ord to Charles Waterton, April 23, 1832, MS: William Wood to TRP, May 11, 1833, MS.

[53] See *ibid.* for comments on Plate XIII and Plate CLII.

In the fall of the same year Waterton wrote to Ord, expressing interest in details of Peale's trip and adding his own praise for Peale:

I met no one in the United States half so knowing or so keen after Natural History as Titian Peale.[56]

Several Philadelphia newspapers and magazines carried laudatory articles, such as the one in the June 26, 1832, issue of the *National Gazette and Literary Register*:

Through the liberality of Mr. Silas E. Burrows, the Curator, Mr. T. R. Peale, was enabled to make a magnificent collection of the Lepidopterae of Colombia, South America, the beauty and extent of which can scarcely be conceived, besides an extensive collection in every department of Zoology, all the articles of which are now in process of preparation, in appropriate and characteristic groups, illustrative of their habits. . . . The birds consist of about 500 specimens, with all the characteristic beauty of the tropical regions.

The Museum has established correspondences in every quarter of the world. Mr. W. W. Wood, a gentleman of established reputation in natural science, at present resident in Canton, has at his disposal funds for investment in objects of interest. From him the Museum has received a fine specimen of the Bos Arnee, or East India Buffaloe, and information of the transmission of several of the large animals of China, and also, a collection of the Birds and Insects of New Holland. . . .

From Dr. Joseph Mechlin, Governor of Liberia, have been received several important additions, among them the Python of large size, two specimens of Manis, a rare and curious animal. . . . The articles received from Governor Mechlin, and a fine specimen of the Ostrich, the whole forming an interesting African collection, are now placed in the Rooms.

In the tradition of showmanship established by C. W. Peale, the Museum itself awarded a gold medal to S. E. Burrows:

---

[56] George Ord to Charles Waterton, April 23, 1832, MS. Irwin, R.A., ed., *Letters of Charles Watterton of Walton Hall, near Wakefield*, 22, London, Rockliff Publishing Corporation Ltd., 1955.

FIG. 26. Sketch made by Titian R. Peale while on South American expedition. "a. head (front) Nat[1] size/ b. Mandible double the Nat. Size/ c. Labium double the Nat Size/ it is contracted and never down except when the Jaws are closed. / Carthagena April 4 1831/ Nat: Size / Coloured from the living/ Spec[m] T R Peale."

FIG. 27. Water color. "Lacerta Iguana/ Length 2 feet 3¾ inches/ tail broken [illegible] / Gaudalope TRP."

May 3, 1833

Sir:

The Board of Trustees of the Philadelᵃ Museum Co., beg your acceptance of the accompanying Gold medal, as a slight testimony of their gratitude, for the liberal and generous manner in which you have advanced the interests of the institution under their charge.

The medal may be of more interest to you, from the circumstance of its being formed from native gold from the Province of Antioquia, procured by the expedition sent out to South America under your patronage, and from its presenting a striking likeness of the venerable founder of that national institution which you have munificently aided.[57]

However much the newspapers praised the enlightened nature of the collections of the Museum, and however much the trustees and the managers aspired to maintain the "moral purity" and high character of the institution as an "unrivalled school of Nature," and however illustrious were the Museum connections with Canton, Liberia, and Europe, the Museum did not attract the crowds it once had. Part of the problem was location, for it was so buried within the extensive caverns of the new building it might just as well have been underground.[58] The entrance to the Museum was obscure and people passed by without noticing it; there was no street floor, no festively lighted façade to attract visitors in the evening as there had been at the State House. Since the lofty rooms on the upstairs floor no longer provided sufficient space for the collections, the trustees were already considering another change of location when in June, 1835, the Arcade Building was sold, and forced a move.

Among the family, Rembrandt Peale led in advocating that a new and appropriate structure be built. Since his father's death in 1827, and Raphaelle's death in 1825, Rembrandt had felt increasingly the weight of his role as the oldest member of the family, and was anxious that the Museum continue as the great ornament to the city it had once been.[59] First they attempted to raise funds through a subscription scheme, inviting the public to buy shares. Finally, however, it was through the "liberality" of the Bank of the United States that funds were obtained. Before long the Museum collections were moved to the new building which had been designed on a grand scale. George Ord provided Charles Waterton with a detailed description of the new museum building:

In a few months (say July) [the Museum] will be removed to a house, now nearly completed, built by the company expressly for its accommodation. This house is at the corner of ninth and George Streets; its exterior length is upwards of 238 feet, the height 73 feet. There are two great rooms, the lower for the accommodation of Chinese models of machines, and other artificial curiosities: an unique collection made by a gentleman, at great cost, in China. The upper room for the Museum proper, is 233 feet in length, 64.6 feet in breadth, height 32 feet. There are preparing rooms, etc. and a spacious lecture room. The whole establishment is on a grand scale; and no cost has been spared to render it of advantage to Science, and an ornament to our city. The liberality of the directors of the Bank of the United States has enabled the directors of the Museum company to effect this great object.

A new collection of Chinese objects, owned by a Mr. Dunn, was installed by Titian and set up as a related, smaller Chinese Museum. The new arrangements attracted crowds, and the programs even included orchestral music. At the moment it seemed as if they were off on another era of success.[60]

The prosperous years of the late twenties and the early thirties made them easy to ignore, but there were probably deep-seated reasons for the diminishing popularity of the Museum, even in its new quarters and with its new program. The Peale Museum had proved much too interesting and profitable an institution not to have developed imitators. If one reads the pages of newspapers of the period, one finds that a number of smaller competitors had arrived, all artful borrowings from the Peale pattern. Most combined a painting gallery, natural curiosities, and often a small menagerie. The odd and the grotesque, such as wax figure displays, were sometimes stressed. The Peales, most of them talented showmen (Titian perhaps less so than his brothers), had not been above attracting attention to the unique and the curious, but they succeeded in keeping their programs fairly educational and eminently respectable. Quaker Yearly Meeting time was always a good season for them.

Not only had their Museum become less distinctive as a popular and educational mecca, but it was proportionately less important as a scientific center. This came about despite the fact that the natural history collection no doubt showed steady improvement in an absolute sense at least until 1838. After its beginning in 1812 the Academy of Natural Sciences in Philadelphia had built up gradually a collection of its own for strictly study purposes, and Titian was one of its regular contributors. Further, in 1828 it had opened its museum gratuitously to the public.[61] Thus the serious students were using the Academy collection and Peale's Philadelphia Museum was more a center for popular educational efforts and amusement. An even subtler development was that the generalized enthusiasm for nature and the study of natural history was on the wane; this subject was becoming more technical and specialized, and the dabblers were turning to other

[57] Draft or copy of a letter which appears to be in TRP's handwriting, May 3, 1833, MS, Peale-Sellers Papers.

Though Peale must have made a notable collection of then new neotropical forms he did not publish these. Thus in publications such as F. W. Chapman, The distribution of bird-life in Colombia; a contribution to a biological survey of South America, Bull. Amer. Mus. Nat. Hist. 36: 1917, one finds no mention whatsoever of Titian Peale's expedition or collections. This is but another example of Peale's failure to achieve recognition because of his slowness or failure to describe his findings.

[58] Rembrandt Peale to President & Directors of Museum, May 5, 1836, in Museum Material box, MS.

[59] Ibid.; Atkinson's Saturday Evening Post, June 13, 1835: 3.

[60] George Ord to Charles Waterton, March 27, 1838, MS; Rubens Peale's Autobiographical Notes, 43, MS.

[61] Meisel, Max, A bibliography of American natural history, 2: 133, Brooklyn, Premier, 1926.

and new interests.[62] Museums are still seeking to define and fulfill successfully their various roles as centers for serious research, conservators of valuable collections, and as educational centers aiming to reach a wider public, and most museums today are operated as non-profit and partially subsidized institutions. Nobody could deny that C. W. Peale had had a handsome income from the Museum in its early days, but as its first popularity had waned he seems to have recognized that, if the educational and higher level aspects of entertainment which were so dear to him were to continue, he would need what would now be a non-profit status. At the same time, he was always reluctant to give up control or income. He and his family dreamed of a National Museum and hoped for and tried to receive municipal or national support, and for a time in the State House had enjoyed a kind of subsidy in the form of low rent. They never achieved their goal and hence were forced into constantly having to devise new and special attractions in order to attract a paying public.

The two younger men were not always attentive to Museum affairs, and, true to the tradition of their father, found diversion in other activities as well.

Since a happy day in the spring of 1829 Franklin and Titian, along with a select circle of friends, had become dedicated toxophilites, devotees of the sport of archery. It all began when Titian and Franklin and three other young men of "social disposition and scientific proclivities," were looking for some new kind of outdoor sport and had decided to experiment with archery. An arrow brought back from the Missouri by Titian was part of their initial equipment. They soon decided that they needed a systematic organization and better equipment, and the United Bowmen of Philadelphia was formed by five members. Membership was quickly expanded, though always limited to twenty-five at one time, and in its entire history included upwards of fifty enthusiastic members. They turned to England, to students of the medieval art of archery, for information and equipment. Armed with these, they rapidly developed their skills, organized regular meets, and kept complete records of each shoot, the members always being listed by their chosen symbols. Titian's was the symbol of eternity, a snake in a circlet swallowing itself. Their annual prize meets and their Fourth of July picnics became famous social events in Philadelphia. Crowds turned out to see the gala shoots. The 1836 meet, held in a Mrs. Kuhn's woods, was memorable. A general invitation was given to the community, and the carriages of approximately two thousand guests crowded the lane from Broad Street to the Ridge Road.

The members were garbed in new uniforms. Earlier they had worn sporting caps of black bombazine and iron-gray jackets bound with black braid and white pantaloons. For the 1836 event they were decked out in uniforms described as follows:

...a single-breasted frock coat with standing collar, of *drap d'été* Lincoln green in color, and trimmed with gold lace, with a gold arrow worked on the collar; a straw hat covered with the same material, and turned up on the left side with three black ostrich feathers couchant; white pantaloons, guard and belt of black patent leather, with a large gold buckle; from the belt depended grease-box and tassel. This was a very pretty, picturesque, and appropriate dress as:
"Hard by the shady greenwood tree,
The merry, merry archers roamed."

As often happened on these occasions, Titian carried off one of the prizes, though Franklin was the outstanding archer of the entire group.[63]

The United Bowmen formed a tight and devoted friendship group. One can virtually check the presence in the city of its members by referring to the attendance records. Through the years, whether one of them was in Canton or Australia, "give my love to the Toxies" was often included in a letter. Members included doctors, lawyers, and painters. The painters Thomas Sully and John Neagle were among its members. The enthusiasm for the sport was but one of the common interests all these professional men shared:

Music, painting, art, science, architecture, medicine, law, and commerce were all represented in the Club, and a better feeling never existed than among the members of the United Bowmen of Philadelphia.[64]

In later years the pipe and the bowl probably held the attention of the members more than the bow and arrow, but they were to continue regular meetings until the death in 1870 of Franklin Peale, a long-time president of the group. The last formal meeting, a sumptuous banquet, a few years before which they had turned their papers over to the Historical Society of Pennsylvania, was held in honor of Titian Peale, last surviving member of the original group,

our highly valued associate [Peale's symbol was drawn in], (familiarly called "Pelican" or "Moose"). Although now four score years old and with silver locks, he is as bright and cheerful as when he used to entertain the Club with his adventures in the Indian Territory, or on "The Imploring Expedition."[65]

The story of the United Bowmen is a period-piece study of the Romantic Age. Here one has intelligent and spirited young men of America's first city, decked in coats of Lincoln green, with dashing hats trimmed

[62] Smallwood, William Martin, and Mabel S. C. Smallwood, *Natural history and the American mind*, New York, Columbia Univ. Press, 1941, Chapter XII, The passing of the naturalist, 337–353, has an especially good discussion of the changing attitude towards natural science. See also John C. Greene, Science and the public in the age of Jefferson, *Isis* 49: 13–25, March, 1958.

[63] Davidson, Robert B., *History of the united bowmen of Philadelphia*, Philadelphia, 1888; MSS, United Bowmen Collection, HSP; and *Cabinet of Natural History and American Rural Sports* 1: 211–214, 1830; 2: 161–163, 1832. This magazine hereafter cited as *Cabinet*.

[64] Davidson, 7.

[65] Minutes, May 28, 1881, MS, United Bowmen Collection, HSP.

FIG. 28. Engraving showing the first uniform of the United Bowmen, worn until 1836. Engraved by C. G. Childs and T. Kelly, from a sketch by Thomas Sully, who was a member of the group. Engraved for the *American Turf Register and Sporting Magazine*.

with ostrich plumes, exercising and displaying their skills in the great out-of-doors, indulging in a sport common to the savages of America and the Sandwich Islands, and to the merry medieval heroes of a bygone era. It seems appropriate that those who lived beyond this age gave the records of the club to a historical society.

Another enterprise with which some of these same energetic young men were involved was the publication of Doughty's *The Cabinet of Natural History and American Rural Sports*. It was a short-lived enterprise, lasting only three years from 1830 to 1833, but the magazine is an extremely interesting period-piece document. It has become something of a collectors' item because it contains some of the finer early hand-colored lithographs executed in America.[66]

In 1830 Titian Peale, Dr. R. E. Griffith, and William Wood, all toxophilites, were busy with plans for a zoological work to be issued periodically. Titian was experimenting with lithographs of animals, shells, and insects.[67] In May, 1831, Franklin sent the first proofs to Titian, who was then in South America. The next record one finds is in an 1833 letter from William Wood, then in Canton, China, to Titian, in which he said, "From what you tell me of Mr. Doughty's success,

I am very sorry our *cabinet* was never published."[68] Very possibly the plan was given up while Titian was in South America, or when Wood departed for the Far East. The *Cabinet* published by John and Thomas Doughty seems to have fulfilled a similar purpose; it is probably the first American sports magazine. Thomas Doughty, a friend of the Peales, was later to become known as the artist whose work gave impetus to the Hudson River School of landscape painting. The lithographs after Doughty reproduced in this now rare magazine are from among his earlier efforts. Several lithographs after drawings by "TRP" are included, several of which have western themes; the 1819–1820 Long Expedition had been a decisive influence in Peale's life.

One of the finest of these is a lively, animated picture of an Indian shooting a buffalo (fig. 29). Peale had dipped into his little sketchbook from the Long Expedition and composed his drawing (see figs. 10 and 11). Even though there is a certain wooden-sculpture quality to the horse in Peale's scene, it has rightly been cited as an excellent example of early American hand-colored lithography[69] and suggests the excitement of

[66] Bennett, 35; Carl W. Drepperd, *Early American prints*, 178, New York, Century Co., 1930.

[67] Reuben Haines to C. L. Bonaparte, March 6, 1830, Film 542, APS—original in Bibliothèque Nationale, Paris.

[68] Franklin Peale to TRP, May 5, 1831; William Wood to Titian Peale, May 11, 1833, received Aug. 7, 1833.

[69] Drepperd, 174–198. Drepperd was not able to identify the artist as Titian R. Peale. The bear study, with a similar TRP cipher identification, and Peale's known close relationship with this magazine make it virtually certain that the lithograph was taken after a sketch of Titian Peale.

FIG. 29. Lithograph. "American Buffaloe. Drawn on Stone by M. E. D. Brown from a sketch by TRP." From *Cabinet of Natural History and American Rural Sports* **2:** opp. p. 169, pl. 15, 1832. Courtesy of the Smithsonian Institution.

FIG. 30. Lithograph. "Buffaloe Hunt on The River Platte. Painted by T. R. Peale. P.S. Duval Lith^r Phil^a." From J. O. Lewis's *Aboriginal Portfolio,* Part 10, pl. 78, *ca.* 1836. Courtesy of the Indiana Historical Society Library, Indianapolis, Indiana.

FIG. 31. Water color by Titian R. Peale. Probably one of the "finished" water colors made after sketches and specimens collected while on the Long Expedition. Caption reads, "T. R. Peale delin: / MISSOURI BEAR. Ursus horribilis: Ord." This is probably the water color exhibited under that name in the 1822 exhibition of the Academy of the Fine Arts in Philadelphia. It also appears to be the original drawing from which a lithograph was made, published in the *Cabinet of Natural History and American Rural Sports* in 1830.

the buffalo hunt on the wide prairies—an excitement Peale knew intimately. The bow and arrow may have been modeled from one brought back from the expedition. Peale's depiction of a buffalo hunt is very probably the first of what was to become one of the favorite and romantic themes of such American painters as Albert Bierstadt, Charles Wimar, John Mix Stanley, George Catlin, Karl Bodmer, and others, such as the unknown artist who painted a stunning primitive painting now owned by the Santa Barbara Museum of Fine Arts in California.

Peale reworked this theme for another splendid lithograph which appeared in the now exceedingly rare tenth part of J. O. Lewis' *Aboriginal Portfolio*, published around 1836 (fig. 30).[70] This lithograph bears the caption, "Buffaloe Hunt on the River Platte," and on the left side, the notation, "Painted by T. R. Peale." This suggests that Peale had by this time elaborated one or more of his earlier sketches into a larger water color or possibly an oil painting, which may yet come to light. In this lithograph a second Indian on a swiftly moving horse has been added to the foreground, and a group of white men on horses taking charge of a kill as well as two figures chasing still more buffaloes are seen in the middle distance to the left, giving a full panorama of the hunt. The majestic Rocky Mountains are seen in the background.

Another lithograph from a Peale water color appear-

ing in the *Cabinet* was that of the Missouri Bear, *Ursus horribilis,* Peale's old friend, the grizzly bear, which Ord had named. In both the original water color (fig. 31) of this and the lithograph the figures lack much sense of organic form. Peale was too much aware of academic techniques ever to be what one would call a naïve or primitive artist, yet he seldom achieved a convincingly life-like sense of animation in his animal figures. His careful, meticulous procedure may have contributed to this. Though this man knew bone and structure better than most, he does not seem to have been able to interpret these by artistic means. Despite these awkwardnesses, these lithographs of Peale, as well as others in the *Cabinet,* are among the better early American lithographs.

Less than a decade before, in 1822, Charles Alexandre Lesueur, one of the artist-naturalists of Titian's acquaintance, had executed what are generally accepted as the first two true lithographs ever done in the United States. These were used to illustrate an article in the *Journal* of the Academy of Natural Sciences. Lithography was hailed by the men in the natural sciences as a boon to their work since it provided a much cheaper means of obtaining exact reproductions of those illustrations so necessary to their articles. The Franklin Institute, after its founding in 1824, had also shown a special interest in lithographic techniques and encouraged new developments by the awarding of prizes. In 1827 Rembrandt Peale had received a silver medal for his lithograph of his portrait of George Washington. This is another of the new technical developments of the time with which the Peale brothers were intimately associated.[71]

The articles in the *Cabinet* include many dealing with technical aspects of natural history, and shorter articles reflecting bluff masculine enthusiasm for hunting, fishing, skating, and archery. Most of the articles are anonymous, but quite evidently they were written by the circle of persons of "social disposition and scientific proclivities" whom the Peales knew. Mr. T. R. Peale is frequently cited for providing a specific answer to a question of natural history, or an anecdote recalled from Peale's trip to the Rocky Mountains is cited to give interest and detail to an article. One article comments on the hunter's joy in eating fresh buffalo flesh:

Some fastidious persons may turn from this as an Abyssinian repast, but there is no squeamishness of this kind to be found in the prairies. Ask Mr. T.R.P. whose looks bespeak him a very gentlemanly as well as amiable man, what

---

[70] This lithograph is Plate 78, Part 10, of J. O. Lewis' *The aboriginal portfolio*, Philadelphia, owned by the William Henry Smith Memorial Library of the Indiana Historical Society. A former researcher indicated in notes left at this Library that it was probably published in February, 1836.

[71] Eckhardt, George H., Early lithography in America, *Antiques* 28: 249–252, 1935.
Maurice E. Phillips has called my attention to an earlier lithograph occurring in Vol. 2 of the *Jour. Acad. Nat. Sci.* In an article published October, 1821, there are two species of fish illustrated by engraved plates. However, there are only one or two copies known, with a plate—a rough lithograph by Lesueur—of the same two species. This apparently was not considered good enough, so the engravings were substituted. This lithograph is earlier than the ones mentioned by Eckhardt, which were published in June or July of 1822.

he thinks of the relish of the buffalo hump, eaten in that way, in the western prairies.[72]

In another, one reads:

For the following account of the Rough billed Pelican, we are indebted to Mr. T. Peale, whose well earned reputation in natural history, requires no eulogy from us.[73]

There is an article about the Skating Club, of which Franklin Peale was president, and there are several amusing articles about the toxies, or United Bowmen. A letter by George Catlin, written from the Upper Missouri, indicates that he was keeping in touch with his friends among the scientific and artistic groups of Philadelphia.[74]

In 1833 both Titian and Franklin were asked to join the American Philosophical Society, one of the country's most distinguished learned associations. Titian Peale attended its meetings and served on some of its special committees from this time until his departure from the United States in 1838. Franklin continued a more active membership throughout his life, serving for a long time as one of the curators of the organization.[75]

In March, 1833, Titian Peale issued a prospectus for what he hoped would be his most important scholarly work, a publication to be entitled *Lepidoptera Americana*. It was to come out in regular issues containing four plates each, with a new issue every two months. A total of one hundred plates was planned. He hoped it would be in the new tradition of work coming from the American presses, all excellent books rivaling work of the sort which had previously been done only in Europe.[76]

In the fashion of many such prospectuses, he wrote:

The correctness of their illustrations, and the faithfulness of their descriptions, have not only been calculated for the scientific but also open a rich mine of rational enjoyment to all classes of society.

He hoped his work would be of interest to the farmer and the horticulturist, and to the casual gardener and outdoor enthusiast as well. In keeping with his strict scientific standards, he would give no species which he had not seen himself.[77] He received little encouragement from the public, and the project was temporarily abandoned as too expensive. A cheaper manual without illustrations might have been attempted, but Peale felt that the book would have been of little value with-

out the figures.[78] A book covering some of the same subject matter as Peale's proposed work had come out in Paris during the years 1829 to 1833. Peale, however, did not receive a copy of this book until 1835.[79] A constant problem of the pioneer naturalists of America during the early nineteenth century was this lack of books. If even a publication as distinguished as Say's *Entomology* produced little that was new, it was all too often because the naturalists did not possess or have access to the necessary reference books. In the letters of Say and Peale, for example, one comes across frequent complaints concerning this deficiency.[80]

Peale's failure to push through to publication on his book was justified for the reasons just given. Without being redundant, it is probably fair to say that Peale's strong points were the observation and collection of data, and that the procedures of writing and editing, or the fine points of classification and nomenclature which sometimes preoccupied his colleagues, did not attract him.

He did publish at this time a short article on the black-tailed or mule deer. In addition to the information it gives, the article is pertinent because it states Peale's convictions concerning the practice of the study of natural history. It was written to correct some facts published in an 1829 English book on American quadrupeds, in which the author had explicitly stated that he had never seen an authenticated specimen of the animal he was describing and classifying. Peale's drawing and measurements were, instead, "taken by myself, from a recently killed specimen." He reasserted the nomenclature suggested by Thomas Say,

as his description was drawn up from the animal and not from the vague information of others. We are glad of an opportunity of protesting against this eagerness of naturalists, in grasping at every notice, however imperfect, in hopes of anticipating others and establishing their own acuteness. This procedure instead of advancing science, only tends to embarrass and to retard its progress, by increasing a list of synonymes and fictitious species, already the bane of natural history.

Peale also pointed out that in making the accompanying illustration he had taken great care to make "an accurate representation of the country in which these animals were found." Both the drawing and the text had been prepared several years previously, "for publication in a periodical, which like many of our scientific journals in this country, came to a premature end."[81]

[72] R. H. R., Communications from Susquehanna County, *Cabinet* 1: 145, 1830.

[73] Rough-Billed Pelican, *Cabinet* 1: 63, 1830.

[74] *Cabinet* 2: 184–185, 1832.

[75] On July 19, 1833, T. R. Peale of Philadelphia was elected to membership, and on Oct. 18, 1833, Franklin Peale was elected. See Phillips, Henry, Jr., Old minutes of the society, from 1743 to 1838, *Proc. Amer. Philos. Soc.* 22: 638 and 640, 1885.

[76] See Meisel, Max, *A bibliography of American natural history* 3: 392–411, Brooklyn, Premier, 1929.

[77] TRP, Prospectus, *Lepidoptera Americana*, Philadelphia, 1833.

[78] TRP, The butterflies of North America, MS, AMNH.

[79] de Boisduval, J. B. A. D., and John Le Conte, *Histoire générale et iconographie des lépidoptères et des chenilles de l'Amérique septentrionale*, Paris, 1829–1834; TRP to Fred E. Melsheimer, Dec. 6, 1835, Microfilm from Museum of Comparative Zoology at Harvard.

[80] TRP to Frederic Melsheimer, March 2, 1836, contains one such typical complaint, Microfilm from Museum of Comparative Zoology at Harvard.

[81] TRP, Black-tailed or mule deer, Cervus macrotis, *Advocate of science and annals of natural history* 1: 11–13, 1834. Peale was

FIG. 32. Drawings. Designs for a coin by Titian R. Peale, 1835–1836. The design used for the Gobrecht dollar is closest to that in the lower sketch. A medal of the United Bowmen also seems to be patterned after this design.

FIG. 33. Water color. Design for coin by Titian R. Peale, 1835–1836.

Franklin Peale's mechanical and engineering knowledge attracted the attention of the officers of the U. S. Mint, who asked him to become Assistant Assayer. Franklin undertook a two-year visit to Europe to study mechanical and metallurgical developments.[82] Very probably because his brother was connected with the Mint at the time, Titian Peale was asked to execute an accurate design of an eagle to be used on a new coin. On August 1, 1835, Robert M. Patterson, Director of the U. S. Mint in Philadelphia, wrote to Titian R. Peale, Esq.:

The law establishing the Mint requires that "upon the reverse of each of the gold and silver coins, there shall be the figure or representation of an eagle, with this inscription, United States of America." Wishing, in a new die which we propose to make, to fulfill this law in a manner more accordant to good taste and to *nature* than in the present coin, let me pray you to draw, for the Mint, a sketch of the American Bald Eagle, in the attitude of flying, and somewhat rising in its flight, amidst a constellation of 24 stars, irregularly disposed around it, and bearing in its talons a scroll, with the words "E Pluribus Unum," the whole surrounded by the legend "United States of America."[83]

A number of studies for such a coin design are in the Titian Peale scrapbook now in the American Philosophical Society; three are shown here in figures 32 and 33. The design finally chosen is nearest to the lower sketch in figure 32, showing the eagle, in flight, in profile to the left.

Coins with this eagle were first minted in 1836. Peale's design appears on the reverse, while the seated figure of Liberty is on the obverse, the latter design probably by Thomas Sully. Gobrecht, the engraver, executed the dies, and some of the earliest coins show his name under the figure of Liberty. These are known as Gobrecht dollars, and are considered to be among the handsomest dollar and half-dollar designs in the whole series of United States coins.[84]

There is documentary evidence to suggest that Titian Peale also designed dies for the Mint in 1848 and in 1868.[85] A smaller profile sketch of the eagle among these same drawings appears to be the original design for one of the silver medals of the United Bowmen and now in the collection of the Historical Society of Penn-

referring to the description of the black-tailed deer given in *The quadrupeds,* Part One of *Fauna boreali-Americana or the zoology of the northern parts of British North America,* 254–256, London, 1829. Though Richardson had not seen a live black-tailed deer, he had been surgeon and naturalist on several land expeditions in western North America under the command of Sir John Franklin, R.N., and hence had seen and studied at first-hand a large number of the animals he described. The book was made possible through the "liberal aid" of His Majesty's Government, a fact which piqued Peale and other naturalists who could not obtain similar aid from the U. S. government.

[82] Sellers, *CWP* **2:** 382.

[83] TRP, Sketches, MSS, Notes & Photographs, MS, AMNH.

[84] Adams, Edgar H., and William H. Woodin, *United States pattern, trial and experimental pieces,* 9, New York, American Numismatic Society, 1913.

[85] Franklin Peale to TRP, Aug. 8, 1848; Franklin Peale to TRP, Aug. 15, 1868.

sylvania. Possibly it was discarded as a design for the coin, but retained as an attractive design for a toxophile award.

When Franklin Peale accepted the position at the Mint in 1833 he resigned as Museum Manager, and Titian was in full charge.[86] But by this time the latter was already preoccupied with plans for participating in another, more ambitious, adventure.

Since the early twenties there had been talk in the newspapers and among scientifically minded people of a proposed United States Exploring Expedition. The initial inspiration seems to have come from Ohio, where an army captain named Symmes promulgated the theory that the earth was formed in several concentric spheres, with polar openings. A Mr. J. N. Reynolds encouraged the idea of an expedition to prove this theory. Reynolds' lectures brought the idea to the attention of the public, and soon the more practical commercial groups involved in whaling and fur trade began to push the idea for their own purposes. By 1828 plans were afoot to send out an exploring expedition to the South Seas within the year.[87] From the personal letters of men in Peale's circle one learns that Titian was mentioned as a possible candidate for the scientific corps.[88] The plans fell through because Congress did not provide adequate funds to cover the costs of equipping such an expedition. The idea was dropped for a time, "Symmes' Hole" happily forgotten, until 1836 when Reynolds again succeeded in catching the attention of Congress. He delivered an address in the House of Representatives which was widely publicized; once again plans were underway for an expedition.[89] The matter had now become closely interwoven with the mercantile interests and "the honor and dignity of a great nation." The country was prosperous, not only free of debts, but with the Treasury overflowing; the government had never accomplished anything for science as had the governments of other great nations; the solemn obligations of duty were intoned. The "national aim" must be extended to forward the interests of science, as "such progress must lead to the furtherance of national objects." The whaling industry faced unnecessary hardships because its ships often sailed in uncharted seas, so that whaling was a "fearful, but immensely lucrative employment." There was the Pa-

cific Coast area of the American Northwest to be explored more thoroughly, now that railroads were soon to bring this area closer, an area over which the United States was still fighting a diplomatic battle with the British for ultimate possession. The fields of knowledge for which more data could and should be collected—topography, hydrography, astronomy, and natural history—were outlined and a suggested plan for a proposed expedition presented.[90]

Thus in May, 1836, in the last year of Andrew Jackson's administration, Congress,

having in view the important interests of our commerce embarked in the whale fisheries, and other adventures in the great Southern Ocean..., authorized an expedition to be fitted out for the purpose of exploring and surveying that sea, as well as to determine the existence of all doubtful islands and shoals, as to discover and accurately fix the position of those which lie in or near the track of our vessels in that quarter, and may have escaped the observation of scientific navigators.[91]

Following a procedure used in planning earlier expeditions, the important scientific and learned bodies of the country were called upon to advise on policy and personnel. The Philosophical Society declined to nominate persons, but appointed a committee of seven, of which T. R. Peale and Charles Pickering were among the members, to prepare a report containing their recommendations about the scientific work of the expedition. In their report they hesitated to make an exact recommendation concerning the size of a scientific corps as this would, of course, be dependent upon the size of the total expedition. They noted the French expedition to the South Seas earlier in the century had suffered a great deal from sickness and death, and therefore recommended that, if possible, a full complement of scientific men be provided for each of the chief vessels. They suggested a corps of at least eleven experts which would include an astronomer and surveyor, both of whom would be provided with several assistants; a meteorologist; a zoologist, a botanist and geologist, and for each of these three they recommended at least one assistant; a landscape painter; a portrait painter; a philologist; and, finally, a historiographer who would be responsible for writing a general narrative of the expedition and who would have access for this purpose to the journals, charts, drawings, etc., of the other members of the corps.

Detailed recommendations concerning suggested lines of inquiry and concerning current scientific problems were then presented under each of the major departments. The recommendations in the field of zoology, which Peale and Pickering had helped to prepare,

[86] Franklin Peale to Board of Trustees of Philadelphia Museum Company, April 30, 1833, in Museum Materials box, MS; TRP, Manager's Reports, Philadelphia Museum Company, Sept. 12, 1833, through June 18, 1835, MS, HSP.

[87] Thomas Say to P. S. DuPonceau, Dec. 28, 1828, MS, ANSP; William Cooper to C. L. Bonaparte, July 3, 1828, Film 542, APS—original in Bibliothèque Nationale, Paris. TRP, Surveying.

[88] William Cooper to C. L. Bonaparte, Feb. 25, 1829, Film 542, APS—original in Bibliothèque Nationale, Paris.

[89] Review of J. N. Reynolds' Address on the subject of a surveying and exploring expedition to the Pacific Ocean and the South Seas, delivered in the Hall of Representatives, on the evening of April 3d, 1836, National gazette and literary review, Oct. 29, 1836.

[90] Ibid.

[91] Paulding, J. K., Secretary of the Navy, Aug. 11, 1838, in his Instructions to Lt. Charles Wilkes, as quoted in Charles Wilkes, The narrative of the United States Exploring Expedition 1: xxv, Philadelphia, 1845. (On reverse of title page: "Stereotyped by J. Fagan, Printed by C. Sherman.") This publication hereafter cited as Wilkes, Narrative.

were broad and general, and partially slanted to the commercial interests who were supporting the proposed tour of duty:

> The Zoologists should observe, draw and describe the various animals inhabiting the Countries which may be visited by the Expedition. The Assistants should be qualified to collect, draw or prepare specimens for preservation. . . .
>
> The Zoologists should be instructed to collect information of the habits, localities, times of gestation, food, etc. of all the large Mammiferous Animals, such as Seals and Cetacea, that inhabit the Southern Oceans, and which constitute the great source of Commerce in those seas. . . . To make themselves particularly acquainted with the times and places where the numerous Sea fowl of those regions resort to breed, the eggs and young of which are known to add largely to the comfort of Seamen engaged in the above Commerce; To observe the various Turtles, and Molluscae with the same views; the Pearl fisheries; To dredge in deep as well as shallow water for the numerous inhabitants of the Ocean, and to ascertain as nearly as possible, the different depths at which these animals exist. . . .
>
> To accomplish all the above views, it will be requisite for the persons employed to collect and prepare specimens, as far as practicable, of all the animals noticed, both as Vouchers to the accuracy of the observations made, and to correct errors which might be committed in the hurry of varied occupations. It will be imperatively necessary that the Zoologists be liberally provided with appropriate Nets, Dredges, Boxes, Casks, Spirits, and all the various instruments and materials used for procuring and preserving Specimens. They should also be provided with Books of reference, which they will require in order to be constantly aware of the labours of their predecessors in the same field.[92]

It was suggested that, if possible, some of the members of the Scientific Corps be sent to Europe for the purpose of procuring appropriate instruments and books. The members of the American Philosophical Society were anxious that the best possible preparations be made so that the expedition should fulfill its purposes according to the highest possible standards.

As will be seen, some, if not all, of the Society's recommendations were incorporated into the official orders of the expedition. Others, if not officially stated, remained the philosophical basis for the work of those who eventually participated in the venture. One of the recommendations of the Philadelphia group which was to become a part of the official procedure, and whose mode of eventual execution was a source of at least minor friction, was that concerning the handling of the data collected:

> We would recommend as a measure of necessary precaution, that before entering port on the return of the Expedition, the Commanding Officer should require all Journals, Charts, Collections, and Drawings made by Officers, Members of the Scientific Corps, or others, to be given up into his hands for the Navy Department, to be there retained until after the Journal of the Expedition shall be published

under the directions of the Government, when such papers and other Articles as may justly be considered the private property of individuals shall be restored to them.[93]

A "fair Copy" of the Society's recommendations was made and Mr. Peale was asked to deliver it to the appropriate persons in Washington.[94]

During this Washington trip Peale talked with President Jackson and was advised by the latter that he had been appointed a member of the Scientific Corps for the Squadron. Furthermore, according to Peale, the President told him that the appointment was made in part because the government had been making plans in connection with a legacy of an Englishman, a Mr. James Smithson. This legacy was to be used to found a new Institution for the increase and diffusion of knowledge—and it was understood that a national museum was to be created. No specific or written orders could be given Peale, because the money had not yet been received, but he was given to understand that one of his chief purposes was to "use all [his] energies in forwarding this object, with the assurance of being sustained by the Government in [his] efforts."[95]

On December 28, 1836, Peale received his official letter of appointment from the Navy. As a member of the Scientific Corps he was to receive $2,500 per year, plus one ration per day while on duty under the direction of the Department.[96] Arrangements apparently were made for Rembrandt to take charge of the Philadelphia Museum in Titian's absence.[97]

It is impossible to discuss here the confusion and political wrangling that took place during the next two years.[98] The objectives of the expedition as finally stated were largely the work of Joel R. Poinsett and James Kirk Paulding, Secretaries of the War and Navy, respectively, under Van Buren. Both were well-informed men who, like so many early nineteenth-century intellectuals, were active in scientific societies in their own communities. Thanks to them, the emphasis of the expedition was most sharply focused on the geographical exploration and natural science, rather than upon the achievement of "National Glory," the display of naval might, and the emphasis on commer-

---

[92] Letter (Signed by committee members: Peter S. DuPonceau, Robert M. Patterson, N. Chapman, James P. Espy, Titian R. Peale, and Charles Pickering. Prof. Rogiers' name was affixed in his absence) from the American Philosophical Society, Philadelphia, October, 1836, to Wilkes, MS, Wilkes Papers, Library of Congress.

[93] *Ibid.*

[94] Phillips, Henry, Jr., Old minutes of the society, *Proc. Amer. Philos. Soc.* **22**: (Sept. 7, 1836) 690–691; (Nov. 18, 1836) 694, 1884.

[95] TRP, Surveying.

[96] Mahlon Dickerson to TRP, Dec. 28, 1836; copy included in TRP, Surveying.

[97] Rembrandt Peale to the President and Directors of the Philadelphia Museum, Jan. 31, 1837, asked to be chosen successor to Titian as curator and superintendent during the latter's absence. In *McElroy's Philadelphia Directory* Rembrandt is listed as a naturalist in 1840, 1841, 1842, and 1843.

[98] The best discussions of various aspects of the Wilkes Expedition are to be found in the series of articles in the June, 1940, issue of *Proc. Amer. Philos. Soc.* **82**(5). Most of these were originally given as papers read February 23, 1940, at a Centenary Celebration of the Wilkes Exploring Expedition. Daniel C. Haskell's excellent bibliography, *The United States exploring expedition, 1838–1842, and its publications 1844–1874—a bibliography*, New York, N. Y. Public Library, 1942, is an equally valuable source.

cial prestige which Reynolds and others had increasingly stressed.[99]

The commander first appointed resigned, and Lieutenant Charles Wilkes, a young officer with experience and training in hydrographic work, was appointed in his stead. Though his appointment met with criticism from several quarters, he was probably the best possible choice that could have been made. Very early in his life he had proven himself skillful and knowledgeable in the field of nautical astronomy, and his skill and dexterity in the use of instruments had occasioned favorable comment. He had studied under Ferdinand Hassler, an eminent Swiss geodesist who was the first superintendent of the United States Coast Survey, and from him had learned the most accurate and up-to-date methods then in use in Europe. At the time he was appointed to lead the United States South Seas Surveying and Exploring Expedition he had several years of nautical surveying experience behind him, having been on the survey of Narragansett Bay in 1832,

and having been in charge of the survey of Georges Bank in 1837.[100]

In 1838 Wilkes was already something of a controversial figure, and was to become a figure about whom controversy swirled when the squadron returned four years later. At that time some of his officers brought court-martial charges against him, while he brought certain counter-charges. He again became a center of controversy in the Civil War. Often overzealous in the performance of his duties, quick to criticize, and given to independent and often high-handed interpretations of his orders, he was not an easy man to get along with. At the same time, his superiors and subordinates readily recognized that he had the drive, determination, and perseverance, as well as the ability, to perform the task at hand. When the expedition finally set sail on August 18, 1838, its record was already marred by a series of unpleasant and public quarrels. Nonetheless, it also enjoyed the blessings and high hopes of the entire country.[101]

[99] For a good discussion of the roles of Poinsett and Paulding see Harley Harris Bartlett, The reports of the Wilkes Expedition, and the work of the specialists in science, *Proc. Amer. Philos. Soc.* **82**: 601–705, 1940.

[100] Cooley, Mary E., The exploring expedition in the Pacific, *Proc. Amer. Philos. Soc.* **82**: 707, 1940. Also Daniel Henderson, *The hidden coasts*, 29–45, New York, Sloane, 1953. The latter is a biography of Wilkes.

[101] TRP, Surveying; George Ord to Charles Waterton, March 27, 1838, MS; Edmond S. Meany, ed., Diary of Wilkes in the northwest, *Wash. Hist. Quart.* **16**: 49–51, 1925.

VII

On The Wilkes Expedition— Outward Bound

THE STORY of the Wilkes Expedition, or, to use its official title, the United States South Seas Surveying and Exploring Expedition, is the story of an extraordinary episode in the history of American exploration. The story is compounded of the aggressive economic motives of the Eastern shipping and whaling interests, and of the highest moral and intellectual purposes. It is part of the story of the penetration by whaling men and missionaries into unknown areas of the Pacific, and of their often high-handed breaking-up of the patterns of life enjoyed by the islanders of the isolated lands of the vast Pacific. It is a story of courage, purposefulness, and amazing accomplishments on the part of pioneer scientists, and it is the story of endless monotonous days at sea with the attendant enforced idleness. In some of its aspects it represents a sense of nationalism so intense that one finds a small note on the title page of the published narrative which reads, "Nothing has been used in its preparation that is not STRICTLY AMERICAN";[1] on the other hand, some of the scientists and officers on the expedition were the most cosmopolitan of men. From its records one gets glimpses of life in many parts of the globe: of the vintners of the Madeira Islands, of fashionable life in Peru, of fur traders in California, of missionaries in Hawaii, of cannibals in the Fiji Islands, and of ranchers in Australia. Yet, curiously enough, the story seems virtually unknown except among maritime historians and scientists with an interest in history. One looks in vain for more than a paragraph or two in the standard histories. The information brought back affected in part the American policy towards the Oregon Territory, and doubtless aided the whaling industry immeasurably, yet in general its impact was diffuse and indirect rather than immediate. The scientific reports published after the voyage were slow in coming out and limited in distribution. Today their importance is fully appreciated by historians of science, but in general they are virtually unknown.

The story is told in lengthy and often dull detail in Wilkes's five-volume *Narrative* of the expedition, and in the twenty-one specialized volumes that resulted from the venture. Many of the journals of the men who took part in the expedition still exist, as do most of Titian Peale's, and there is an abundance of other materials. The degree of this abundance is indicated by the fact that the New York Public Library has issued an excellent one-volume bibliography of available materials concerning the expedition and the publications which resulted from it.[2]

One needs a globe at hand to follow the crisscross routes of the six vessels that made up the squadron (see map 2 on back end leaves). During the almost four years they were absent they spent the majority of their time among the islands of the South Pacific, and they had circled the globe by the time they returned. Briefly, they departed from Hampton Roads, Virginia, in August, 1838, and sailed with the prevailing winds to Madeira. From there they recrossed the Atlantic and spent six weeks in Rio de Janeiro. In January, 1839, they departed that city, sailed round the Horn, two ships penetrating deeply into the Antarctic Sea. In April they were at Valparaiso, Chile, and then enjoyed a busy social life during brief stops elsewhere in Chile and in Peru. They soon set sail for the Pacific Islands, where they arrived in July, 1839, and they reached Sydney, Australia, at the end of November, 1839. Most of the first year they were on the high seas, and there were few opportunities for the scientists to fulfill their assigned duties.

During the first half of the second year the Scientific Corps stayed in Australia and then in New Zealand while the ships cruised in the Antarctic. The squadron then visited the Fiji Islands, and went on to Hawaii,

---

[1] Wilkes, *Narrative* 1.

[2] See note 98, Chap. VI. This will hereafter be referred to as Haskell, *Bibliography*.

which they reached in September, 1840. They were six months in the area of the Hawaiian, or Sandwich, Islands. In April, 1841, they departed for the Columbia River on the Northwest Coast of what is now the United States, arriving in this then-disputed territory at the end of the same month. Here they lost one of their ships in a wreck at the mouth of the Columbia. Some of the party went overland from Oregon to California; altogether the squadron was several months in this area, exploring the harbor facilities and examining the terrain of the area the nation hoped to acquire.

They left San Francisco on November 1, 1841, and recrossed the Pacific, visiting Hawaii once again, and then the Ladrone and Philippine Islands. They spent some time in the latter area during the first half of 1842. The return route was by way of Singapore, the Cape of Good Hope, and the Island of St. Helena. They arrived in New York Harbor on June 9, 1842.

Among Peale's journals and letters of this period one finds an affectionate father's letter to his daughters, describing the ship and his cabin on the eve of the departure:

U. S. Ship Peacock
Hampton Roads
August 13, 1838

Florida & Sybilla, My dear Children,

... The little stateroom in which I live is just about as large as your mother's bedstead; in it I have a little bed over and under which is packed clothes, furs, guns, Books and boxes without number, all of which have to be tied to keep them from rolling and tumbling about, and kept off the floor as it is sometimes covered with water. I eat with the Lieutenants and Surgeons in the *Ward room* down underneath the surface of the sea, where we have to have candles burning in the day time, the water we drink is kept in barrels and Iron tanks, it is very warm and now smells very bad, but as we do not come on board ship to be comfortable we content ourselves with anything we can get. ...

Tomorrow afternoon if the wind is fair we will sail and before night will be on the wide ocean.

Kiss your Mother, Brothers & Mary and bid them adieu for me, and take the blessing of your

Affectionate Father,
T. R. Peale

He was leaving behind his wife, two daughters aged thirteen and eleven, two sons, one eight years old and one aged three-and-one-half.[3]

The *Peacock* was a small sloop of war of six hundred and fifty tons, already ten years old and a veteran of two round-the-world voyages.[4] It was not a particularly sturdy ship, and frequent stops for repairs were necessary during the voyage. Captain William L. Hudson was second in command of the expedition and captain of the *Peacock*. Peale was to stay on the *Peacock* during most of the voyage.

The squadron was smaller than had been originally anticipated, and these reductions necessitated reductions in the size of the entire organization, including the scientific corps. The vessels which composed the squadron that left Hampton Roads in August, 1838, consisted of the following: *Vincennes, Peacock, Porpoise, Sea-Gull, Flying Fish,* and *Relief.* The *Vincennes,* the flagship and a sloop of war, was somewhat larger than the *Peacock,* being seven hundred and eighty tons. Like the *Peacock,* it had been outfitted with a light deck for the protection of the men, and to provide a little more room. The *Porpoise* was a gunbrig of two hundred and thirty tons; the two tenders, the *Sea-Gull* and the *Flying Fish,* had been New York pilot boats of one hundred and ten and ninety-six tons, respectively. They had been purchased on the third of August, 1838, and in three short days had been outfitted, and masts, sails, etc., reduced and made ready for the expedition. The last vessel was a new one, the *Relief,* designed as a store ship for the Navy and when launched was assigned to the expedition. Her slow rate of sailing was a distinct disadvantage. This band of sailing ships which set forth in 1838, the same year that the first steamship crossed the Atlantic, made up the first and last great United States government-sponsored expedition under canvas.[5]

The Scientific Corps, as finally organized, consisted of nine men. During the voyage they changed ships from time to time; their official titles and assignments were summed up by Wilkes in the final report:

On the *Vincennes:*

Charles Pickering, Naturalist.
Joseph Drayton, Artist.
William D. Brackenridge, Assistant Botanist.
Joseph P. Couthouy, Naturalist. He left at Sydney and was detached from the Expedition at Honolulu, November, 1840.

On the *Peacock:*

James D. Dana, Mineralogist. Joined *Vincennes* at San Francisco.
T. R. Peale, Naturalist. Joined *Vincennes* at San Francisco.
Horatio Hale, Philologist. Joined *Vincennes* at New Zealand, *Peacock* at Honolulu, and was left at Oregon to cross the country.

On the *Relief:*

William Rich, Botanist. Joined the *Peacock* at Callao and the *Vincennes* at San Francisco.
Alfred T. Agate, Artist. Joined the *Peacock* at Callao and the *Vincennes* at San Francisco.[6]

[3] TRP to children, Aug. 13, 1838, MS, Franklin to Titian letters; Sellers, *CWP* 2: 422. Most of the genealogical information has been obtained from Sellers, who in turn obtained much of it from Joseph Peale, now deceased. I have examined the papers of the latter; though his records were very carefully organized he did not always list his sources. I have been able to check most of the facts against the records of St. John's Church, 13th and Market, Philadelphia, and in only a few cases are there discrepancies. Sellers records a son, John Godman, b. July 27, 1829 and d. Sept. 1838. There is no record of either the birth or death of this child at St. John's, but since TRP in the letter just quoted refers to brothers, the Sellers data are probably correct. Moreover, in a letter dated Jan. 8, 1830, from George Ord to TRP, MS, HSP, Ord mentions son named Godman.

[4] Wilkes, *Narrative* 1: xv.
[5] *Ibid.,* xv and xvi.
[6] *Ibid.,* xxix and xxxiv–xxxvi.

In point of age, Peale and Pickering were among the senior members of the corps. Peale's long-term interest in the expedition and his reputation as an experienced collector, able observer, and field man had led to his selection, though he had published comparatively little.

Charles Pickering (1805–1878) was also a native Philadelphian and a distinguished doctor of medicine. He had graduated as an M.D. from Harvard in 1826, and in 1836, when the plans for the expedition had first been formulated, his reputation was such that he had been named as the principal zoologist. He, like Peale, had been active in both the Academy of Natural Sciences and the American Philosophical Society. His writings before and after the expedition dealt largely with the geographical distribution of plants, animals, and men. He was to be responsible for two of the scientific reports eventually published after the expedition's return. One, *Races of Man and Their Geographical Distribution,* came out in 1848, and the other, on *The Geographical Distribution of Animals and Plants,* was published in 1854. Wilkes and others were to rely heavily on his comprehensive journals for their reports. These journals, which are now in the manuscript collection of the Academy of Natural Sciences in Philadelphia, are models of record-keeping and observation. It would appear, in fact, that he kept rough notes and then later organized his notes into a systematic form, rather than simply keeping a narrative journal of each day's events as did most of the other men. Thus he usually wrote a general summary of the history and people of a given place, then a day-to-day record of his observations, and then a very detailed and systematically written summary of the natural history of the area, under such general headings as Vegetation, Maritime Vegetation, Extratopical Forms and Analogies, Review of Families, Zoology: Mammalia, Birds, Reptiles, Fishes, Crustacea, Insects, Mollusca, etc.

He and William Brackenridge (1810–1893), also on the *Vincennes,* made many excursions together. Scottish-born, Brackenridge had been head gardener to Dr. Patrick Neill of Edinburgh and was attached for a time to the Botanical Garden in Berlin before coming to the United States in 1837 as an employee of a Philadelphia nurseryman. The plants and seeds he brought home from the expedition formed the nucleus of the Botanical Gardens in Washington. Subsequently he was superintendent of the public grounds of the Capitol and laid out the Smithsonian grounds.

Joseph B. Couthouy (1808–1864), conchologist in the *Vincennes,* was destined to leave the voyage before its completion, partly because of sickness and also because of differences with Wilkes. A Bostonian, Couthouy had been educated at the Boston Latin School. He first went to sea on one of his father's ships and, by 1836, when he was elected to membership in the Boston Society of Natural History and presented his first paper on conchology, he was called "Captain." In 1838 he presented a "large and splendid collection of foreign shells" to the Harvard Natural History Society, founded in 1837, and thus had established a local reputation as a conchologist. The story goes that when plans were underway for the Exploring Expedition, Couthouy went to Washington and applied in person to President Andrew Jackson for a position on the scientific corps. Upon learning that all the appointments had been filled,

the irrepressible young sailor replied: "Well, General, I'll be hanged if I don't go, if I have to go before the mast." This pleased "Old Hickory," who told him, "Go back to Boston, and I will see if anything can be done for you." There, a few days after his return, his commission as a conchologist of the scientific corps was received.[7]

Two of the most brilliant young men on the expedition were James Dwight Dana (1813–1895) and Horatio Hale (1817–1896). Indeed, one present-day scientist has said, "The opportunity it gave Dana to become one of the greatest American leaders of science was undoubtedly one of the Exploring Expedition's greatest benefits to the nation."[8] An assistant to Professor Benjamin Silliman at Yale, Dana had at the age of twenty-four written a major work on mineralogy. He was one of those people able to absorb and organize a vast amount of detailed information into broad wholes. During the voyage he specialized in geology, mineralogy, and corals, and his experience on the expedition was to provide one of the foundations for his voluminous and specialized publications of his later life. One of the giants of American science, he has often been compared with Darwin.

Hale had graduated from Harvard just a year before his embarkation. Though he was only twenty-one when the corps was made up, he had already published a small pamphlet on the language of the St. John's or Wlastukweek Indians. He was named as philologist and ethnographer of the corps, and his duties included observation of the habits and customs of primitive people, the study of native dialects, and the gathering of information concerning Polynesian migrations across the Pacific.

Little is known concerning the botanist, William Rich, who had first been named assistant botanist and then eliminated, but who was again appointed very shortly before embarkation when the well-known scholar and close friend of Dana, Asa Gray, felt compelled to resign his post. In a personal letter to Gray written during the expedition Dana said, "Rich has done so-so."[9] Rich did not finish his proposed report on botany at the end of the voyage and this was eventually completed by Gray.

Though Drayton and Agate were the official artists of the expedition, and it is from their drawings that

[7] Dall, William H., Some American conchologists, *Proc. Biol. Soc. Wash.* **4:** 95–134, 1888.

[8] Bartlett, Reports, 640.

[9] Dana to Gray, Fiji Islands, June 15, 1840, as quoted in Daniel C. Gilman, *The life of James Dwight Dana,* 122, New York and London, 1899.

most of the engravings and lithographs of the Wilkes report were made, both Dana and Peale chose to do their own drawings, and Peale was frequently busy with his brushes during the voyage.

Wilkes decided that the duties relating to astronomy, surveying, hydrography, geography, geodesy, magnetism, meteorology, and physics should be the responsibility of the naval officers and selected his men accordingly. He quite willingly undertook some of the heaviest duties himself, and, further, decided to direct the work of all these departments.

Some, if not all, of the officers were interested and excited about the scientific aspects of the voyage, while others were less so. Lieutenant Henry Eld, on board the *Peacock,* was eager to do his job well, and was interested in natural history and the broad scientific purposes of the cruise. The two years of delay and intermittent wrangling that had preceded the departure, however, had tempered his enthusiasm. The sardonic mood in which he wrote to his father on the eve of the departure was probably shared by other officers:

> ...A General Order was read to the Officers & crew on preparation to sailing from Capt. Wilkes, which read as those ... generally do. Subordination. Honoring our countrys expectations, patriotism, etc. All I can say a very little of either is flowing in my veins at present. My day has gone by so far as that goes, all the zeal that I ever felt for the service of my country has evaporated, gone, vanished inevitably. You speak of curiosities. I certainly will make collections if circumstances will permit. Am fond of it and as much a mind to so do so as you are to have me. But if I am to judge from such expeditions heretofore we shall be obliged to give up all curiosities to government when we return, as well as all Journals and information in any way collected, and if I mistake not we shall be enjoyned to keep our mouths Hermetically sealed from the time we leave the Capes thro the cruise. This has been the case with Ross's and others.[10]

After a few months at sea, Dana, writing to a friend at home, felt that many of the officers were unsympathetic to the work of the scientific men:

> Mr. Eld is very accurate in his observations & I doubt not that the table he keeps will be the only one of any value aboard our ship. I have no idea of accuracy of naval officers, especially on duties in which they take no interest. They take the temperature at the mast's head, but the thermometer is half the time in the sun & half the time in the shade! But you must not tell everybody of this. In fact the Naval officers have very little interest in anything connected with the Expedition. I would except however Capts. Wilkes & Hudson. Wilkes is quite enthusiastic and in every respect has proved a far more agreeable man than was expected.[11]

Hudson seems to have been a mature, humane, and capable leader of men. Four years older, and with a higher rating than Wilkes, Hudson had been prevailed upon to serve under Wilkes because of the latter's more specialized knowledge. Throughout the voyage

Hudson seems to have done what he could to make life on board the *Peacock* peaceable and businesslike, and there were fewer of the inter-officer squabbles on his ship of the sort which dot the story of Wilkes's relations with those on board the *Vincennes,* or with those commanding the smaller vessels.

The five extant journals of the seven or more which Peale kept while on the expedition are reproduced in their entirety in the second section of this study. From them one gets a record of the day-to-day events of the voyage as seen by Peale, along with recorded observations and notes on natural history. In these chapters I shall not begin to discuss all aspects or events of the expedition, but rather shall try to summarize some of the major events and to give a general picture of the story of the expedition and Peale's role in it.

The problem of determining the role of civilians on a Navy ship still exists, though it is no longer new as it was on this expedition. Very early in his journal Peale perceived and commented upon this problem:

> *Sept. 2, 1838.* ...I cannot but feel that our government has done us injustice in not assigning a nominal rank to the members of the scientific corps; while all appear in their respective places & dress, we alone are left as idle spectators, by courtesy only being considered officers without grade, subject to the usual etiquete of a man of war without any privileges. ...
> Our ships also have been constructed without any design for their future opperations, and are totally unfitted for the service. It is true state rooms on the gun deck have been constructed for our accomedation, they are wet and dark—where neither drawings or preparations of specimens can be made. The Capt^{ns} Cabin is the only place on board where such opperations could be carried on and these only at the sacrifice of his private convenience. ... The usual Naval etiquete prevents our working on deck and the want of air and light below![12]

Wilkes was not unaware of the fretting of some of the scientific men during the long days of enforced idleness at sea, and in his published narrative makes note of this and states his side of the case:

> I am aware that some dissatisfaction was occasionally felt at the outset by a few of the naturalists, because they were not allowed all the opportunities they desired of making investigations. It was not to be supposed, from the many interests, and their inexperience in naval duties, that all could agree that the particular objects of their several departments received the proper consideration. Each would naturally look upon his own as the most important. They were not aware of my instructions, and of the duties that were enjoined upon me; and I think did not take into consideration the loss of time I had met with from various causes, and that my intentions were at times unexpectedly frustrated. Besides, it was my duty to look to the essential objects of the Expedition, which were entirely unknown to them. They are now, after the cruise has passed, I believe fully satisfied that it was not possible, without sacrificing the greater interests, to give more attention than I did to sub-ordinate parts.[13]

---

[10] Aug. 17, 1838, MS, Henry Eld Papers, Library of Congress.
[11] Dana to Edward Herrick, New Haven, Conn., Jan.. 2, 1839, MS, Dana-Herrick Letters, Yale University Library.

---

[12] TRP, Journal # 1, MS, Library of Congress. TRP's Journals numbered 1, 2, 3, 5, and 7 are all in the Library of Congress and are published in their entirety in the second section of this study.
[13] Wilkes, *Narrative* 1: xix.

The Instructions to Wilkes from the Secretary of the Navy had stated:

Although the primary object of the Expedition is the promotion of the great interests of commerce and navigation, yet you will take all occasions, not incompatible with the great purposes of your undertaking, to extend the bounds of science, and promote the acquisition of knowledge. For the more successful attainment of these, a corps of scientific gentlemen ... will accompany the Expedition, and are placed under your direction.[14]

Wilkes's orders for the first phase of the expedition were to shape his course for Rio Janeiro and,

crossing the line between longitude 18° and 22° W, and keeping within those meridians to about latitude 10° S, ... to determine the existence of certain *vigias* or shoals laid down in the charts as doubtful, ... whose position, should they be found to exist, it is deemed useful to the interests of our commerce to ascertain.[15]

Though there was comparatively little to observe during the first weeks at sea, Peale and others eagerly made notes concerning the birds and fishes seen. Lieutenant George Emmons, another of the *Peacock's* officers, was interested in ornithology and mentions birds, and Peale's work, quite regularly in his journal, *viz.*:

Oct. 20, 1838. A small Land Bird came on board of us & a drawing of him was taken by Mr. Peal.

Oct. 31, 1838. Passed a large flock of Sea Gulls and Tern that were busy diving for fish, & for the last week noticed that the Mother Cary's Chickens that hovered around the Vessel were much larger than those we generally meet with near our coast, although in every respect apparently the same—some of them were entangled in twine & retained as specimens by Mr. Peal who was ever on the *que vive* to add to his collections.[16]

Some of the sailors were probably bemused by Peale's eagerness to secure specimens of what must have seemed commonplace birds and fishes, but others were excited by the work of the specialists. Wilkes writes, "It was amusing to see all entering into the novel occupation of dissecting the fish taken, and to hear scientific names bandied about between Jack and his shipmates."[17] More sensitive and even compassionate is the prose of the seaman, Joseph Clark, one of the *Peacock's* crew. From his published journal one feels that Clark was one of those philosophical and discursive seamen that Melville liked to create, thoughtful and knowledgeable if not learned. On the dissection of a fish on board ship September 4, 1838, Clark had this to say:

This morning we had the first sight of a dolphin, one of the most beautiful inhabitants of the sea. The usual length of this fish appears to be about two feet. In its shape it bears

but little resemblance to the representation of it seen on vases, etc., and in marine emblems, and armorial bearings, but is very similar to the white salmon trout found in fresh water lakes. When swimming in the water, its colors appear exceedingly delicate and beautiful. The head, back, and upper part of the sides, vary from the hue of burnished steel to that of deep azure and nazarine blue, shading off toward the under part in pea green and light yellow. The dolphin is often taken with a hook and line, but this morning one was struck with a harpoon and brought upon deck. I hastened to witness its colors while dying. I found them to be as truly beautiful as they have been described, consisting of rapid transitions, from the deepest purple approaching to black, through blue, green, gold of different hues, and several shades of silver, to almost a snow white, and then to purple again. The sight, however, was painful from a kind of sympathy with the beautiful sufferer. I could but feel that the gratification of my curiosity was at the expense of its life.[18]

Clark seems to have been a sensitive, observant, God-fearing New Englander, very Protestant in his views, promissionary and anti-liquor, whose chief purpose in publishing his journal was to describe the life of the sailor, particularly the problem of "land sharks" who all too often bilked sailors of their earnings the day they landed. His writing lacks the almost deadly objectivity of some of the scientists and officers, who knew that their journals were to be used in the compilation of the official report, and which apparently were scrutinized from time to time by Wilkes. Thus at times Clark's insights often have a freshness and enthusiasm that others lacked; unfortunately he did not always write in great detail and spoke little of the other men or specific incidents on board ship. He felt and saw a romance in the life of the sea, and in the varied natures of the men who felt its call; to him it was only right and natural that scholars should be on board:

Yet there is a far greater number who are high-minded, generous and worthy, who have selected an ocean-life—not from a blind fatality—but have been drawn to it by a love of the grand and wildly sublime, which the ocean ever presents to the lover of nature's wonders. The scholar is often found here, whose romantic predilections have induced him to leave the halls of science, and study nature in her more imposing forms. There is a grandeur in ocean scenery, a majesty in the strides of a stately ship, as she moves, like a "thing of life," over the heaving bosom of restless waters;—an awe in the tempest, when the mighty voice of the Omnipotent is heard in thunder-tones, pealing amid the roar of winds and the dashing of billows, which can divert the man of letters from his more quiet letters.[19]

Seamen, naval officers, and scientific gentlemen alike were delighted when, on the sixteenth of September, 1838, they landed at Madeira, where they stayed for nine days. Some of the officers and scientific gentlemen divided themselves into small parties and made short jaunts into the country in order to collect as many specimens and as much information as possible in the time available. As was often the case, Lieutenant Em-

---

[14] *Ibid.*, xxix.

[15] *Ibid.*, xxv.

[16] Journal of George Foster Emmons, No. 1, MS, Western Americana Library, Yale University. Hereafter referred to as Emmons, Journal 1.

[17] Wilkes, *Narrative* 1: 4.

[18] Clark, Joseph G., *Lights and shadows of sailor life*, 19–20, Boston, 1848.

[19] *Ibid.*, x.

FIG. 34. Drawing. Madeira, Valley of the Coural. Notes indicate such things as "Ferns with green tops & cienna brown dead leaves," "Road," "Stream," and "Dry grass." Courtesy of the American Museum of Natural History.

mons and Peale were members of the same group; Dr. Sickles and Lieutenant Perry, also of the *Peacock*, were in the party. Peale's journal includes a description of their trip in the mountains to a place called the Coural, where they joined about twenty of the officers and scientific men from the other ships. Some were occupied in making barometrical observations, while Peale and several others occupied themselves with sketching. Peale, who was awed and delighted with the scenery, was not content with making only "eye sketches" but chose to return equipped with his *camera lucida*. This was a simple gadget often used by artists so that they could draw in true perspective, and consisted of a piece of plain glass set at an angle of 45° so that it would reflect the objects before it on a sheet of paper placed beneath.[20] Several of the other officers, as well as both Agate and Drayton, made use of the *camera lucida* when making drawings and paintings. It was a tool which they deemed necessary in order to make the kind of records and paintings they considered most desirable and useful in the collection and promotion of "useful knowledge." It appears that

Peale usually made one or more sketches on the spot, and then in the tradition of studio painting, completed the compositions later, in this case, at his leisure on board ship. Thus, after leaving Madeira, Peale found his time passing more pleasantly, as he was busy taking care of his specimens and drawings. A number of neat, almost ascetic, *camera lucida* sketches, as well as several more finished water colors by Peale survive (fig. 34).

Though Peale was often fretful when forced to be idle on board ship, he also regretted the absence of an assistant to help him in caring for his specimens and in making drawings and records. When the size of the squadron had been cut, this is one of the positions which had been eliminated. Wilkes, who was willing to take on any number of extra duties for himself, seemed to have felt that Peale could handle all phases of his own department in the same fashion. Wilkes also suggested that one of the seamen might be willing to help him out. Peale probably remembered his own services to Say on the Long Expedition and had hoped and expected to have an assistant of equal caliber. From time to time he was provided with an aide, but not regularly, and the men probably did not

[20] Phillips, Sir Richard, *A dictionary of the arts of life and civilization*, 335, London, 1833.

begin to possess Peale's own skill. In one of the very few extant letters of Peale which were written while on the expedition he outlines some of his frustrations, though the general spirit is good natured. The letter is dated November 13, 1838, and is to R. M. Patterson of the U. S. Mint in Philadelphia:

We are now rolling and plunging merily before a strong trade wind, with studden sails below and aloft, on both sides, in a way that surpasses any Eagle with spreading wings, designed for coin; *all* the men are scrubbing, holy stoning, and sluising the ship, to be ready for painting inside and out, buckets and swabs fly in all directions; Saturday in Phil[a] is a fool to it; I sought refuge in my room, not safe here for even now the water is spurting in jets through the key hole; every one heaves with a good will, and well they may, we have been three months at sea,—early and expect to be in Rio Janairo in as many days, there?—you'd not be bothered to know whats there if you could hear either men or officers,—everything from an onion up to a bullock is to be had.

The service thus far has been pleasant, but tedious, we have been on fruitless searches for some half dozen shoals, of course little or nothing for *me* to do; I had a few days at Madeira, and one at the Cape de Verde, they were overwhelming because I had to do everything myself; shoot, write, draw, and explain to the uninitiated; there is not an individual in the Scientific Corps but who is now before the world for the first time, some who do not know even the rudiments of the service they are on; of course fuss, and mystified dignity, is constantly elbowing with quiet labor. The selection of officers has been a very happy one,—we get along very happily—I feel lucky in getting with Capt[n] Hudson, and only regret suffering them to take Williams from me, and if I cannot supply his place in Rio Janairo, it is questionable with me whether I ought not to leave the expedition, for I can be little more than the stuffer of skins—or be considered a churl, no one in the whole squadron understands it, and without vouchers Nat[l] history is questionable, particularly that of beginners. Capt Wilkes's assertion that I would find sailors ready and able to do anything, and that I should have their services whenever required, arose merely from the wish to remove impediments to the sailing of the expedition as quietly as possible, *all* the sailors are required for their own immediate duties, and they are not willing to have more imposed on them than they can help: There will be a "beggarly account of empty boxes" and in this one respect at least the English and French will hold their way. Our "Scientific Corps" is precisely in the state of our Militia in Penn[a]; the officers must be their own boot blacks, and washerwomen, because they have no men.

Last night or rather this morning was the anniversary of the "Meteoric Shower" we had sundry observers but the greatest number observed in one hour was 71, of these I strongly suspect a large proportion were caused by the rolling of the ship, indeed when she pitches sometimes it looks as though the whole firmament was coming down; we saw what was more singular a few weeks since, which was the aurora australis, or aurora from south of the line. . . .

Rio Janairo Nov[r] 20th 1838

We arrived here this afternoon, but to our surprise and disappointment found we were the first of our Squadron from which have parted since we have been searching for shoals near the equator; the Relief we have some apprehension for, as she was to meet us at Porto Praya; the frigate Independance Com[r] Nicholson is here expecting to sail in a few days. The scenery of this harbour is Magnificent beyond anything I have ever seen, and as we expect to be detained some time I shall probably have some time to attempt a

description, at present remember me to all enquiring friends.[21]

Unfortunately, Peale's journal kept during the time spent in Rio de Janeiro, where they landed on November 20, 1838, is missing, so we lack his verbal descriptions of the city. One precise sketch (fig. 35) survives, showing the animated street life of the city at that time. While in Rio the *Peacock* underwent extensive repairs.

At Rio, as at other major ports, the scientific men were busy organizing, labeling, and packing the numerous specimens they had collected. Franklin Peale, at the Museum in Philadelphia, had agreed to receive some of their shipments and to turn them over to an appropriate agent of the Navy when they were called for. Thus on Christmas Day, 1838, Wilkes wrote to Franklin Peale, informing the latter of a shipment via the brig *S. Orient* of boxes of specimens in "Natural History, Botany, and Mineralogy." And on June 18, 1840, Franklin Peale officially acknowledged the receipt of eighty "Boxes, Barrels, Half Barrels and Bundles" which, according to the accompanying detailed list, included a wide variety of specimens from Madeira, St. Iago, the Cape Verde Islands, and Rio itself, and included specimens collected by all of the scientific men.[22]

Later during the voyage the shipments of specimens were sent directly to the Navy Department in Washington. Wilkes wrote to the Secretary, stressing how carefully the boxes were packed and labeled, and pleading that they be kept unopened until the squadron's return—an idle hope:

I would impress upon the Hon[l] Sect[y] of the Navy, that in order to keep them in a state of preservation, and thereby insure success to this branch of the enterprise, it is of the highest importance, that they be moved as little as possible, and kept unopened, in a safe and dry depository, until the return of the Squadron, when with the assistance of the Catalogues, they can be arranged in order without difficulty.[23]

Peale's friend Emmons had a mild brush with Wilkes during their Rio stay. They had heard that no Americans had yet succeeded in climbing Sugar Loaf mountain; hence, he and several others felt challenged to give it a trial. Much to their pleasure, they succeeded in the first attempt, and:

. . . then returned on board with a large variety of botanical plants that we had collected in a bag on our decent—for this & the labor & fatigue which we had undergone in reaching a point which had so long been talked of by the different officers of the squadron (but never before attempted by them) we had flattered ourselves, would at least entitle us (under the circumstances) to the silent approbation of the com-

---

[21] TRP to R. M. Patterson, U. S. Mint, Philadelphia; written at sea, Nov. 13, 1838, MS, Misc. MSS Collection.

[22] List of specimens sent to Franklin Peale, MS, Smithsonian Institution.

[23] Wilkes to Paulding, Nov. 9, 1840, MS, Smithsonian Institution.

FIG. 35. Drawing. "Rio Janairo / Rue Direshe/ By T. R. Peale." Marginal comments on margin of upper left read: "No. 1 Dirty white. The pediment [?] granite; ornaments on front dº. 2. 3. dº. signs black with white letters. 4. green grass. Rails of balconies black, doors green. Jams lead colᵈ. Caps of the bells green. Street well-filled with figures."

mander of the Expedition—but in this it appears we were mistaken as the following document will show—

U.S.S. Vincennes
Rio de Janeiro
Dec. 15, 1838

Sir

I learn with surprise & regret that an officer of your ship made an excursion to an important height in this vicinity without obtaining the necessary instruments for its correct measurement; as it results only in the idle and boastful saying that its summit has been reached, instead of an excursion which might have been useful to the Expedition.

I am Sir

To Capt. W. L. Hudson   Very Respectfully
  Comdg U.S.S. Peacock   Your Most Obt Servant
                           Chas Wilkes

My "surprise" if not "regret" upon reading the above, I presume equalled that of Capt. Wilkes, for we had contemplated all that we had not accomplished and had even accomplished more than we had reason to expect upon the *first trial*—after the many reports which we had depended upon, all of which were unfavorable to an *attempt, even without instruments.*[24]

---

[24] Emmons, Journal 1, Dec. 14, 1838.

Wilkes's martinet manner was here exemplified. In this particular case measurements were eventually taken from the sea and the episode probably soon forgotten. The record of the Expedition is dotted with small episodes of this sort; Wilkes's quixotic manner was frequently to exasperate and surprise the men under him.

As Peale had early perceived, there was a certain amount of confusion as to the role of the scientific men on the expedition, and the rights and privileges which were theirs, but no real crisis arose until January, 1839. At that time the squadron was anchored off the mouth of the Rio Negro, in what is now Argentina. This was their second landing in South America, and Wilkes's instructions were "to make a particular examination of Rio Negro, which falls into the South Atlantic, about latitude 41° S., with a view to ascertain its resources and facilities for trade."[25] Consequently, plans were made to land the members of the scientific corps so that they could make some short exploratory excursions. Their stops to date had been in settled and civilized areas where, though men like

---

[25] Wilkes *Narrative*, I: xxvi.

Peale busied themselves with painting and collecting, they had not made any real expeditions to gather new materials. Wilkes called all the members of the scientific corps on board the flagship, *Vincennes*, and issued orders concerning their duties. He expressed the hope that there would be no difficulties between the officers and the scientific men, and hoped all would have a proper understanding as to their relative position in the squadron. Mr. Couthouy, who was stationed on Wilkes's ship, said that he had *not* felt the officers had been as prompt in aiding him as seemed reasonable to expect, but that he hoped to have no further cause of complaint. After a half hour's meeting, they agreed all around that they must all work unceasingly for the general good. Hudson's journal reports that "the meeting broke up with the greatest good feeling,"[26] and includes no mention of the episode which followed, recorded by Peale years later:

> Our orders from Captain Wilkes were sufficiently explicit about landing, duties on shore, etc., but no provision was made for returning to the ships, or subsistance while ashore. Captⁿ Ringgold [a young officer in charge of another of the squadron's ships] was charged with the survey of the River, and unfortunately issued orders to the officers in charge of the boats, to hold no communication with the gentlemen of the Scientific Corps after landing them. The weather was very warm; our only drink, such as we could find, was brackish water, and fortunately game on the pampa was abundant, or the writer, and two Surgeons, Dʳˢ Fox and Holmes would have suffered more. As it was, the two Surgeons were overcome by the sun's heat, on the sand hills, as there was no vegetation to afford shade.
> Captⁿ Hudson, who was a humane officer, saw the difficulty, and ordered a boat to our relief, or matters would have been worse. The animal specimens collected, were almost all spoiled by the heat of the weather, as they could not be sent to the ships.
> Captⁿ Wilkes required me to prepare Court Martial charges against the conduct of Lᵗ Ringold [*sic*], but this was declined, and a request to be returned to the United States, by the first opportunity, was substituted—unless I could have the assurance of better protection, and assistance, for myself and colleagues of the Scientific Corps, during the remainder of the voyage. This was obtained orally at Callao, Peru, many months afterwards. No serious complaint could be made, of improper treatment during the time we were afloat.[27]

In this situation Peale would appear to have displayed a combination of high-minded nobility and independence of position which had positive results in alleviating an unpleasant situation for Ringgold and achieving more definite status for the men of the scientific corps. But his action was not such as to please Wilkes.

The frustrations and exasperations were seen as hindrances to the main purpose, which for Peale was to collect information and specimens of birds and animals from the remote parts of the globe they visited. To achieve these objectives Peale took advantage of every opportunity afforded, and appears to

have performed his work with competence and thoroughness. Even while at sea, or on the ship when near shore, Peale shot and secured many specimens of sea birds. During the first year out, at the time when the ships were rounding Cape Horn, he felt it his duty to volunteer to accompany the *Peacock* on a peregrination, as Hudson called it, into the Antarctic Sea. Plans for a short cruise into the Antarctic were made after the squadron had arrived at Orange Harbour in Tierra del Fuego. Wilkes's Instructions were to "stretch towards the southward and westward as far as the Ne Plus Ultra of Cook, or longitude 105° W., and return northward to Valparaiso, where a store-ship will meet you in the month of March, 1839."[28] Consequently the *Peacock* and the *Flying Fish* were ordered to the westward, as far as the Ne Plus Ultra, and the *Porpoise* and the *Sea-Gull* were ordered to pass to the south in order to explore the southeast side of Palmer's land. (The *Sea-Gull* was never to be heard from again.) The *Relief* was ordered into the Straits of Magellan. Members of the scientific corps were to accompany the latter ship for some land explorations or to stay with the *Vincennes*, moored in Orange Harbour.[29]

Peale volunteered to accompany the *Peacock*, and thus was the only member of the scientific corps to go into the cold regions of the Antarctic.

> I have considered it a duty to volunteer, although the product in Natural history may be small, yet be it what it may, it will be looked for with interest.[30]

It was an exceedingly difficult passage with heavy winds and squalls of rain and snow. One man was knocked off the yard and thrown overboard, and, though quite miraculously rescued, died within a few days and was buried at sea. They began to see icebergs regularly, and the cold increased as they pushed southwards. The ship was covered with ice, the deck constantly wet, and the ship damp throughout. The beauties of the *aurora australis*, lighting the southern skys, contrasted with the misery on board. The men bore up well under the difficulties, and Captain Hudson good-humoredly recorded their hardships in his log:

> Sunday, March 17, 1839.... Had Divine Service on the half Deck—read the Episcopal Service and a sermon—perhaps the first time it was ever done within the Southern Antar[c]tic circle. I should indeed rejoice to extend the requirements of the Gospel and knowledge of salvation from Pole to Pole.... I must here again repeat how wet and uncomfortable our gun deck is—enough of itself to make all hands sick—most of the water passing over it *freezing*.... For the last 14 hours we have had the strongest gales and heaviest sea that we have experienced since I took charge of this ship and I feel quite ready to retract...all I asserted a few days since in my Journal—of our having reached a more equable & uniform climate...nor am I prepared to allow that cruising amongst icebergs in *thick* hazy weather, when

---

[26] Hudson, Journal I, Jan. 26, 1839, 98–99.
[27] TRP, Surveying.

[28] Wilkes, *Narrative* 1: xxvi.
[29] *Ibid.* 1: 120.
[30] TRP, Journal № 1, Feb. 25, 1839.

you have them popping up suddenly in your face to bid you defiance, and that without any previous notice—to be quite so agreeable as being seated *tate a tate* at your own fireside—*this fancy kind of sailing* is *not all that* it is *cracked up to be.*[31]

On the twenty-second of March, Peale recorded:

. . . our difficulties increased as the wind rose, for we soon found that we were surrounded [by icebergs] and detached floes; at one time there was about 30 of enormous size, which seemed to say, "thus far shalt thou come, and no further."[32]

On the twenty-fourth of March, Lieutenant Walker and his small crew of two officers and ten men in the sturdy little *Flying Fish* reached latitude 70° 14′ S, thus penetrating further south than any other ship of the squadron during this and the later voyage into the ice pack. The *Peacock* had come almost as far, having reached latitude 68° S, 97° 58′ W. The edge of pleasure in having achieved a United States record was taken away by the regret that they had not surpassed Cook's record of sixty-five years earlier, which was 71° 10′ S.[33]

On the twenty-fifth of March, with conditions steadily worsening, the officers held a council and Hudson decided to return northward. By the first of April they were in warmer and calmer seas.[34]

Captain Hudson's journal contains a number of simple topographical sketches delineated by Peale, and it is not surprising to find entries in Peale's journal similar to this:

This morning I was roused early to make drawings of some of the icebergs which we were passing.[35]

Peale's skill was a handmaiden to his science. He constantly was sketching specimens he had obtained. In these he strove for accuracy, so that, if, as sometimes happened, circumstances made it impossible to preserve the specimens, he had his drawings and data.

In Valparaiso, Chile, their first important stop after the Antarctic venture, Peale, along with the others, not only enjoyed a few days of civilized social life in South America, but visited the public gardens. Here he had the pleasure of seeing some of the fruits of his earlier labors:

They [the gardens] are on the Almendral, closely walled in, and kept in tolerable repair, in them great pains is taken with foreign plants & flowers, among which are some which I assisted to introduce from the prairies of Arkansas in 1822

—coreopsis tinctoria, Centaurea Americana, and which are now common all over the civilized world.[36]

In Peale's journal, in the journals of the other scientists and officers, and in Wilkes's published *Narrative* one finds a great and varied combination of facts and observations. The sheer mass of data gathered by the entire expedition was to give tremendous impetus to certain specialized scientific developments of the second half of the nineteenth century. In addition to the scientific data he collected, Peale often commented incidentally upon the arts and crafts of an area visited —the paintings in Madeira and Peru, or the pottery of one of the tribes of the South Seas. Hudson's journal is generally a straightforward account of the ship's movements, but along with this are some refreshing descriptions such as that of the social life enjoyed in Peru, where, however attractive and well-groomed the ladies were, with their hairdressers stationed in a powder room just off the ball room, family-man Hudson longed for a "*certain lady of my acquaintance* dangling on one arm, and her daughter on the other."[37]

In some of the other journals one finds excellent descriptions of their stay in Peru. Dr. Pickering was moved and touched by the life there:

Ever since I had been in Peru I had not been able to get it out of my head, that we had somehow gotten back into those old times that Poets and Novelists are so fond of, familiarly called the "Dark Ages"—the knife produced at the slightest affront, the mode of travelling, the frequency of highway robbery, a Walled city, Women covering their faces; the language I heard spoken so much like the Latin, even the forms of the Roman Catholic Religion.[38]

However diverting and interesting had been the stops in Madeira, Rio de Janeiro, Rio Negro, Orange Harbour, Valparaiso, and Callao, they were few and far between, and most of the first year was spent at sea. Peale and other members of the scientific corps were understandably depressed by the lack of accomplishment during this time.

On August 10, 1839, almost a year after they had left the United States, they sighted the Island of Clermont Tonnere, the first of the Paumotu or Tuamotu, Group. The ships began a running survey of the island, but no attempt was made to land the members of the scientific corps. Peale described his frustration in his journal:

No canoes were visible and as we made no attempt to land, we learned no more about them or their islands than was visible through our spy glasses. . . . The land was a very narrow strip of apparently coral rocks, enclosing a lagoon of about five miles in diameter with here and there a cluster of trees among which cocoanuts were conspicuous.

It is a very sorry business that our government should have a Scientific Corps to collect information and make a "Survey" (in the present day this term includes all the Nat[l] Sciences)

[31] Hudson, Journal I: 151.

[32] TRP, Journal ⚓1, March 22, 1839.
Parts of collections made by Titian R. Peale while on the Wilkes Expedition are now at the Academy of Natural Sciences of Philadelphia. Some of the shells collected by Peale are identified and discussed in R. Tucker Abbott, The Titian R. Peale shell collection, *The Nautilus* **68**: 123–127, 1955. A rare and valuable collection of Samoan prints and other Polynesian ethnica are described in William Churchill, The earliest Samoan prints, *Proc. Acad. Nat. Sc. of Phila.* **67**: 199–202, 1915.

[33] Henderson, *Hidden coasts*, 67–68.

[34] Hudson, Journal I: 128–77.

[35] TRP Journal ⚓ 1, March 20, 1839.

[36] TRP, Journal ⚓ 2, May, 1839.

[37] Hudson, Journal I, June 7, 1839: 197.

[38] Charles Pickering Journal, **1**, May 25, 1839, MS, ANSP. Hereafter referred to as Pickering, Journal.

of the countries we may visit, when the officer under whose charge it has been placed should consider it quite unnecessary to appropriate a single boat out of the whole squadron for their use, in consequence of which we must remain on board admiring through our spy glasses that which it is utterly out of our power to avail ourselves of; I hope in the next twenty-four hours he may see his error, and retrieve the credit of his country and the expedition, by allowing us to work as well as himself.[39]

On August 18, 1839, one year from their date of departure, Peale unhappily recorded:

It is natural to form an estimate of the labors of the past year, which it grieves me to find have been unproductive.[40]

Several days later Captain Hudson allowed some of the scientific men to land, only to be censured by Wilkes, who regretted "that he had seen officers collecting specimens." Peale felt

the order was insulting to the Scientific Corps but being addressed to Capt. Hudson I have to regret not having a copy, as it is quite a litterary curiosity as coming from the commander of a Scientific expedition, and wholly unworthy that branch of our government which allowed him to have the command.[41]

This may have been a misunderstanding on Peale's part as the published narrative of the expedition indicates that Wilkes specifically enjoined the officers to make collections of specimens which were to become the property of the government.[42]

However, often during the first year, when the expedition was chiefly involved in reaching its main area of operation in the South Seas, the scientific men like Peale were concerned that they would not accomplish their purposes. Peale confided this exasperation to his journal a number of times:

August 27, 1839. . . . We [are] under obligation to the world at large to add something to the general fund of knowledge; but as those whose duty it has become to do so are at the mercy of a petty tyrant, no remedy remains but the mortifying one of reporting the truth to the world, in our own defence, the people of the United States expect much from us, after our long delays and vexations to them we owe a long apology.[43]

For Captain Hudson, Peale always had high praise, saying that "few strive harder to make those around him happy."[44]

---

[39] TRP, Journal ≸ 2.
[40] *Ibid.*
[41] *Ibid.*

[42] General Instructions, April 18, 1839, in Wilkes *Narrative* 1: 416.
[43] TRP, Journal ≸ 2.
[44] *Ibid.*

VIII

On The Wilkes Expedition— In The South Pacific

ONCE into the South Pacific, Peale and the other men had less cause to complain of inactivity. From August, 1839, to June, 1841, the *Peacock* and the other ships of the squadron were to range the seas of the South Pacific, carefully, precisely, conscientiously, surveying and charting the numerous island groups. The scientific men frequently were landed and were allowed and encouraged to make shorter or longer excursions, gathering specimens, observing the habits of men and beasts, and collecting native artifacts. As a result, they accumulated an untold amount of factual information, often in a rather undigested manner, concerning the flora and fauna and the human life of the scattered islands of the Pacific. Their records provide detailed descriptions of native dress, habits, buildings, modes of worship and patterns of government.

The charting of the islands was the chief purpose of the expedition, and the Instructions to Wilkes read:

> ... to verify, if possible, the existence of certain islands and shoals, laid down in the charts as doubtful, and if they exist, to determine their precise position, as well as that of all others which may be discovered in this unfrequented track. When you arrive in those latitudes where discoveries may be reasonably anticipated, you will so dispose your vessels as that they shall sweep the broadest expanse of the ocean that may be practicable, without danger of parting company, lying-to at night in order to avoid the chance of passing any small island or shoal without detection.[1]

The basic method of surveying which Wilkes and the squadron used has been admirably summarized by Miss Mary E. Cooley in a paper she read at the Centenary Celebration of the Wilkes Expedition in 1940, sponsored by the American Philosophical Society:

> Most of the surveys were to be made among the low coral islands of the Pacific, and Wilkes devised an effective procedure for accomplishing them. When an island was to be surveyed, the larger vessels took stations off-shore, and smaller boats were dispatched to positions along the reef or on land. Each of the larger vessels in turn, after hoisting a signal, fired a gun so that the distance to that vessel from each of the others and from the small boats could be measured by sound, and at the same time angles were taken to the different ships and to objects on shore. From the smaller boats angles were taken between the different vessels stationed off-shore. At the time of each set of observations, the altitude of the sun was taken in order to ascertain the exact time, angles were measured to calculate the azimuth of some one of the objects, and the altitude and azimuth of the mast of one of the ships were observed. When all of the desired observations had been made, one of the larger vessels moved into a new position, and a new set of observations was taken. In this way the survey progressed around the island. Frequently the ships engaged in the work would split into two parties, one going around the island in a clockwise direction, and the other counter-clockwise, and the two parties would meet and close the survey on the opposite side of the island from the starting point. The deck boards were then sent to the flagship where the survey was calculated and plotted. By this method an island about seven miles long was surveyed in three hours and thirty-five minutes. [Fig. 36.]

The manner in which the observations were taken and recorded was very definitely prescribed by Wilkes, and a syllabus of instructions was issued to the officers. Any officer who failed to follow the methods indicated to be taken to task, and in a number of instances surveys were required to be done over again when the first results did not come up to the high standard set by the commander.[2]

During the summer and fall months of 1839 the *Peacock* and other ships of the squadron moved across the South Pacific, surveying the islands of the Tuamotu Archipelago and the Society Islands. They made a longer stop at Tahiti, and then visited the Samoan Islands before arriving in Sydney, Australia, late in November, 1839.

The journals of all the men and Wilkes's published *Narrative* contain accounts of their relationships with

---

[1] Wilkes, *Narrative* 1: xxvi.

[2] Cooley, *Pacific*, 709–710. Also see Wilkes, *Narrative* 1: 429–432.

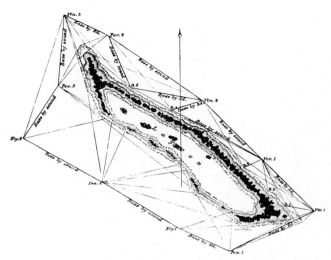

Fig. 36. Map illustrating surveying method. From Wilkes, *Narrative* 1: 452.

the various native groups, and of the numerous instances when the men of the squadron intervened in the affairs of these natives. Wilkes's volumes are rife with accounts of such episodes, and in his preface he says that the expedition carried "the moral influence of our country to every quarter of the globe where our flag has waved."[3] The concepts of law and justice held by these men were often consciously or unconsciously imperialistic. Though they sometimes described and dealt with the native tribes with the objectivity and respect of anthropologists, they also felt no qualms in dealing out their own brand of ruthless justice in order to protect themselves and to protect future United States ships which might be in these waters.

In their dealings with the natives the Navy had ordered the expedition to

neither interfere, nor permit any wanton interference with the customs, habits, manners, or prejudices, of the natives of such countries or islands as you may visit; nor take part in their disputes, except as a mediator; nor commit any act of hostility, unless in self-defence, or to protect or secure the property of those under your command, or whom circumstances may have placed within reach of your protection.[4]

Despite the fact that Wilkes issued further orders to the squadron supporting these general directives, his handling of their first encounter with the natives of Clermont Tonnere was such that some of the officers who brought charges against him at the end of the voyage included this incident as an example of unnecessary cruelty to natives. (The charge was thrown out of the court-martial as groundless.)

Probably because of the pressures brought to bear by men like Peale, boats were lowered and sent on shore for the purpose of landing. Several of the officers

and naturalists managed, by swimming through the surf, to reach the beach and spent two short hours making collections, and then returned.

The next day they wished again to effect a landing, but this time a small group of natives, the men armed with spears, lined the beach. Through the squadron's interpreter, John Sacs, a petty New Zealand chief—a half-naked tattooed savage similar to Melville's Queequeg—they learned the natives were shouting, "Go to your own land; this belongs to us, and we do not want to have anything to do with you."

Undaunted, they tried throwing presents to the natives, which were eagerly taken. Though Wilkes told John Sacs to assure them of their peaceful intentions, the New Zealander was soon engaged in a vociferous argument. Sac's ire had apparently been aroused by the chief's obstinacy; "his eyes shone fiercely, and his whole frame seemed agitated." Several officers attempted to swim ashore, only to retreat hurriedly as the natives, now more numerous, advanced. "This evidently gave the natives confidence, and their conduct became more violent." Mr. Couthouy asked to make an attempt to land, and swam towards shore, pausing only now and then to show he had trinkets. He managed to reach the rocks at the edge of the shore, but as he advanced,

the chief stopped, raised his spear, . . . made a pass at Mr. Couthouy, who at once dropped looking-glasses, trinkets, etc., at his feet, and quickly made for the boat. . . . This precipitate retreat gave them still more confidence; they now began throwing pieces of coral, numbers of which struck the men in the boat.

Wilkes wished to do them no harm, "and yet I had no idea of letting them see and feel that they had driven us off without landing." He ordered blank cartridges to be fired, but, according to John Sac, the natives only hooted at them and dared the men to land.

In his narrative report Wilkes continues the story:

Then, Mr. Peale, who was near by me, was requested to draw his ball, and load with mustard seed, which he did; and Lieutenant North likewise fired, which caused the chief and all the rest to retreat, rubbing their legs. The officers were now permitted to land, under strict injunctions, in order to avoid all contact with the natives, not to leave the beach.[5]

Because so much time had been lost and because the situation was such a delicate one, only the officers were allowed to land. Needless to say, they were able to make only the most superficial observations about the island and its products. Peale's prowess with a gun, a consistent theme in his experiences while on the Long Expedition, was to be a theme of this one as well. The other men mention his achievements in their journals and he himself often notes, sometimes with pride and sometimes in a very matter-of-fact manner, the results of his skill.

Though they met with more welcome native receptions at other islands, many of their landings were al-

[3] Wilkes, *Narrative* 1: xxiii.
[4] *Ibid.* 1: xxviii.

[5] *Ibid.,* 312–314.

most equally brief. In reading Wilkes's own narrative as well as the journals and the official scientific publications, one realizes the pressures the scientific men were under. Their work was often done on the run. Seldom could they stay even a part of a season, and they could not observe the changing aspects of plant life, or the nesting and mating habits of birds and animals. Their observations of the habits and customs of the people they encountered were hampered by the same limitations. They could describe native buildings, canoes, weapons, costumes, and other artifacts. But they could only glean fairly superficial information about the religion, the kinship patterns, the nature of the economy, or the other living habits of the natives. Hence Peale's journals, as well as those of the others, often have an episodic and unfinished quality about them. One only begins to know something of the story of the war between the Christians and the heathens on one island, or of the "Joe Gimblet" religion on another, or of the relations of Phillip to the other members of the "royal" family on another island, or of the form of idol worship at still another atoll, when the narrator moves on to the next location. They did not have time to make observations in depth. In his published narrative, Wilkes, by being able to combine information from all the men's journals, and by a compilation of related factual data gathered during the trip from missionaries, consuls, sea captains, stranded seamen living on the islands, and still other sources, was able to make more of his information meaningful by placing it in context. But in addition to a writing style often lacking grace or zest, he presents such a vast amount of varied and specific information, without sufficiently organizing it, and with very little theoretical or philosophical framework, that this is difficult for the reader to assimilate. The information in Wilkes's report is now of exceedingly interesting historical value, and a number of lively and interesting episodes are recorded, but the reader must be selective in order to extract meaning from it.

Melville may well have had the men of the Wilkes Expedition in mind when he wrote in *Typee*:

The fact is, that there is a vast deal of unintentional humbuggery in some of the accounts we have from scientific men concerning the religious institutions of Polynesia. These learned tourists generally obtain the greater part of their information from the retired old South Sea rovers, who have domesticated themselves among the barbarous tribes of the Pacific. Jack, who has long been accustomed to the long-bow, and to spin tough yarns on a ship's forecastle, invariably officiates as showman of the island on which he has settled, and having mastered a few dozen words of the language, is supposed to know all about the people who speak it. A natural desire to make himself of consequence in the eyes of strangers, prompts him to lay claims to a much greater knowledge of such matters than he actually possesses. In reply to incessant queries, he communicates not only all he knows but a good deal more, and if there be any information deficient still he is at no loss to supply it. . . .
Now when the scientific voyager arrives at home with his collection of wonders, he attempts, perhaps, to give a description of some of the strange people he had been visiting.

Instead of representing them as a community of lusty savages, who are leading a merry idle, innocent life, he enters into a very circumstantial and learned narrative of certain unaccountable superstitions and practices, about which he knows as little as the islanders do themselves. Having had little time, and scarcely any opportunity, to become acquainted with the customs he pretends to describe, he writes them down one after another in an off-hand, haphazard style; and were the book thus produced to be translated into the tongue of the people of whom it purports to give the history, it would appear quite as wonderful to them as it does to the American public, and much more improbable.[6]

One of the first longer trips Peale was able to make was an overland excursion on Tahiti, beginning Friday the thirteenth, in September, 1839. The party totaled sixteen persons and included Lieutenant Emmons, Dana, Peale, two seamen, four guides, and an interpreter. If possible, they were to ascend the highest point of the island and to ascertain the nature of the products of the island—animal, vegetable, marine, and mineral. They had hard slogging, occasionally fording a river and occasionally having to swim. These efforts were rewarded by the enjoyment of the results of the native method of cooking succulent pig and fowl, wrapped in great green leaves and cooked over coals, producing an effect between steaming and baking. Both Peale and Emmons relished this native cooking.

Rains poured down, but they still managed to obtain a few specimens, and at the summit they found "a most magnificent view" on each side.

A miserable night was spent when,

having nothing to eat and great difficulty in getting any fire to burn, we were constrained to go supperless and dripping to a cold bed on the muddy bank, during a heavy thunderstorm, but had to have a ditch dug round us in the night to carry off the water which collected beneath us in the cavities made in the soft soil by our bodies.

Happily, the next day they arrived at the house of one of the guides and the miseries of the night before were forgotten in the pleasures of a warm fire, dry clothes, and excellent food served by the hospitable natives. The hardships were a part of the accepted day's work for the enterprising naturalists. They often complained, but the hardships did not deter them, and they showed a high degree of physical stamina.

The party returned to Papeete, where they joined the *Vincennes* temporarily. A number of *camera lucida* sketches (figs. 37, 38) show that Peale spent part of his time on the hills outside Papeete sketching and painting. Some of Peale's sketches were eventually used as backgrounds for the plates which accompanied the expedition publication, *Mammalogy and Ornithology*. Peale no doubt intended to use most of his sketches and paintings in this manner; these were his notes which provided him with accurate habitat information.

In Tahiti and in other islands of the South Pacific

---

[6] Melville, Herman, *Typee*, 183–184, New York, Bantam Books, 1958.

FIG. 37. Drawing. "Papeete, Island of Tahiti. Taken from hill back of the Town / Looking
W N W." Detailed notes in upper left corner include, "2. Peacock. 3. Charles Carroll, Whaler (*too large*). 4. Queen's Palace, white with a thatched roof. 5. hill covered with Guava bushes... 7. French Consulate. 8. U.S. Sch. Flying fish ... 10.
British Consulate." Courtesy of the American Museum of Natural History.

the men of the expedition frequently came to know
the missionaries and generally felt that the religious
endeavors were positive in effect. But whereas Seaman
Clark wholeheartedly applauded the efforts of the
Protestant emissaries, Wilkes, Peale and others of the
officers and scientific men were more objective in their
judgments, and recognized some of the shortcomings.
Wilkes, for example, was critical of the discriminatory
schools set up by the missionaries in Tahiti for their
own children and those of other "respectable white
parents."[7] And later in his narrative Wilkes was to
discuss at length the pros and cons of the missionary
influence in the Sandwich, or Hawaiian Islands.

Like many who felt the charm of Tahiti, Peale's
Philadelphia colleague, Dr. Pickering, found little "to
corrupt the heart" in the Tahitian manner of living:

I know not why this island should have been pointed at
at all times on account of its licentiousness.—The difference
from the rest of the World is not so striking, at least so far
as I have had an opportunity of observing. Besides, these
people are not to be judged precisely by the same rule as
ourselves—their Social institutions are in some respects different. They are a plain-spoken set, who call things by their
right names—and it seems their conversation among themselves is often of the broadest cast—without any body sup-
posing any harm—as though, we are tempted to say, they
had not the *refinement* of indecent *ideas*. Their *dances* have
been nearly put an end to by the Missionaries, to whom
some blame has been attached on this account, but as far
as we can learn, they were not far wrong; with them however, according to Mr. Drayton the Native *Music* has almost
entirely disappeared.... The Missionaries have taught them
to read and write, but the only Literature they have furnished them, consists of some parts of the Bible, a small
Hymn & Prayer-book.... The Missionaries too claim the
credit for having abolished *infanticide*, said to have been
formerly extremely prevalent. The Women on meeting a
near relation after a long absence, always have a long continued spell of crying, and we witnessed the commencement
of one of these meetings.... On the whole taking these
people and their institutions, as well as I was able to understand them—though I would not by any means be understood to recommend them—I am satisfied there is less to corrupt the heart, than in our "Civilized Communities."[8]

[7] Wilkes, *Narrative* 2: 57.

[8] Pickering, Journal 2, Sept. 21, 1839.

FIG. 38. Drawing. "One tree hill. Tahiti." Detailed notes in upper right corner. Courtesy of the American Museum of Natural History.

Land excursions were also made in the Samoan Islands, and provided a rich harvest in ornithological collections. On October 29, 1839, Peale and several others "set off south through a beautiful valley of great fertility, abounding in heavy timber and wild Pigeons (Col[umb]ª Oceania)" many of which Peale shot without leaving the path. In the mountains Peale was impressed with the sight of a waterfall which he estimated at about 900 feet perpendicular:

The water makes but a single leap, and is lost in spray before reaching the bottom. Numerous Tropic birds and Petrels breed in the precipice, and large as they are in hovering below the cliff many are lost to the eye in the vast space below.

Since it was rumored that there was a cave on the opposite side of the island inhabited by swallows which never saw the light of day, Peale and a small party were directed on November 2 to visit it and to obtain specimens. They found perfectly ordinary swallows, but there was a certain eerie quality to the cave, where the "bat-like" voices of the birds resembled "the rattling of small pebbles."

Lieutenant Emmons, when on their subsequent visit to the Islands, recorded a tender encounter with a child that made him understand why sailors often "went Samoan":

In entering some Chiefs House I was met at the door (if an open entrance deserves the name) by two very pretty little native girls both apparently about 11 years of age—with their hair tastefully dressed with natural flowers, who after saluting me with a sweet smile & shake of the hand, retained possession of my hands and led me to a screen on the opposite side of the House behind which there was an elderly woman laying upon mats.... She rose & saluted me—offered me a seat upon a mat & a cocoanut to drink—having satisfied my curiosity and distributed some little presents, I was leaving the house when one of these little sylphs after bidding me goodbye with a tender of her hand *asked to seal it with a kiss*—which of course she was allowed to do—and received interest in return. This purely innocent mark of friendship from one so young & pretty, quite captivated me—and had I felt my existence as much of a blank as some foreigners who have taken up their residence in these Islands, and forgotten my own Land of Liberty I am sure I should have turned "Samoa" too.[9]

On December 26, 1839, the expedition reached Sydney, Australia. They slipped into the harbor at night "and lay snugly at anchor when the good people of Sydney looked abroad in the morning. Much to their

[9] Emmons, Journal 2, Feb. 28, 1841.

surprise they saw a Yankee squadron and their streets alive with the officers half wild at being once more in a civilised community who spoke their own language." Despite the nasty shock the Australians had as they realized how easily they might have been attacked had the squadron been an enemy, they treated the new arrivals magnificently.

While Wilkes, Hudson, and the naval officers made preparations for their second and major effort to penetrate into the Antarctic region, Peale and the other scientific men made various preparations for inland excursions. They also packed and shipped their specimens. At this time Peale turned over to Wilkes a total of 119 drawings and sketches as well as several notebooks.[10] A great number of these drawings appear to have been lost.

When the squadron departed at the end of December, Peale left by steamboat to visit an acquaintance, Lachlan Macallister, in the Argyle district. Peale had time to hunt and to shoot on this extended jaunt and to observe the varied natural phenomena of the Australian continent. Before his departure from Sydney in Feburary another acquaintance, Mr. McLeary, gave him a collection of butterflies and Miss McLeary, probably of the same family, a collection of birds. He wrote to his brother Franklin that these were private gifts and were sent on a ship bound for Boston, along with the public collections, but separately directed to himself at the Philadelphia Museum.[11]

In mid-January, 1840, Peale joined the other scientific men in Sydney, and early in February they departed for New Zealand. Here they spent a month waiting for the return of the squadron from the Antarctic, and during this time, as Peale wrote to his brother, they:

> ...gathered all the plants, shot all the birds, caught all the fish, and got heartily sick of the natives, in spite of their tattooing and carving; they won't bear a comparison for good qualities with the worst of the Polinesians [12]

They welcomed the return of the *Vincennes* and the other ships from the Antarctic, and were pleased and proud of the news that a continent had been discovered. With grim determination and a perseverance that won him the grudging admiration of all his men, Wilkes had pushed further and further along the barrier, until he felt sure it was indeed a continent.

Wilkes's claim was to be disputed by the British before his ships reached Hawaii, and in subsequent years there was much controversy concerning the accuracy of his claim. Though disagreeing on various points, modern experts generally agree that, though his measurements may have been incorrect as to where the land began, he was correct in proclaiming the existence of a continent. Thus, though Wilkes was not the first to discover Antarctic land, for this had been done by Pal-

mer twenty years earlier, he was the first to explore the coast line for a sufficient length to prove its continental character.[13]

The old and plucky *Peacock* was considerably worse for wear after this second Antarctic tour of duty. Peale described its plight to Franklin in Philadelphia:

> ...The poor ship has had her ribs terribly squeezed in the ice. She was embayed and carried stern foremost against an enormous "burg" the shock loosening great masses which fell fortunately astern of her, some however carrying away some of her upper spares, while the masses below "chewed" up the rudder, keel and stern, besides all her starboard abaft the gangway. Yet by a miracle and the good management of her officers she got clear steering by her sails, and went to Port Jackson to repair, when she will join us again at Tongataboa, or the Feejees.[14]

The survey made of the Fiji Islands was one of the most thorough made by the squadron, and they spent well over two months there. When they arrived in Tongataboa a small war was going on between the heathens and the Christians. For the first time, they saw a large assembly of warriors in full war regalia, their faces painted with tumeric, charcoal, and vermilion, and carrying heavy clubs, spears, and some muskets. Wilkes volunteered to mediate, and a meeting was held on neutral ground, but nothing was achieved. Peale noted with asperity that the war had been provoked by the Wesleyan missionaries, and that the odds were against the ill-equipped heathens: "The ultimatum of the allies is Christianity and a Missionary amongst you or—Extermination—the result ought to be obvious, when we know that the Mission[ry] party is the strongest and best armed."

When the *Peacock* joined the squadron on May 3, 1840, Peale wrote:

> ...All [were] glad to join our friends & shipmates—1st Lieut. Walker excepted, he refused me his hand—the remains of his old grudge for reporting sundry inconveniences he has placed me at in taking my assistant for ships duty, refusing my stores on board, etc.[15]

There were other men on this expedition as proud and individualistic as Peale. A subtle war of nerves went on between Peale and the First Lieutenant, or so it would seem from scattered comments in the former's journal. Peale, possessing a mellower sense of humor than in the days when his spleen was aroused in arguments with his father, could take these episodes somewhat philosophically. On April 24, 1841, he ruefully recorded in his journal:

[10] Peale to Wilkes, Dec. 21, 1839, MS, Smithsonian Institution.
[11] TRP to Franklin Peale, April 5, 1840, MS.
[12] *Ibid.*

[13] For a good discussion of this subject see William Herbert Hobbs, the discovery of Wilkes Land, Antarctica, *Proc. Amer. Philos. Soc.* 82: 561–582, 1940. Also see Henderson, *Hidden coasts*, chapter 9, 133–145. Wilkes' claims have most recently been upheld by two Australian experts, B. P. Lambert and Phillip G. Law. Their conclusions were presented at an international symposium on Antarctica and are briefly described in the *New York Times*, Jan. 10, 1960.
[14] TRP to Franklin Peale, April 5, 1840, MS.
[15] TRP, Journal # 3.

The first L^t issued his orders to the boats, running thus, "2d cutter, Lt Emmons will take 10 water bags, 2 buckets, 1 shovel & Messrs Hale & Peale." One at Sandalwood Bay was worse—"bring off the yams, hogs and scientifics."[16]

As the ships systematically moved among the islands, Peale and the others gathered their materials. The birds Peale found to be similar to those in Samoa, but he kept observing, making notes, and gathering specimens.

Throughout the voyage Peale was also responsible for collecting and assembling miscellaneous ethnographical artifacts. He collected tapa mats, pottery jugs and bowls, a wooden idol, models of boats, and other similar articles, many of which are on display in the Smithsonian Institution today. Always he was fascinated with the various weapons used, and particularly the bows and arrows; the toxophile was eager to enlarge his knowledge of the varieties of this supple weapon. He noted that the Fiji Islanders' method of holding the bow was exactly similar to that prescribed by the British archery manuals.

In addition to charting the islands so that the whaling and commercial vessels of the United States might more safely traverse the seas of the South Pacific, Wilkes's duties included a certain amount of policing "for protection," and administering of justice, attempting reconciliations among native factions, and making commercial treaties with chiefs. In the course of the expedition, for example, Wilkes made a treaty with "The Principal Chiefs of the Samoan Group of Islands," effected November 5, 1839, and duly signed with the marks of seven chiefs;[17] Hudson effected a set of commercial regulations made by the principal chiefs of the Fiji group of islands on May 14, 1840, and signed with the mark of the chief, Tanoa;[18] and Wilkes still another treaty with the Sultan of Sooloo made February 5, 1842.[19]

One of the cases in which it was decided to administer justice, the better to define to the natives that the vessels of the United States should be respected, was at Rewa in the Fijis, and involved the native chief, Vendovi. There are qualities of farce in this episode, which took place in part on Peale's ship, the *Peacock*. Seven years earlier, in September, 1834, according to a deposition from a former member of the crew of the brig *Charles Doggett* from Salem, Massachusetts, the chief, Vendovi, had ordered his people to attack and murder the white men, and thus had been responsible for the murder of ten members of the crew.[20] The ship had been in the harbor getting a cargo of *biche de mar*, a sea-slug which was gathered, cured, and then sold to the Chinese.

The facts in the deposition had been confirmed to Wilkes by Paddy Connel, an Irishman who had been living among the Fijis for some time and who had been present at the time of the massacre. Paddy seems to have been one of the sea-rover types mentioned by Melville. Wilkes found him,

...a very amusing fellow, and possessed an accurate knowledge of the Feejee character.... He gave me a droll account of his daily employments which it would be inappropriate to give here.... On my asking him if he did not cultivate the ground, he said at once no, he found it much easier to get his living by telling the Feejeeans stories, which he could always make good enough for them.... [He spent his time] rearing pigs, fowls, and children. Of the last description of livestock he had forty-eight, and hoped he might live to see fifty born to him. He had had one hundred wives.

Wilkes listened to Paddy's life story, but,

I told him I did not believe a word of it; to which he answered, that the main part of it was true, but he might have made some mistakes, as he had been so much in the habit of lying to the Feejeeans, that he hardly now knew when he told the truth, adding that he had no desire to tell any thing but the truth.[21]

Having confirmed the story of the massacre which had taken place seven years before from the redoubtable Paddy, Wilkes dispatched a message to Hudson, recommending "that some steps should be taken to obtain the chief, or perhaps destroy the town where the offence occurred."[22]

When Hudson received the message, Dr. Pickering and the artist, Agate, had already met Vendovi during an excursion on May 20:

We fell in with three men, one of whom was taller than the others, and from his appearance we should have taken him for the fop of the Village. His face was painted of a shining black, except the lower part of the nose which was Vermilion, carefully "squared off"; and his hair from behind had much the appearance of an inverted iron pot. This we subsequently found was Vendova, with whom we were destined to be better acquainted. A sketch of him was fortunately made by Mr. Agate, before he was robbed of his locks.[23]

On the twenty-first of May, 1840, Hudson called a council of the royal family on board the ship, hoping that Vendovi would appear. When he did not, Hudson informed the group that he desired Vendovi and that they would be retained as prisoners until the guilty man was forthcoming. "This announcement threw them all into great consternation, while it was, at the same time, a matter of surprise to all the officers of the ship." Peale, of course, was a witness and participant in the events that followed. The royal party consisted of about seventy or eighty natives, but Hudson had laid his plans carefully and soon persuaded two of the chiefs to return to the island and to take Vendovi by surprise. While they waited for them to re-

[16] TRP, Journal ⅍ 5.
[17] Wilkes, *Narrative* 2: 428–430.
[18] *Ibid.* 3: 408–409.
[19] *Ibid.* 5: 532.
[20] *Ibid.* 3: 412–414.

[21] *Ibid.* 3: 69–70.
[22] Wilkes to Hudson, May 17, 1840, in Wilkes, *Narrative* 3: 411.
[23] Pickering, Journal 2.

turn, the natives were given "plenty of hard bread and molasses, which they enjoyed exceedingly, and afterwards performed several dances."

The king and his party were served their desired evening brew of ava, and then:

... theatricals were resorted to for the amusement of their majesties. This was a business in which many of the crew of the Peacock were proficients, having been in the habit of amusing themselves in this way....Jim Crow's appearance, on the back of a jackass, was truly comical: the ass was enacted by two men in a kneeling posture, with their posteriors in contact; the body of the animal was formed of clothing; four iron belaying-pins served it for feet; a ship's swab for its tail, and a pair of old shoes for its ears, with a blanket as covering. The walking of the mimic quadruped about the deck,...and the audience, half civilized, half savage, gave the whole scene a very remarkable effect.... The whole company seemed contented and happy; the king had his extra bowl of ava, the queen and chiefs their tea and supper; and all enjoyed their cigars, of which they smoked a great number.[24]

Early next morning the two chiefs sent to get Vendovi appeared in a large canoe, and he was

...at once brought on board and delivered to Captain Hudson, who forthwith examined him before the king and chiefs, and in the presence of the officers of the ship, assembled in the cabin. Vendovi acknowledged his guilt in causing the murder of part of the crew of the Charles Doggett, and admitted that he had held the mate by the arms while the natives killed him with clubs. Captain Hudson now explained why he had thought proper to retain the king and the others as prisoners, saying that the course the affair had taken had saved them much trouble, and probably fighting, for he would have thought it incumbent upon him to burn Rewa, if Vendovi had not been taken. The king replied, that Captain Hudson had done right; that he would like to go to America himself, they had all been treated so well; that we were now all good friends, and that he should ever continue to be a good friend to all white men. Vendovi was now put in irons....

When the time for leave-taking came, all of the party were much affected:

All shed tears, and sobbed aloud while conversing in broken sentences with their brother.... The king kissed the prisoner's forehead, touched noses, and turned away... whilst the common people crawled up to him and kissed his feet. One young man who belonged to the household of Vendovi, was the last to quit him.... In bidding farewell to the chief, he embraced his knees, kissed his hands and feet, and received a parting blessing from Vendovi, who placed both his manacled hands on his head. The young man then retreated backwards towards the ladder, sighing and sobbing as though his heart would break. The last request the king made to Captain Hudson was, that his own barber, Oahu Sam (a Sandwich Islander), might accompany Vendovi. This was readily assented to, as he would be a useful man on board ship, having sailed in a whaler, and having some knowledge of the English language.[25]

It is difficult to know exactly how the Fiji Islanders interpreted this odd piece of American justice. Wilkes himself talked to the missionary at Rewa several weeks later and reported that "he spoke in very high terms of the conduct of Captain Hudson, and the manner in which he had conducted the whole business at Rewa. He also told me that the chiefs often spoke of it, and were fully sensible that it was just that Vendovi should be punished."[26] Pickering, however, noted in his journal that the episode had possibly had a very different effect from that anticipated and that it was rumored "that the Rewa people had even gone so far as to build a house for the presents he was to bring back from America!"[27]

Vendovi, the Fiji chief, was something of a showpiece during the rest of the voyage, attracting attention among the Indians of the American Northwest as well as among the inhabitants of Malay. His health gradually declined, and then took a turn for the worse when, during the return voyage, Mr. Vanderford, an officer who had especially befriended him and who had lived for a time among the Fijis, died.

Poor Vendovi could not be persuaded to look at his friend's corpse; his spirits evidently flagged; a marked change came over him; and he no doubt felt as though he had lost his only friend. His own disease, henceforward, made rapid strides towards a fatal termination, and he showed that such was the case by his total disregard of everything that passed around him, as well as by his moping, melancholy look.[28]

When the squadron finally reached New York, the pathetic and declining Vendovi was placed in the Naval Hospital, where he soon after died. A final sequel is the listing of the "Cranium of Vendovi" as item No. 30 in a handwritten catalogue of the collections of the United States South Sea Surveying and Exploring Expedition originally prepared in 1846, and a copy of which was presented to the National Museum in 1877 by Mr. Titian R. Peale. Vendovi's skull is still carefully stored among the ethnological collections of the Smithsonian Institution.

All told, the men of the squadron had had peaceable and pleasant relationships with the bushy-haired inhabitants of the Fiji Islands and had had a profitable time making collections and conducting their surveys. The legendary cannibals had been amiable, peaceful, and friendly. But at last, on July 3, 1840, they had occasion to witness cannibalism. The journals of Emmons and others are closely parallel; one can almost hear them discussing the episode together on deck. Dr. Pickering recorded the event as well:

We had hitherto been so well treated by the Natives, had found them always so obliging, and so "timid"; that many of us began to think they had been maligned. Some even doubted whether they were really *Cannibals*; and the question had been seriously discussed at the Wardroom table the previous evening. It so happened that though we had been nearly two months on these islands, no one could say that he had actually witnessed the fact, or name a person of credit who had. We were on the point of returning, and only

[24] Wilkes, *Narrative* 3: 128–130.
[25] *Ibid.* 3: 135–137.

[26] *Ibid.* 3: 137.
[27] Pickering, Journal 2, May 21, 1840.
[28] Wilkes, *Narrative* 5: 418.

FIG. 39. Oil painting. Inscription on back reads, "Volcano of 'Kaluea Pele' as seen from the side of 'Mauna loa,' looking SE. Nov. 21, 1840." Courtesy of the American Museum of Natural History.

adding "mud to the stream of knowledge." "There are none so blind as they that wont see," but it turned out that these were even forced to see. We were anchored off the village on the island before visited by us, and some one learning that there was a feast on shore, desired evidences of the fact. Presently 3 or 4 Canoes came about, bringing part of a skull, and several human bones with the flesh adhering. One fellow was seen on Deck to pick out the eye, and biting off a piece, chew it with the greatest unco[n]cern; saying that it was "Venaka." I was myself below at the time, but afterwards saw some of the bones, pretty well "gnawed," and obtained the remnant of the eye, . . . which I gave to Mr. Peale. The incident was witnessed by Messrs. Spieden and Dana, Dr. Palmer, and others who were on deck at the time.[29]

Appropriately enough, Item No. 29 in the Smithsonian Institution catalogue compiled by Peale is:

Cranium of a Fiji who was killed, with others by a neighboring tribe, and portions of their cooked bodies taken on board the U.S. Ship Peacock for sale, at Naloa bay, Island of Vanu-levu, July 3d, 1840.

A bitter end to the stay in the Fijis was an episode that took place between the islanders of Malolo and

[29] Pickering, Journal 2, July 3, 1840.

the men of the *Flying Fish* while the latter were completing their survey. Though the natives thronging on the shore had seemed hostile, one of the lieutenants, Underwood, had gone on shore to parley for provisions. After a series of rapid-fire events a melée occurred in which both Lieutenant Underwood and Lieutenant Henry, Wilkes' nephew, were brutally killed. As retribution, one of the villages was burned, and a dramatic surrender according to the customs of native warfare exacted. Though some of the officers were later to charge Wilkes with unnecessary cruelty in this case (the court-martial exonerated him), he felt he had acted with restraint and that his actions were motivated, not by revenge, but by a desire to leave an impression of fair but firm action among the islanders.

The squadron spent several months in the Sandwich, or Hawaiian Islands. This somewhat longer stay was necessitated by their late arrival in September, 1840. Wilkes felt it was then too late in the season to go to the Northwest Coast of America, where they next intended to make surveys, and consequently their time was spent in laying in supplies, in making complex

FIG. 40. Oil painting. Interior of Kileuea. Courtesy of the
American Museum of Natural History.

FIG. 41. Water color. "The tree near which Capt Cook was
killed Caurcacoa bay / Hawai." A woodcut after
this was used in Wilkes, *Narrative* 4: 93.

pendulum observations on the summit and base of Mauna Loa, in examining the craters and effects of recent eruptions of the volcanoes, and in making shorter surveying and collecting trips in the area. Peale's own journal is missing for this period, but a number of sketches and oil paintings from this season are again testimony to Peale's collecting and observing activities (figs. 39, 40, 41).

The most effective of these is his portrayal of the volcano crater of Kilauea. As seems to have been customary with him, he first prepared a careful sketch and then did an oil painting afterwards. In the painting the appearance of the glowing, smoldering, fiery sea of lava is caught. The "boil" he noted in his sketch (now in the collection of the American Museum of Natural History) is there, as are the "dark" and "light" in the sky. The minute, sticklike, figures of the men in the foreground are dwarfed by the fiery grandeur of the scene. The painting has many of the dramatic effects of terrible and awesome nature that preoccupied artists and writers of the period. This is because the scene itself was dramatic. Peale, the artist-scientist, would not over-dramatize or romanticize a scene. But he did put forth his best efforts to record for others a little-known and exotic world.

While the *Vincennes* stayed on at Hawaii, Captain Hudson and the men of the *Peacock* as well as those on the *Flying Fish* were instructed to depart on December 2, 1840, to return to the Samoan group to re-examine some of the surveys made by the *Flying Fish* which Wilkes deemed inadequate, and to visit the little-known groups of the Ellice and Kings Mill Islands. Several policing investigations, similar to the Vendovi episode, were included in their list of duties. As they moved from island to island, Hudson was generous in giving the naturalists many opportunities to enlarge their collections.

One tense episode in which Peale played a role of some prominence occurred in April, 1841, while they were in the Kings Mill group of islands. They were surveying an island where they had found the people of one of the villages to be aggressive and seemingly hostile, and Hudson had cautioned his men to be particularly correct in their behavior toward the natives. Nonetheless, at the end of the day John Anderson, seaman, and "one of the most prudent & correct men in

the Ship," failed to appear. The natives threw stones at some of the other men and brandished spears, but did no further harm. The next day they attempted a parley with the natives, promising a gift of tobacco if they would present Anderson. The natives seemed sullen and the white men became convinced that Anderson had been murdered; it was decided that the villagers should be punished.[30] Peale's journal describes the episode which followed:

April 9, 1841. Receiving no intelligence of the missing man Anderson we are now fully satisfied that he was murdered by the savages on the 7th, therefore chastisement was indispensable for the security of the numerous whalers who visit the vicinity of this group; accordingly 7 boats with about 80 men were fitted out & started for the village Uteróa where the murder was committed.... We found about 500 natives armed & on shore to receive us, flanked by several hundred more behind the fences, and above and below the town, about 300 waded off towards the boats with the intention of forcably draging them ashore, a short parley was held and we demanded the lost man, but they treated the demand with contempt....

I was in the left division with Lt. Emmons and while the men were forming had occasion to single out two chiefs rallying their warriors to the attack. The shots were both long rifle range, the last being 217 paces and both fell dead in their tracks: this was too much for warriors who heard the sharp crack of the rifle for the first time: they were at first incredulous about the death of their leaders, but when once satisfied they would not suffer me to approach so near again, retreating as we advanced.[31]

The men then landed and set fire to the town, which was soon reduced to ashes. About twenty natives were killed, but no whites. The latter, though outnumbered, obviously had the advantage in fighting equipment. A sorry ending was provided by the further looting and plundering of the village by a neighboring tribe.

Wilkes's narrative records Mr. Peale as the best shot in the group. The latter was pleased to learn, upon their second stop at Samoa, that the natives affectionately called him "the Good-Shot," though on this island it was only in honor of his skilled marksmanship when shooting game.[32]

[30] Hudson, W. L., Journal II, Aug. 11, 1840, to Feb. 19, 1842: 184–191, Southern Historical Collection, University of North Carolina. Microfilm.
[31] TRP, Journal ⚓ 5, April 9, 1841.
[32] *Ibid.*, Feb. 6, 1841.

On The Wilkes Expedition—
Shipwreck And Homeward Bound

WHEN the *Peacock* and the *Flying Fish,* after thorough and leisurely surveys of the island groups they had been ordered to chart, returned again to Honolulu on June 16, 1841, they discovered that the *Vincennes* and *Porpoise* had left on April 6, expecting to meet the *Peacock* at the mouth of the Columbia River shortly thereafter. After quickly replenishing supplies, they were off again in little over a week, bound for the northwest coast of America. A carefully compiled "List of miscellaneous curiosities collected by the Officers and crew of the *U.S. Ship Peacock,* during her cruise from the Sandwich Islands to Columbia River, from December 1840 to July 1841" indicates that Peale was busy assembling and cataloguing all the curiosities collected by the men of the *Peacock.* It was a varied assortment, including shark's tooth swords, necklaces, fishing nets, tapa mats, the unusual coats of mail of the Kings Mill islanders, coils of sinnet (a kind of cordage), cocoanut scrapers, daggers, knives, and articles of tortoise shell. He also probably spent time checking over and organizing his specimens of bird and animal skins, and his butterflies, while the crew fiddled and danced the time away. The last six months when, without the *Vincennes* immediately at their heels, they had moved at a slower pace (albeit they were behind schedule) the scientific men had been able to gather masses of data and material. Peale apparently kept most of his especially fine and rare items with him, fearing they would be badly handled or destroyed if shipped.

When they reached the treacherous mouth of the Columbia River on the northwest coast of North America, the collections were the least of their worries. July 18–19, 1841, were fateful days for the men of the *Peacock.* Titian wrote about them to his brother several months later:

It was Sunday and a fine breeze was blowing to enter the Columbia river. We waited until after church and then the tide changed, before we attempted to enter, but most un-fortunately struck the bar—at first not very heavy as the tide was running out, but on the turn it was too much for the poor ship, and the shocks were so heavy we could not stand on the decks. The boats were cleared and one hoisted out (1st cutter) but she was immediately stove to pieces by the sea, which was constantly rising, and at night most had given all hope of saving the ship, or indeed our lives—by morning, however, the sea has somewhat abated, and we were directed to attempt saving only our papers, and watching a smooth time, the boats shoved off from the wreck with a few of the crew, papers and scientifics, myself with the rest, arrived to protect the above mentioned journals, etc., from the Ind[ns] who were seen collecting on Cape Disappointment where we intended to try and land, in which we were successful and the boats were sent back to the ship for the rest of the crew, but could not succeed in gaining her untill a change of tide.

In the meantime the ship was constantly beating to pieces, her masts were gone and we had little hopes of all the lives being saved,—but by hard labor all were landed before night with nothing but the clothes they had on their backs and thankful at that. One of the whale boats was absolutely capsized endwise in the breakers and lost—crew picked up by another boat near, several men wounded.

Next morning not a vestage of the ship remained, all our collections (the most valuable of any obtained) all my knick-knacks, clothes—everything but my rifle and the clothes on my back were—gone—[1]

Within a few hours many of the results of three years' work were irretrievably lost in the waters of the Columbia.

Lieutenant Emmons, who played a strategic role in the rescue operations, was in charge of the boats during this harrowing time and in his journal recapitulated some of the events of the two days:

Before Mid. the ship laboured so hard that her timbers and planking commenced working when she made water so fast that it was considered useless to attempt to free her—when the crew were consequently allowed a respite from the pumps—but there was no such as *repose* on board for on all decks one was subject to a continual shower bath and the pitching and rolling of the ship had become so violent that there appeared but little probability of the ship holding to-

---

[1] TRP to Franklin Peale, Oct. 30, 1841.

gether until daylight, *and upon this only depended our safety*. In the meantime we were gradually forging farther upon the bank, when at Daylight we were left for a short time stationary, the united action of the current & sea having piled up the sand about us and the breakers having owing to the low state of the ebb receded just to seaward of us—still the water was quite rough inshore of us. This first opportunity was seized upon to commence a landing with all our available boats which were given in my charge. As soon as I had landed in Bakers Bay and discharged my load of marines, invalids & c—, I dispatched the smaller boats back to the wreck and soon after followed with the Gigs with the intention of bringing on shore the remainder of the officers & crew. Upon doubling the cape found that the sea was very rough and breaking heavy between us & the ship, the latter labouring hard some of the head boats were already among the breakers & could occasionally be seen standing almost on end. Directly, saw the ships masts go over the side, one by one, commencing with the foremast, the mizzen going about 10 feet above the deck—upon the stump of the latter immediately afterwards disc'd the signal of distress flying (Ensign, Union down) this led me to believe that the ship was fast going to pieces & I redoubled my efforts to get through the surf to her. Still the sea was fast increasing with the rise of the tide & it required considerable management to keep the boat afloat, finding the rudder rendered useless by the roughness of the sea shipped a steering oar which answered my purpose better—although it did not lessen my chances of being knocked overboard. At this time I disc'd one of our boats that was in charge of our Gunner Mr. Lewis capsized *end first* by a heavy roller & all disappeared for sometime.

Another boat under Pass^d Mid^n Davis or Harrison being near succeeded in rescuing all hands of the crew—when the swamped boat was soon drifted out of sight among the breakers.

Capt. H. witnessing the fate of this boat and our fruitless exertions to reach the ship—reversed the Ensign and hoisted it *Union up* which I at once understood to mean *return with the boats*. Seeing how useless my efforts were, and that by continuing to persevere, I was not only risking the *means*, but jeopardizing the *lives*, that were *looked to for success*. I turned back. And with feelings that I will not attempt to describe, nor shall I soon forget.

Immediately upon reaching Bakers bay again I sent an officer to the top of the Cape to keep a lookout upon the Sea & Ship—& to let me know of any change in regard to either—in the interim employed all hands that were well (nearly all the crew of the boat that was lost, being disabled) in erecting temporary tents out of spruce boughs for officers & men. Found here Messrs Frost, & some members of the American Methodist Mission, who have lately established themselves on Point Adams from where they witnessed our situation & had come over with their tents, some articles of provisions, and cooking utentils to afford any assistance in their power.

Mr. Burnie, the agent for the H.B. [Hudson's Bay] Company in charge of Fort George, Astoria, also came soon after similarly prepared. And Indians arriving from different quarters with fresh salmon for sail relieved many of our cares and immediate wants. Our only anxiety however was for the safety of those on board, and as soon a favorable report came from the officer on the lookout I despatched the boats again & before dark welcomed their return with the commander & all the remaining officers & crew with three hearty cheers.

Early the following morning I sent off in the Launch for the Wreck accompanied by several other boats, in hopes of saving some personal or public property but upon a near approach found only the extreme end of the bowsprit and the stump of the mizzen mast projecting above the water— could see that the spar deck had been washed away and even the planking forcibly torn from the bulwarks by the force of the sea. The tide was at this time setting out over the wreck with such rapidity that it was dangerous to venture very near in a seaway—we were therefore obliged to return, which we did at a snails pace the boats for some time barely steming the current.[2]

Since Emmons had served his first days as a midshipman on board the *Peacock*, its loss was all the more poignant to him:

Thus I have witnessed the beginning and end of the Peacock, having been launched in her at New York in 1828. And wrecked in her on the Columbia River in 1841.—She may be ranked among the first vessels in our service for the good she has done the country—having as I consider *more than thrice paid for herself this cruise,* and when her future usefulness is considered—this cruise being near its close— when from her defective state she must have been torn to pieces—and having rescued all our survey notes—and other ship's papers together with chronometers & seven instruments—the *public* loss is of no importance. And there is some consolation in knowing that after the many narrow risks she has run this cruise, that her fate has finally been prolongued until reaching her native shore where she was only deserted after all hopes of saving her had sunk with her.

The saving of *all lives,* under the circumstances, I regard as one of the most remarkable & providential things that has occured during the cruise. And one which we all have reason to be thankful for.[3]

The *Peacock* was not the first ship to be lost in an attempt to cross the bar at the mouth of the Columbia River. The report of the Wilkes Expedition emphasized the commercial desirability of the ports of San Francisco and those along the Straits of Juan de Fuca, to the north of Oregon. The information transmitted by Wilkes after his exacting study of the islands and sea lanes of the entire West Coast was responsible in part for the cry of "Fifty-four forty or fight." His conclusions about the potential maritime and commercial importance of these ports influenced immeasurably the men who were negotiating with England and with Mexico for the Northwest, and who made possible an American empire on the Pacific.[4]

Just as Captain Hudson had maintained the ordinary routine of ship's duty as the ship was falling to pieces under him, even to piping to dinner which was served on the spar deck,[5] so did the scientific men almost immediately continue their duties of collecting and recording notes. Wilkes reports that Hale and Dana, Peale and Rich visited the country around the mouth of the Columbia during the first days after the wreck.[6]

After the shipwreck, Emmons, exhausted and soon to become ill with fever, was ordered to take charge of an overland party to California that was to include Peale and other members of the expedition as well as

---

[2] Emmons, Journal 3. Emmons wrote this account five months (December, 1841) after the episode took place.

[3] *Ibid.*

[4] Wilkes, *Narrative* 5: 182–183; Norman A. Graebner, *Empire on the Pacific,* 219–228, New York, Ronald Press, 1955.

[5] Emmons, Journal 3.

[6] Wilkes, *Narrative* 5: 115.

a group of settlers and trappers to be engaged to accompany them. Because of changes in orders as to the route to be taken, several of the best people he had engaged as guides refused to go. Then followed a whole series of delays and disappointments; some of the members of the party became ill; some of the settlers decided against going because they felt their crops needed attention; rumors were circulated of hostile Indians who intended to cut off the party; animals were lost or strayed away; higher wages were demanded; Emmons himself became ill. Peale, Rich, and Agate also suffered from ague and fever at this time, though it would appear from the subsequent record of the trip that Peale recovered quickly. The others continued to suffer from the disease.[7]

When the party was finally organized, it included marines and sailors, several hired hunters and trappers, and several families that had come to settle in the West. They were altogether twenty-eight men, two white women, six children, and three squaws who were wives of trappers. In a letter to his brother describing the party, Peale underlined the "to settle," as if it seemed preposterous that settlers had already begun to arrive in these far-western territories.[8]

It was sometime during these first weeks after the shipwreck that Peale and Emmons apparently had a quarrel. Emmons refers to the episode somewhat elliptically in his journal, and though he doesn't name the "scientific gentleman" in question later journal entries lead one to believe that he means Peale. It is impossible to tell what the quarrel was about, but there is no doubt that Peale, with his prickly pride and rigid principles, was quite capable of being self-centered. Both men were tired and sick. Emmons' journal entry is dated July 25, 1841, but he was obviously writing in retrospect:

Wishing to obtain some fresh salmon at a fishery some distance farther up the river, it was past mer. when we breakfasted. A little circumstance occurred just previus to landing which developed some traits of character in one of the Scientific Gentlemen belonging to the Party, which I may not otherwise have learned on ship board, and while it confirms the predictions of several of my shipmates cautions me to be more guarded in my future bestowal of confidence.

I have treated the individual with much friendship for the 3 Years that he has been both a shipmate & messmate, but hereafter, shall [not removed with ink remover] recognize him as an acquaintance. An allusion to personal matters however brief, is unpleasant, and would not have found its way into this journal, had not the subsequent conduct of this gentleman while on the route to California evinced vindictiveness highly unbecoming an officer and gentleman.

Having placed this conduct in its true light before the Commdr of this Expedition my present ends are answered in showing as I believe I now do that I am not unmindful of the past, and am prepared to answer in future any complaints which may possibly reach the Department out of the official channel through the presumptions of this gentleman attached to the Scientific Corps.[9]

Shortly before they received their final orders for the overland journey, Emmons encountered a chief of the Kalapaya tribe, and the conversation caused him to record another type of short soliloquy in his journal concerning the fate of the red man. His views very probably represented those of many sensitive mid-nineteenth-century men:

I was met by the principal chief of this Tribe with several of his followers who addressed to me a short speech—accompanied with considerable gesture—the amount of which agreeable to the interpretation of Mr. Rodgers—was to inform me that he was chief of the Kalapaya Tribe—& that all this portion of the country belonged to them. I gave him to understand through the same channel, that I had not come to contest his claims, & hoped that he might still live many happy years upon his soil, when he retired apparently contented. Poor fellow, like the rest of his race he is *doomed* to vanish before the *White Man*. Out of 20,000 who 10 years ago peopled this country, there scarcely now remains 6,000. Whole Tribes have been completely swept off—and but a few years longer at this rate, & there will be none left. How melancholly the reflection! How little do we know of this once numerous people? & yet how much have we done to shorten their existence!!! By *we*, I of course mean the white men generally, they having introduced fatal diseases before unknown among them.[10]

Emmons received final orders for the overland journey on September 1, 1841, and the party was off immediately thereafter. During their first days and weeks on the trail they had difficulties in getting over the rough paths, with the occasional straying of some of the pack-mules, and in accustoming themselves to the hardships and routines of trail life, such as the howling of wolves at night. Typical entries in Emmons' own journal are similar to the one on September 21, 1841: "5 of the party on the sick list, myself included."[11]

They had been on the trail only a little over two weeks when they encountered two grizzly bears; Eld recorded the event:

There has been a good deal of excitement today along the road. . . . The party ahead fell in with two Grizzly bears, the first was small & scampered off the moment he spied the van, but the next was of an Enormous size and seemed to despise getting out of his usual route, but trotted along toward the party turning neither to the right or left. This led to the supposition that it was one of the pack mules, that had got ahead in some way & was now returning; the round and whitish appearance of his back deceived many until he got very near, he came boldly up within a few feet & placing himself upon his hind legs with his fore arms massed in defiance. In this position Mr. Peale gave him a ball in his lungs and he bounded away in an instant. [12]

The rest of the party were no doubt grateful for Peale's dependable marksmanship and cool familiarity with *Ursus horribilis*.

Peale's journal for this journey does not begin until the twenty-second of September, the day on which he

[7] Ibid. 5: 218.

[8] TRP to Franklin Peale, Oct. 30, 1841.

[9] Emmons, Journal 3.

[10] Ibid., Aug. 8, 1841.

[11] Ibid.

[12] Journal of Henry Eld, Jr., U. S. Navy, Sept. 6 to Oct. 29, 1841; Sept. 20, 1841 entry, MS, Western Americana Library, Yale University. Hereafter referred to as Eld, Journal.

began a new one because the other, begun after the wreck, was lost along with more of his precious notes. His journal records this episode:

September 22, 1841.... The days journey was a most arduous one, one or two horses fell down the steep sides of the mountains with their packs, but were recovered with some little delay; the bag containing my bed^g and wardrobe was torn open by the brush and carelessness of the men in charge, and the case containing my drawing instruments was broken, and all the instruments, my sketch book and Journal lost—with all my notes and drawings from the time of our landing in Oregon after the wreck of the Peacock; a loss the more serious by reason of my being destitute of the materials to continue my observations.

Encamped on the south side of the mountains before night, at which time only I became acquainted with my loss; the men returning a *boot* picked up in the road.

Thursday 23^d. The party were delayed today, to allow me time to try and recover my Journal, etc., I returned over the mountains with two men (Wood & Black)—I succeeded in finding my camera lucida only, and continued searching until afternoon, when meeting some Indians in the path concluded it was useless to search further, and that my book, and the remaining instruments and paint box were irrecoverably lost.[13]

This loss, added to his others, was an extremely hard blow for Peale.

Emmons' fuller account describes the same events in greater detail. It was one of the most arduous of their trip, and one can readily imagine the exhaustion of the sick and tired men:

Sept. 22, 1841

... The mountain had lately been set on fire by the Indians (doubtless to obstruct us*) and large trees had fallen across our path so that we were in many instances obliged to cut our way through or around them.

And as the mountain path was always more or less obstructed by broken limbs & brush which was now tough & blackened by the fire, by keeping up a continual dodgeing, we were unable to escape many hard rubs and scratches which I fancy made us look more like a band [of] devils on horseback than anything human.

Having reached the first summit (about 3000 feet above the valley) decended again at about the same angle, crossing a small rivilet & immediately commenced another & if possible, worse ascent passing above a narrow burnt ridge—cutting our way as before—transferring some of the pack from the weak to the stronger animals, that the former might hold out, and for similar reasons each of the party that was able walking & leading his animals up & down all bad placed.

I had hopes that the atmosphere would have been clear so as to have allowed me a view of the surrounding country upon crossing these mountains, but I was disappointed, and as long as it continues in its present state I feel that I am groping my way along half blindfolded, & consequently learning but little about the country beyond my reach.

During the day, being in advance of the Party, I was caught by one of the Indian snares, & swept off the horse without receiving any injury.

A rifle was discharged among the party owing to the lock' catching a bush—no one receiving injury.

After a gradual descent of about 3 miles reached a beautiful valley at the foot of the mountains, having disc^d several tracks of wild cattle, and passed on our way a pen that had evidently been erected by the Indians to entrap them. These are doubtless the same cattle or the progeny of those that have at different times been lost by the H.B. Co^s Party while passing through this country. After pitching tents sent out Hunters in hopes of getting one, but was unsuccessful.

Upon one of the last packs that arrived in camp was a bag belonging to Mr. Peale, the mouth of which had been torn open on the way, & several articles of importance lost, among others a Camera Lucida, Journal, etc.

During the night I was wakened by the cry of ho! ho! and upon looking from under my tent disc^d that one of the horses had become entangled in the adjoining tent streatchers, & after kicking furiously for some time finally pulled the whole fabric down upon the Marines who were the principal inmates, & who took no further trouble to extricate themselves until daylight.

19th Encampment   Sept. 23^d, 1841   *Land*

Light Westerly winds, latter part fresh, flying clouds & smoky atmosphere. Smith the Marine added to the sick list, ague & fever, had become so weak that he had fallen from his horse several times within the last few days, and it became necessary to appoint a man to look especially after him, as it was evident that his senses had become impaired.

To comply with Mr. Peales request, and allow the animals some additional feed & repose, both of which they were much in need of, I did not start camp this day, but sent the band about a mile to the southward, and despatched two men back accompanied by Mr. Peale in search of his lost articles part of which were finally found....

A lazy fellow by the name of Wood who I engaged to make up my number in the Party, but more especially for two mules which he could furnish for pack animals, having been reported to me by Mr. Peale for neglect of duty, and having become quite worthless, I gave him his discharge. He however still continued along with the Party, as it would have been dangerous for him to have separated from it in this country.[14]

It was a trying two days for both Peale and Emmons, and both seem to have done all they could to solve the problem. Nevertheless, their petty quarrel seems to have continued, as evidenced by comparing parts of their respective journal entries on October 8, 1841:

On this day Peale wrote:

... After traveling 13 miles we came to a pleasant valley with open groves, and abundance of grass for the horses. There we pitched our tents, and being destitute of meat, all the hunters started out. I killed three deer, but lost one of them. Meeting one of the horse guard I sent one carcase into camp for supper, and on my return reported the other to Mr. Eld with a request that men might be sent for the meat, but Mr. Emmons considered the report *informal* in not being made to *him,* and refus^d permission to the men to bring the meat. I therefore gave directions to the camp followers (Wacca & Mrs. Warfield) who consequently were better supplied than we were.[15]

On the same day Emmons again wrote in an elliptical fashion:

Encamped early (about Mer.) on account of the Sick, in high grass, & on the East side of the C. River. Two [of] our

[13] TRP, Journal ⚹ 7.

* The boughs were in many bad places artfully tied together from opposite sides of the path, so as to entrap the riders & sweep them from their horses backs. Found a cutlass of considerable service to us in this particular.

[14] Emmons, Journal 3.
[15] TRP, Journal ⚹ 7.

pack animals were reported missing, one of them a large mule that carried most of our powder. Immediately dispatched 3 men back in search, & returned about 2 miles to accompany in a small sick party under Mr. Eld.

Two deer were shot & brought in and divided among the Party, including the families as usual.

Connected with the fate of these Deer & Mr. Agate's chill are two circumstances which I shall not soon forget.[16]

All was not hardship, illness, and personal bickering on the journey. In Peale's journal and in those of Emmons and Eld as well, one finds good descriptions of the countryside of the Far West and fairly objective pictures of the hardships and joys of the days on the trail. Peale, as usual, made notes on the flora and fauna of the region. In other parts of his journal he reports on the beauty of the view from the top of Mount Tchasty (Shasta), and upon the kinds of bows and arrows used by a group of Indians they encountered. Eld shared some of Peale's enthusiasm for ornithology and occasionally paused to make notes on the habits of birds they saw. In spite of themselves, the men had to laugh at their own sorry condition. Emmons devoted a page and more to the story of the irascible horse, Frying Pan, who managed both to exasperate and to amuse:

Oct. 19, 1841. . . . In an open prairie, came upon a large herd of Elk nearly all bucks. They first disc'd us when about 2 mile distant & watched us attentively until within about 1 mile when they frequently altered their positions—moving about in circles, then halting, & erecting their heads to obtain a better view of us. And when within about ½ mile, they started & all moved off rapidly at right angles with our line of march, for a piece of woods to the west'd. Ere they had entered this cover two of our Hunters were side by side with some of them, but did not succeed in killing any. With fresh horses, well equipt, such a chase, with such advantages, would be grand sport, but with our poor worn out animals it is cruel to see them attempt to run except in the case of one today, that has frequently evinced some viciousness & made it an invariable practice of kicking up three times as soon as the bellyband to its load was hauled taut previous to starting camp.

This Horse L gave in charge to one of the sailors by the name of Doughty, who named it Frying Pan in consideration of this article together with pots, kettles, etc. composing its load. On the present occasion while all the band were moving along quietly, Frying Pan commenced kicking & running against the other animals in the band, & making so much noise by shaking up the pots & pans together, that the other animals began to get allarmed. When several men made an effort to catch her, to avoid which she dashed off at right angles across the prairie at the top of her speed, closely pursued by several of the men with their Lasso's, but being accustomed to this game, she escaped by dodging & after taking a wide range, came back in to the band again, & in her effort to do mischief bursted her bellyband, & having created another excitement, away she dashed again ahead of the Party, pots and pans flying in all directions, & it was nearly ½ an hour before she was finally captured.

Some of these scenes are gotten up without much previous notice, and are certainly entertaining, if they are sometimes troublesome & expensive.[17]

The overland journey was virtually ended when the

weary travelers reached the ranch of Capt. Sutter, the "Nuevo Helvetia," in the Sacramento Valley. Peale's journal describes Sutter's prosperous settlement with almost one thousand horses, a cattle herd of three thousand head, and a flock of sheep numbering almost eighteen hundred. Here the party divided. A launch from the Vincennes took Emmons and the sick members of the party down the river, and they reached San Francisco on the twenty-fourth of October.

Eld, Peale, Rich, Brackenridge, and some of the men went the last lap by land. On the twenty-fourth they reached the Mission of San José. They were entertained by the agent of the Hudson's Bay Company, Mr. Forbes, at his farm. At the mission Peale and Eld visited the church and gardens, and in the former Peale noted oil paintings by "some wandering Italian." The mission received its chief income from the hide trade, which was carried on with the merchants of Boston. Peale's word picture of the bleached bones of the slaughtered animals is vivid:

[The] plains in all directions [are] covered with carcases in different stages of decomposition, the hides and tallow only being preserved—as we traveled in the dark last night, the continued rattleing and breaking of bones under our horses feet, had a most singular and unpoetic effect—any but California horses would have been frightened by it.[18]

They also visited Santa Clara before reaching Yerba Buena at the end of October. They were a rough-hewn looking group when they arrived and had difficulty convincing some of the people they met that they were Americans. Eld described the astonishment of one man:

Oct. 27, 1841. . . . I was very much amused at the astonishment expressed by the person who belonged to the launch when he found that I was an American; he seemed scarcely to credit his eyes or ears, although I had not at all tempted from the first anything but broad English, he persisted in speaking Spanish to me, and when I told him that I perceived he was an American I wished he would speak English to me, he looked up at my buckskin attire and scraggy beard that had not been shaved in 50 days & exclaimed My God Sir where did you come from! & when I told him from the Columbia his lower jaw fell and he looked perfectly aghast and amazed, and I think would not have believed me at all had not the state of our poor miserable Horses told but too plausibily the rout they had come.[19]

They had one more sorry task to perform before joining the ship—the sale of their exhausted but cherished horses. Eld's description of their last day is not without feeling:

29th October. The Alcade rode half a mile with us to show us our rout . . . he then left us when we continued on 2½ miles more making in all a league from the Mission, which brought us to two or three houses, one of which I went up to and looking in at a window, was surprised to find some of our men belonging to the ship at a billiard table. I asked where Yerba Buena was, and with some astonishment was told that I had already arrived at the Puebla, which I had expected to find a village with 500 or

[16] Emmons, Journal 3.
[17] Ibid.
[18] TRP, Journal # 7, Oct. 24, 1841.
[19] Eld, Journal.

1000 inhabitants. I soon found Mr E. who had been on shore two or three days expecting me and a boat was in readiness to take our things off to the ship. It was determined however that I should remain on shore to assist in settling with the trappers and woodsmen and disposing of the horses, accordingly notice was written in due form to inform the public (a half a dozen persons) of our intentions and at 2 o'clock a ridiculous but to me rather painful sceen took place. Our poor old worn out & jaded horses that had borne us faithfully, and patiently, through thick and thin from Vancouver to San Francisco a distance by the rout we came about 840 miles, were exposed to public vendue, their hard usage, sore backs and bare ribs, held up to contempt and ridicule in English and repeated with jeers & laughter in Spanish and french and knocked off in lots from *12 rials* to 5 & 6 dollars each

I could with a good will have knocked down the little Alcade who had followed us from the Mission, when he bid the above paltry sum for a sturdy healthy and one of the toughest horses in the band, but they were sold without reserve and we had to let him go.[20]

The men joined the *Vincennes* and it departed from San Francisco for Honolulu on October 31, 1841. They arrived at the Hawaiian port on November 17, and in a week and a half set sail once again. All felt they were homeward bound at last, though their work of surveying and collecting was not yet finished. The voyage westward was monotonous, broken by a brief stop at Wake Island. Christmas day was spent at sea, and was lonely for the men who had been gone from their families so long:

Capt[ns] Wilkes & Hudson dined with us in the ward room and our Christmas passed as pleasantly as could be expected for those who are accustomed to make it a *family* festival.[21]

During January they spent several weeks in the Philippines and in the Malayan group. The scientific men made several excursions inland, and, as before, Peale's journal contains observations not only on natural history, but on subjects such as the practice of cock fighting and the music played by the natives. The last entries in Peale's Journal Number Seven describe the port of Singapore, where they arrived at the end of a Chinese New Year's celebration. This was in February, 1842. Their surveying had at last come to an end, and this meant that the little tender, the *Flying Fish*, had to be sold. It was another symbol of the approaching end of their tour of duty. To Seaman Clark and the others it was a sad moment:

She had been our associate in toils and dangers, and when she passed us with a strange commander and crew, with a foreign pennon streaming in the fragrant gales of this balmy spot, an involuntary sadness filled every bosom on board. There seemed to be something in the nature of our enterprise which strengthened the bonds of sympathy, extending even to inanimate nature. Her companion, the Sea Gull, had probably been lost off the coast of Terra Del Fuego, and her crew found a deep watery grave. The Peacock had been stranded at the mouth of the Columbia River, the Relief had been sent home from New Holland, and the Vincennes and Porpoise were all that remained of the original fleet, which were to return to the United States.[22]

Long days at sea, with welcome stops at Cape Town, South Africa, and St. Helena's Island, were to follow. The series of court-martials that took place after the expedition returned shows that the fires of hate and jealousy kindled between Wilkes and some of his officers earlier in the expedition had not died down. The *Vincennes* returned to the port of New York on June 10, 1842. Again, the nineteenth-century grandiloquent prose of Seaman Clark expresses the emotions that many of the men must have felt as they saw once more the familiar shores of their own country:

The events of the Expedition can not but awaken peculiarly lively emotions in all who participated in deeply interesting incidents. Five hundred men had left Norfolk to visit bleak and untraversed parts of the world, in which cruise a deep, dark uncertainty necessarily enshrouded our undertakings. The sequel proved it to be such; of the five hundred, but two-hundred and thirty-six reached the shore at that time. A portion of the remainder arrived at different times, and some slept in coral beds, to obey the summons of Omnipotence, when the unnumbered millions of ocean's children shall rise above its troubled bosom an august assemblage, and join the vast universe of created intelligences. The remote results of this Expedition cannot easily be predicted. Though the continent discovered may not be, and perhaps may never be capable of being peopled, its discovery was an acquisition to science which may not be easily appreciated. We had visited unknown nooks of the globe, navigated unexplored seas, and surveyed many islands of which there was no previous knowledge. Hidden rocks and dangerous reefs had been laid down upon charts, that future adventurers may not hazard life and property, while extending the conquests of commerce & enterprise.[23]

They had been absent not quite four years in which they had undergone many new and different experiences, four years in which much had also transpired in their own country.

---

[20] *Ibid.*

[21] TRP, Journal ⅟ 7, Dec. 25, 1841.

Maurice E. Phillips has informed me that a shell collector from the Academy of Natural Sciences of Philadelphia, recently returned from the South Pacific, reports a plaque on Wake Island commemorating the visit of the Wilkes Expedition. The name of Titian R. Peale is included among those listed as having visited there.

---

[22] Clark, *Lights and shadows*, 250.

[23] *Ibid.*, 264.

X

The Bitter Years

THE DECADE which followed immediately after Peale's return from the Wilkes Expedition was probably the bitterest and unhappiest of his life. All those things that had provided a framework for his life disintegrated during this time—family, Museum, career were washed away or badly damaged by the tide of events.

In discussing some of these unhappy events years later, Peale reported the hurt felt by the men of the expedition upon their arrival home because of the apparent indifference shown by both the public and the government:

The aggregate material, by observation, and unceasing industry in all branches of science, made an enormous collection; far greater than that of any previous enterprise of the kind. The labor was protracted to four years; we seldom in those times could hear from home in the "out of way" places we were exploring, and looked joyously for approbation on our return. We had encountered the icebergs of the Antarctic regions, if we could not prove the discovery of a new Continent; we had surveyed the Islands of the Canibals and discovered new islands, where our race has since found new homes. Will anyone wonder at our surprise when landing again on our *own* shores,—we were received with a *cold shoulder*!—unfortunately it is too true to be a pleasant memory.

Our organization commenced under President Jackson; we started under the auspices of President Van Buren, and arrived home in the time of President Tyler.[1]

The economic panic of 1837 had occurred before the departure of the expedition; it had left during a period of recovery and revival which lasted from 1838 into 1839. In 1842 the country was in the midst of a more serious and ever-deepening economic depression which had been caused in part by the failure of the Second Bank of the United States.[2] The country was in no mood to interest itself in the results of a scientific expedition. It was a period of great change, a period when increasing industrialization was making a major impact upon the life of the new country. The railroads, to name but one example, were beginning to crisscross the land and had caused a revolution in trans-

portation. In the more specialized field of science, it is worth noting that the Smallwoods, in their admirable study, *Natural History and the American Mind*, cite the decade of 1830 to 1840 as the era which saw the passing of the naturalist. That is, the naturalist, after having become a popular figure in American society, suddenly declined in importance. The natural sciences became specialized and no longer represented a general interest among many people.[3]

Wilkes himself met with a certain initial indifference and aloofness in the Navy Department, and soon had to face the dismaying court martial, from most of which charges he was exonerated. The expedition's achievements in surveying and charting alone were great, if little noticed. They had surveyed 280 islands as well as some 800 miles of coast and inland waters of Oregon Territory and 1,500 miles along the Antarctic Continent. The *North American Review* did take notice of their achievements, and in one review stated that the Secretary of the Navy felt the charts of California and the coast of the Oregon Territory alone were worth the entire cost of the expedition.[4] The expedition had been a little too late to make numerous or important discoveries of new islands in the Pacific, and doubts were being cast on their achievements in the Antarctic. But the geographical work is considered of outstanding importance today because it accurately fixed for the first time the positions of many of the islands in the groups visited, and because they made much improved charts and descriptions of them. The fact that many of the charts prepared by the expedition were still in use in World War II is a tribute to their accuracy and usefulness.[5]

One indication of the indifference and subsequent confusion that occurred at the time of the expedition's return was the immediate dismissal of the members of the Scientific Corps. The Secretary of the Navy, in writing to Peale, indicated that he was

---

[1] TRP, Surveying.
[2] Taylor, 344–345.

[3] Smallwood, 337–353.
[4] *North American Review* **56**: 266, 1843. Also see Cooley, Pacific, 718.
[5] Cooley, Pacific, 718.

of [the] opinion that so far as this Department is concerned, the Expedition must be considered as at an end upon the return of the Ships. I have consequently no authority to continue you any longer in your present position. You will therefore consider yourself as detached from the Exploring Expedition.[6]

As to what would happen next, how and even whether the collections were to be arranged and analyzed, and what was to be published about them, the curt governmental communication only stated:

The subject is now before Congress, & doubtless some suitable provision will be made for securing the results of the Expedition, under the superintendence of those who have been charged with its various departments of duty.[7]

Confusion was being compounded. Who, but the men on the expedition, should be "charged with its various departments of duty?" Three of the expedition's scientific men had been retained as temporary curators. They were Pickering, Dana, and Brackenridge.[8] The governmental action was probably a typical and necessary delay caused by the limitations of the Act of Congress authorizing and outlining the scope of the Expedition, but to the men in Peale's position this did not seem so. To make matters worse, there were already rumors and evidences of the fact that some of the collections had been opened and carelessly handled.

Blocked for a time in his efforts to complete the work of the expedition, Peale, with no other income, returned to Philadelphia and the Museum, to family and familiar friends. Franklin had good news: he had been married in 1839 to a congenial and musically inclined widow of wealth, Caroline Girard, a niece of the famous Stephen Girard. The United Bowmen elected Titian Captain at the annual prize shoot, but even that turned out to be a dismal, rainy day with poor shooting and worse music.[9] Titian's wife, Eliza, and eldest daughter, Florida, were frequently in ill health, or had colds, during the coming months—ominous signs of the tuberculosis from which both were probably suffering. To this daughter, who went off to a boarding school in the fall, Titian wrote affectionate, fatherly letters. She apparently shared his enthusiasm for natural history; he sent her shells for the school cabinet and described the plants—using the Latin names—seen at the flower show. He also told her of the tedious hours spent in New York, where he was one of the witnesses for the defense in Wilkes's court martial.[10] The family was "jog[ging] along as usual."[11]

Titian worked in the Museum, and in January, 1843, was unanimously elected Manager by the Board of Trustees. It was a hollow honor, for the Museum was

in sorry financial straits and his salary, supposed to be $1,000 per year, was dependent upon the income which was steadily falling. In May the lot on which the Museum stood was sold in a sheriff's sale.[12] George Ord, a superb if partisan letter-writer, kept his friend, Charles Waterton, informed of the unhappy train of events that took place during the next few years. On August 23, 1843, he wrote:

I should have spoken of the Museum. In a word, the building, which was erected by the company, no longer belongs to them; it was sold on the 18th of May to satisfy a mortgage; and the morgagee is now the proprieter of the whole premises. He permits the collection to remain one year free of rent; but when that period expires, the whole concern, it is thought, will go to the dogs.[13]

Ord's prediction was quite right. On April 1, 1845, the Trustees of the late Bank of the United States brought a suit against the Museum Company for the unpaid note of $100,000, plus interest, and in June of the same year the Museum Trustees voted that the contents be sold.[14] Ord informed Waterton of the event:

Apropos of the Museum. This ill-fated establishment is at its last gasp. The sheriff has his paws upon it; and it will be shortly sold on a judgment obtained by the assignees of that den of thieves, the United States Bank. The whole affair of the Museum, ever since the purchase of its present location, has been characterized, if not by knavery, yet by the most consummate folly. Poor old Mr. Peale by getting his pet Institution incorporated he would secure its perpetuity. The worthy virtuoso had yet to learn, that, in our free country, an act of incorporation is a nose of wax, *c'est ou camus ou aquilin ou retroussé ou comme vous voudrez.*

Finally, on February 26, 1846, he wrote:

The Philadelphia Museum is sold by the Sheriff; the purchaser one of the Peale Family.[15] It is exhibited in the Masonic Hall; and is merely an appendage to a Hall for the exhibitions of Jugglers and Ballad-Singers.[16]

Titian was probably just as happy to be living in Washington when the denouement took place. It was a sorry end to what had been a grand institution. In the years of its greatest ascendancy, which lasted from about 1800 to 1830, it had played an important role in the development of natural science in America.[17] It was helped by the remarkable group of pioneer scientists who lived in Philadelphia during these years. The Peales in turn had helped to inspire and encourage these men. Most important, the Peales did much to diffuse knowledge of the growing new sciences to a much

---

[6] A. P. Upshur to TRP, July 13, 1842, as quoted in TRP, Surveying.

[7] *Ibid.*

[8] Meisel, *Bibliography* 2: 654.

[9] TRP to Florida Peale, Sept. 1842; Target Book, Sept. 21, 1842, MS, United Bowmen Collection, HSP.

[10] TRP to Florida Peale, Sept. 1842, and Nov. 6, 1842.

[11] *Ibid.*, Nov. 6, 1842.

[12] Minutes of Philadelphia Museum, 1843, 116, MS, HSP.

[13] George Ord to Charles Waterton, Aug. 23, 1843, MS.

[14] Minutes of Philadelphia Museum, 1845, 128–131, MS, HSP.

[15] Edmund Peale, son of Raphaelle Peale, was the purchaser. *Philadelphia Saturday Courier*, Jan. 23, 1847.

[16] George Ord to Charles Waterton, June 22, 1845; Feb. 22, 1846, MS.

[17] See Frank L. Burns, *Wilson Bulletin* 44: 1923, and Harold S. Colton, Peale's Museum, *Popular Science Monthly*, September, 1909, for an evaluation of the Museum. Also see Charles Coleman Sellers, Peale's Museum, in: Historic Philadelphia, *Trans. Amer. Philos. Soc.* 43(1): 253–259, 1953.

wider public. It had been appropriate for Dr. Mitchill of New York to introduce Charles Willson Peale to an 1817 audience as the "father of Natural History in America."[18]

The Museum's contribution to art was perhaps proportionately less, but still significant. It was one of the first important institutions in this country to have a permanent display of paintings. At the same time the Peales helped to found the Academy of the Fine Arts in Philadelphia, so that the picture gallery of the Museum was of less influence than the annual exhibitions at the Academy. The Peales—especially Charles Willson, Rembrandt, Raphaelle, James, Sarah, and Anna—all contributed regularly to the Academy shows. Their contribution to the development of American art, and to the development of a taste and interest in art, is an integral part of the story of the history of art and taste in this country.

The natural history collections were kept together and shown at the Masonic Hall until 1850; what remains of them are now chiefly in the Museum of Comparative Zoology at Harvard University where the specimens form a valuable historical collection. The miscellaneous curiosities were purchased by Barnum, and were most probably burned in the fire of 1865. The majority of the portraits were purchased for a new National Portrait and Historical Gallery in Cincinnati, but the Cincinnatians could not meet their payments and the pictures were returned to Philadelphia. Until very recently a large number of them still hung, appropriately enough, in the upper halls of the Philadelphia State House, or Independence Hall.[19]

The institution which had been so much a part of Titian Peale's world had disintegrated. The immediate cause of the closing of its doors was the failure of the Second Bank of the United States. An indirect cause was that the institution had fulfilled its particular role in history and was not suited to a new age.

In January, 1843, Titian Peale was requested to come to Washington to "review, arrange and label the collections formed during the cruise."[20] He found the collections in even greater confusion than he had expected. Many of the boxes had been opened even before the expedition's return, and some of the collections had been put on display. When they had arrived, Secretary of the Navy Paulding had arranged to have them cared for by the newly formed National Institute, then sharing space with the Patent Office. An effort was made to appoint a competent curator, but politics or sheer negligence apparently intervened, and instead an old janitor, one or two taxidermists, and a clergyman, "doubtless a worthy theologian," were appointed

to care for the collections until the return of the men on the expedition.[21] The story of the condition in which Couthouy, who returned early, found his specimens was recounted in 1887 by a Washington scientist:

He had many valuable drawings and notes, many of which are preserved in the report on the Mollusca and Shells of the expedition. He had numbered his notes with a serial number, and a tin tag, similarly numbered, was attached to the specimen, which was preserved in spirits for future anatomical study and identification. The authorities in Washington had appointed a reverend gentlemen who knew nothing of science, with a fat salary, to unpack and take care of the specimens sent home by the expedition. This gentleman, finding that the presence of some lead in the tinfoil tags was whitening the alcohol, carefully removed all the tags and put them in a bottle by themselves without replacing them by any other means of identification. Twenty years ago I saw this bottle of tags on a shelf at the Smithsonian and heard its mournful history.[22]

Discouraged and disheartened, Peale again returned to Philadelphia. At this point Senator Benjamin Tappan, who was then chairman of the Library Committee of Congress, stepped in and persuaded Peale to continue with the task, promising arrears of pay and ample reward beyond the $120 per month which the Navy had indicated as the rate of pay. Peale accepted and began the work. To Ord he wrote:

One hundred and eighty specimens of birds which *I* collected, are missing, including some new Species;—the agregate of all other branches of Nat history, and the collections of others which are not on my register, I leave you to infer.

It is realy sickening, but I suppose there is no remedy for what is passed; I have about 60 Species of new Mammalia, and Birds, which I am now preparing an account of: they will form a very pretty volume, if completed; after that I shall be pennyless, and out of employment unless my friends will help me look out for some new "berth."—So much for enterprise!—after five years exile, with my children running wild, for want of paternal presence.—I can only expect to be rewarded with poverty, and a broken constitution.[23]

A year later he was to write in an equally bitter vein to another Philadelphia friend concerning the National Institute and its handling of the collections:

I cannot forget the late Exploring Expedition,—my two birds (male & female) made into one,—the legs of one put on another body.—hundreds of fine insects put in "families" without localities, although they came from all parts of the world.—bows in one end of the room,—arrows in another, with their ends sawed off to make them fit into fancy stands, etc.—all for the great end,—promotion of science.[24]

The developments that ensued are complex and difficult to follow. The responsibility for the publications had been shifted from the Navy to a Library Committee of Congress. Wilkes was put in charge, acting for the Committee, and was authorized to have

[18] CWP, June 2, 1817, CWP Diary ✗ 22, 34.

[19] Faxon, Walter, Relics of Peale's Museum, *Bull. Mus. Comp. Zoology at Harvard*, **59**: 119–148, 1915. George Ord to Charles Waterton, Dec. 7, 1854, MS.

[20] Charles Pickering to TRP, Jan. 8, 1843, and A. P. Upshur, Secretary of the Navy, to TRP, Jan. 11, 1843, both as quoted in TRP, Surveying.

[21] Bartlett, Reports, 617–618.

[22] Dall, *Proc. Biol. Soc. Wash.* **4**: 109–110, 1888.

[23] TRP to George Ord, March 14, 1843, MS, Misc. MSS Collection.

[24] TRP to Prof. John F. Frazer, May 15, 1844, MS, John Fries Frazer Papers.

a series of reports prepared, "in a form similar to the 'Voyage of the Astrolabe' published by the government of France."[25] Wilkes had been called to other duty during the year 1842–1843, serving on the United States Coastal Survey, but began to supervise the reports late in 1843 or early in 1844.[26] Both the Library Committee and Wilkes were under various types of pressures. The expedition had departed while a Democratic administration was in power, and returned when the Whigs were in control. Wilkes had also been disappointed in the reception given his squadron upon their return, and seems to have felt the Whigs were unsympathetic to his efforts and eager to disparage the achievements. Throughout the ensuing fifteen years or more when the specialized publications were gradually coming off the press, there was constant pressure from Congress to cut the ever-mounting expenses.

Congress looked upon the enterprise and the publications in a nationalistic manner. These were to prove the superior ability of American efforts. The Committee decreed that nothing should be printed except what was new; further, the works should be strictly American products, with no help from European scholars. (This regulation was later relaxed.) In addition, they said that the scientists should live and work in Washington while preparing their texts. All these regulations drew protests from the scientists, who resented the "quarter-deck insolence" of Wilkes's and the Committee's direction. Dana wrote a friend that "it is perfectly absurd that I should be able to prepare my reports in a city, where there are no books."[27] In 1843 Peale wrote to Tappan with some optimism about the progress of his work. However, he too complained of the lack of adequate references:

The books for which requisition was made last season have not been received; which has rendered much of my labor very unsatisfactory from want of confidence in the originality of discoveries, etc. So much has been done, even during our absence, in scientific discovery, that it is no slight task to overtake the collaborators in their onward pace. The privilege of access to the Libraries of this City has already proved of great service, but they unfortunately do not in all matters "keep up to the day."[28]

Not only were there pressures upon the Library Committee from Congress, but there were pressures from other scientists. For example, the Boston scientist Augustus Gould was writing with regularity to Tappan, urging that he be given permission to do the work on conchology, which Couthouy had abandoned and which for a time Wilkes was recommending be done by Drayton, who had been an artist on the expedition, and who seems to have developed into a kind of assistant or agent for Wilkes during the period the publications were underway. Gould wrote:

It is not the date of *discovery* of an object which gives precedence to it among scientific men, but the date of *publication*. Suppose someone should tomorrow publish descriptions of every new shell brought home by the Expedition; Mr. Drayton and every other subsequent author would be obliged to use the names there given and all further descriptions would be superfluous, because everyone would necessarily have recourse to the first described.[29]

If they were to publish only that which was new, argued Gould, they should work fast; only the best taxonomists (those most skilled in the naming and proper classification of species; those who were most familiar with the specialized literature of scientific nomenclature) should be employed to write the books, quite regardless of who had been on the expedition or done the field work. Since Couthouy had abandoned his work very early, Gould's case was special. But even the implication that others might work on their materials, before those who had gathered them, was irritating to the members of the Scientific Corps; though they had been away from libraries for four years they felt they were up to the task if they had time to organize their materials and complete their research. However, Peale would have agreed wholeheartedly with another suggestion of Gould—that a list of new specimens be published immediately before the completion of the books, so that the Europeans would know and recognize the achievements of the Americans.

The working conditions for Peale in Washington were far from pleasant. He wrote freely of his awkward and precarious position to Ord:

My present, a temporary situation is extremely unpleasant, and is I fear not to last long enough to finish our labor, although we strive to do our duty: I suffer from poverty as well as persecution; the salary is small, and never paid with regularity—we are now three months in arrears; (our masters off electioneering, or have forgotten us?) the Committee are scattered to their homes. Capt. Wilkes in Philad looking after *his book* while we poor devils have to market on credit, whine to our landlords, and bully our shoe-makers: . . . I console myself, wife and children with the old adage, "it's a long lane, that has no turn" but I feel that I have been leaning on a broken reed, in trusting to the honor, or patriot[sm] of public officers. . . .

How goes the Society? let me hear; we might as well be in Oregon as Washington for all but political news;—there's not a reading room in the city. I am painting all my new birds and animals in oil, a few have been sent to the engravers in Philad[a], and if you see them I should like to hear your opinion, that I may profit by it;—it makes a new office to have an agent!!* so that I cannot tell you who the engravers are, or where you will see the paintings.—probably Mr Lea can tell you. . . .[30]

* who gets more than twice the reward of the Naturalist and artist.

[25] *Checklist of Public Documents*, 2d ed., 176, Washington, 1895, as quoted by Meisel, *Bibliography* 2: 655.

[26] Meany, Edmond S., ed., Diary of Wilkes in the northwest, *Wash. Hist. Quart.* 16: 51, 1925.

[27] J. D. Dana to Asa Gray, March 16, 1846, as quoted in Haskell, *Bibliography*, 11. Original letter in Gray Herbarium, Cambridge, Massachusetts.

[28] TRP to Benjamin Tappan, Oct. 27, 1843, MS, Tappan Papers, Library of Congress.

[29] A. Gould to Benjamin Tappan, Dec. 17, 1843, MS, Tappan Papers, Library of Congress.

[30] TRP to George Ord, Nov. 26, 1844, MS, Mics. MSS Collection.

The agent referred to may have been Mr. Drayton or Wilkes's son, both of whom helped him prepare his narrative for publication. Peale and the others resented the commander's privilege to use their materials for the summary narrative. They had fully expected this, but they grumbled about the fact that he had obtained a copyright for additional editions published beyond the minimum number published as government documents. Though all were given the privilege of privately printing (and further financing) their own books after the hundred copies each authorized by Congress had been printed, only Wilkes, with a more popular overall narrative, which was first published in 1844 and went through several editions, could have expected to or did profit thereby. A comparison of Wilkes's narrative with any one of the individual journals shows that he freely used the information and observations recorded in them, making only slight editorial changes. His narrative is, in effect, a vast compilation of the materials in the various journals, including his own. It seemed to some of the men that he had been able to publish as his own, on private speculation, information gathered at public expense.[31]

The general publishing procedure, which made for an exceedingly limited circulation of the scientific books, was criticized by scientists in this country and abroad, by some of the learned societies, and by some Senators, but it was adhered to throughout.[32]

During the years 1843 to 1848, when Peale was working on his text and drawings, there was probably conflict between Wilkes and Peale, both proud and strong-willed men whose individual records are sprinkled with controversy. Doubts arose concerning Peale's ability to write the text. There seems to have been some honest doubt about Peale's ability as a taxonomist; he was not a "closet naturalist" but more of a field man. He had written only one or two articles of his own, and at least one of these was in collaboration with another man. His was not the brilliantly organizing, synthesizing, theorizing mind of a Dana or a Pickering. Apparently he had always received some help and advice from his friend, Dr. Griffith, in the classification work at the Museum. Therefore, overtures of different sorts appear to have been made, in order to have someone work with Peale on part of the text. Precisely how these overtures were handled or presented to Peale is not clear. There is an implication that Peale had quarreled with some of his Philadelphia friends and would not go there for help, or accept any offered. One of the offers for help came from John Cassin, a rising and aggressive young ornithologist, apparently an offer to help in classification and use of nomenclature.[33] Given the history of subsequent

events, it is possible that Cassin's offer was lacking in tact and, if so, was the kind the overproud Peale could not have accepted. Wilkes's reaction was, "Peale is very proud as you well know, and difficult to manage."[34] Virtually all of the scientists appear to have been at odds with Wilkes at one time or another, but others may have believed more in the art of compromise than the stubborn and tenacious Peale did.

It was during these same years, when all events connected with his professional life were going awry, that Peale lost three members of his immediate family. A baby boy died in the summer of 1844.[35] His wife, who had suffered long from colds, died of "consumption of the lungs" on February 24, 1846, and his eldest daughter, Florida, named after the sunny southern state, died of the same disease on February 6, 1847.[36] He was left with a son, Francis Titian, and a daughter, Sybilla. The remnants of the family had to carry on in a precarious fashion. Franklin, in Philadelphia, tactfully helped by inviting Sybilla to stay with them for months at a time, and the son, about to enter his teens, may have stayed with relatives at times. During these acid years there was no warm, comforting home life to sooth and sustain 'the spirit of the head of the family.

Another disappointment of the same period spelled the end to any dreams of association with a National Museum. The promise of President Jackson concerning Mr. Smithson's bequest had been tentative and oral. A National Institution for the Promotion of Science, a forerunner of the Smithsonian, had been founded in 1840, and it was in this institution that the collections of the Wilkes Expedition had been housed. After a long delay the new Smithsonian Institution was organized, and in December, 1846, Peale applied for the position of Curator. In this he had a letter of support from Wilkes and the active support of Ord and some other scientists. For a time Ord entertained hopes of being named Librarian, and had written reassuringly that if the efforts of his friends should be successful, "you may take it for granted that the situation of Curator will be filled by T.R.P." The letters and application were not acted upon; the reasons are not clear, but one seems to have been that it

---

[31] TRP, Surveying.

[32] Senator Pearce, Document 405, Senate, 29th Congress, 1st Session, June, 1846, as cited by TRP, Surveying.

[33] Drayton to Wilkes, June 16, 1850, reports a conversation with Cassin: "It appears he [Cassin] wrote to Peale offering anything in his power to aid him, when P. first began his book. No answer,

but one which was of no importance." MS, Wilkes Papers, Library of Congress.

[34] Charles Wilkes to Benjamin Tappan, May 28, 1845, Tappan Papers 20: 3211–3212, MS, Library of Congress, as cited by Haskell, Bibliography, 55.

[35] This child, Louis Bonaventure Peale, according to the records of St. John's Church, 13th & Market, Philadelphia, was born on July 14, 1843, and baptized Aug. 22, 1843. His name and date of birth are incorrectly recorded in Sellers, CWP 2: 422. The child apparently died in 1844, inasmuch as Peale wrote to Ord on February 11, 1845, saying, "she [Mrs. Peale] has never recovered her health since the death of her son last summer." MS, Misc. MSS Collection. The child's body is reported as having been interred in the Laforgue vault along with his mother on Feb. 26, 1846.

[36] Records, St. John's Church, 13th and Market, Philadelphia; George Ord to Charles Waterton, May 24, 1846, MS; and Sellers, CWP 2: 421–422.

was decided to make no more appointments until the buildings were finished three or more years hence. The office sought had seemed a humble one, but the small honor did not go to Mr. Peale.[37]

The blow was a hard one; as he kept working on his book, Peale worried more and more about the future. He talked of emigrating to California and thought of casting his lot with the new settlers of this area. However wild and difficult it might seem to his Eastern friends, to him it would have seemed friendly and familiar, and he could have made a new start. One of the friends who stayed loyal to Peale during these years was Professor John Frazer of the Franklin Institute, and a member of the United Bowmen. To him Peale expressed his disappointment at not getting the curatorial job at the Smithsonian Institution:

I am now much depressed by my misfortunes, but hope soon to regain my spirits, and will shake the dirt from my shoes and clear out for the west as soon as my present work is finished. It always occasions some mortification to fail, and this failure is perhaps felt more keenly on account of my domestic afflictions, and because I fear that some of my friends in whom I have confided, have not been candid with me. But it is of no use "crying over spilled milk" and as the country is large, and contains others as poor as myself I may change the scene perhaps with advantage. The pursuits of a life time cannot however be changed without a pang. Do not expose my present feelings to Judge Kane, or Dr. Patterson. You shall hear again from me before I close my arrangements here.[38]

Upon completion of his text, in June, 1848, Peale received a letter from Wilkes, on behalf of the Library Committee, informing him that his salary as a member of the Scientific Corps of the Expedition would be terminated at the end of the month. They did wish to have him complete the drawings, however, and would pay twenty dollars each; bills would be paid monthly according to the number of drawings completed. A separate volume containing the plates was anticipated.[39]

In March of the same year a bill had been passed authorizing the appointment of additional examiners in the Patent Office. The position of examiner attracted Peale and he wrote hopefully to Frazer:

Now as the Franklin Institute must be a great mechanical level, can't you fix a fulcrum for me in that quarter.—the political power can be set in motion perhaps by a cane (Kane?)[40]

Friends from Philadelphia rallied around and in August, 1848, he was duly sworn in as an Assistant Examiner in the U. S. Patent Office. Even this had not come without a tempest in a teapot when, because he

was not named an examiner, but only an assistant, he had at first refused the appointment. This time, probably on the advice of the same friends who had helped him to secure the job, he swallowed his pride and undertook his now duties,[41] which, if "not so congenial," were "more harmonious."

His position as a member of the Wilkes Expedition had terminated in June; nonetheless the request or offer to complete the drawings for the accompanying atlas remained open. While at work on the text, Peale had also spent long daylight hours working on the drawings, and had completed a fair portion of these. With his meticulous methods and his passion for accuracy, it usually took him two weeks to complete each drawing.[42] When queried by Wilkes late in October concerning the progress on the illustrations, Peale replied in a properly formal letter, indicating both his hurt and his inability or unwillingness to continue the project. The letter, in effect, severed his connection with the Exploring Expedition:

Your note of the 31st ult° was duly recd. I have always entertained, and expressed a desire to perform to the utmost of my ability, all, and every duty for which I was appointed a member of the Scientific Corps of the late Exploring Expedition.

I am personally interested in the proper completion of the drawings, considering them as I do identified with my scientific reputation; and I would have been much gratified to have been allowed to finish them in accordance with the original plan; but my services as a member of the corps, having been considered unnecessary, I was obliged to seek other employment, and being at present engaged in an office which occupies all my time, I do not see how I can now undertake on any terms to finish the work.[43]

Peale's unwillingness to finish the drawings was probably related to still another argument over the engravings. In making contracts for engravings, the Library Committee failed to request that proofs be submitted for inspection before publication. Peale, however, was determined to examine them, and through the aid of the aging John Quincy Adams, a former acquaintance of his father and a member of the Library Committee, he did succeed in having the engravings submitted for his approval. Of ten which he was allowed to examine he, as author and artist, felt seven were unworthy of publication. Peale, whose previous works had been executed by the superb and meticulous engravers Cornelius Tiebout and Alexander Lawson, could not accept the work of a generation whose standards were formed by increasing demands for quick and mass-production results. Peale failed to appreciate the Committee's need and desire to cut expenses. Their version is that they had decided to have the engraver cut out most of the elaborate backgrounds as a means of saving money, and that they had avowed "scrupulous exactness" in the natural history figures. John

---

[37] Charles Wilkes to TRP, Dec. 14, 1846, and Charles Wilkes to the Board of Regents of the Smithsonian Institution, undated, both as quoted in TRP, Surveying; George Ord to TRP, Aug. 25, 1846, MS, HSP.

[38] TRP to J. F. Frazer, Jan. 30, 1847, MS, Frazer Papers.

[39] Charles Wilkes to TRP, June 14, 1848, as cited by TRP, Surveying.

[40] TRP to Frazer, March 22, 1848, MS, Frazer Papers.

[41] See series of TRP Letters to J. F. Frazer, MSS, Frazer Papers.

[42] TRP, Surveying.

[43] TRP to Charles Wilkes, Nov. 3, 1848, as cited by TRP, Surveying.

Quincy Adams died while this quarrel was going on, and Peale made no further efforts to correct the engravings.[44]

Despite all the difficulties, Peale's book was published in 1848 as Volume 8 of the scientific books resulting from the Expedition, titled *Mammalia and Ornithology* and printed by C. Sherman of Philadelphia. In this quatro-sized volume of 338 pages Peale carefully provided a list of references referred to before beginning the text. The text was divided into two major sections, one on mammals and the other on birds. Thirty-eight mammals and 265 birds are then described; the notes from his direct observations in the field enrich his comments. Finally, there is a catalogue of 762 specimens he collected. This latter list was apparently prepared on the basis of Dr. Pickering's journals. At least, in a letter written June 23, 1847, Wilkes wrote to Senator Pearce, Chairman of the Library Committee:

> When Mr. Peale handed me in his MS . . . I found it wanting in very essential information in his department of Natural History, viz. a catalogue of all the specimens obtained & seen embracing their locality. This he ought long since to have furnished. I have directed him to prepare one but as I well knew his inability to do so from his own notes, I procured those of Dr. Pickering & allowed him to extract the information.[45]

Though a number of small-sized black-and-white illustrations are scattered throughout the volume, the eighty-four plates listed by Peale were not published.

Much to Peale's dismay, Wilkes changed the title from *Zoology* to *Mammalia and Ornithology,* and, more serious, suppressed the author's preface. In a letter to Senator Pearce, dated December 30, 1847, Wilkes stated his position:

> With respect to Mr. Peales Title and Preface, I have declined to allow them to be printed; the first on the ground that the title was not appropriate to the contents of the volume, and agreeably to that given to it by the Committee, and that the Second was irrelevant and I did not deem it proper to authorize it, when a former Committee had expressly declined to print prefaces of both Mr. Hale and Dana's volume. . . . The objections to his title is that is a General title, instead of a Specific one which it ought to be to make it consistent with the whole publication. I recommended to Mr. Peale that he should change it into Mammalia and Ornithology. This he has declined, and insisted upon the general title of Zoology.[46]

Concerning the preface, Wilkes had also written to Pearce on June 2, 1847:

> The tone of this in my opinion is very objectionable & not borne out by the facts to my knowledge.[47]

If one is not apprized of the controversy that existed and does not read between the lines, this unpublished preface seems innocent and honest, the usual effort to state the author's case, some of the problems involved, and the reasons for certain omissions and possible errors. He had not been happy with the Committee's narrow dictum that only new species be listed (Peale was not the only scientist to disagree with this policy):

> The geographical distribution of species over the surface of the earth is a subject of great interest to every philosophic mind. . . . With this view I have recorded the times and places where known species of animals were observed, with such other information as a passing traveller could collect, believing it to be quite as important as the discovery of new species. . . .

He expressed doubts that all the species he included were truly new, and said that he should have been allowed to publish a list of the probable new species immediately upon his return:

> The agents of the government did not allow this to be done, but instructed me to describe and figure as new, all the animals presumed to be new, at the time we discovered them.

In a manuscript copy of the preface he underlined in red the phrase, "presumed to be new." He also mentioned the loss of the butterfly collection in the shipwreck which prevented him from including any information on Lepidoptera. He credited professors at Georgetown University for help in the Latin inscriptions. Near the end of this preface Peale added a comment about conditions during the expedition which would not have pleased Wilkes:

> A civilian on board a ship of war, has much to contend with, particularly where the officers are young and inexperienced.[48]

He did qualify this by adding that there were few occasions during the long and perilous voyage when he was "obliged to feel the dependence of my situation," and that he would always feel proud of having been a member of the Expedition.

Wilkes seems to have held up circulation or printing of Peale's book, already devoid of plates, shortly after the first copies came off the press. It is not known how many copies of the book were printed and distributed before it was suppressed; it is now one of the rarest of books. A few copies were sent abroad. Criticism from scientific quarters in Philadelphia probably most influenced Wilkes's decision to suppress the book. An obvious attempt to discredit Peale's work is revealed in an 1851 notice of Peale's book in a German periodical. Though the reviewer had tried, he had not been able to secure a copy for review. He had had a communication, however, from the "able critic," John Cassin, who was directly quoted as writing:

> I have sufficient knowledge of the book to be fully satisfied that little confidence can be placed in any of Mr. Peale's birds described as new, of which there are upwards of an hundred; the Fissirostres are erroneous to an extraordinary extent.[49]

[44] TRP, Surveying; Haskell, *Bibliography,* 56.

[45] Wilkes Papers, Letterbook 1841–1847, MS, Library of Congress, as quoted in Haskell, *Bibliography,* 55–56.

[46] *Ibid.*

[47] *Ibid.*

[48] As quoted in Haskell, *Bibliography,* 59–60. Original at AMNH. (Several drafts are in TRP Papers, Library of Congress.)

[49] Hartlaub, G., Bericht über die Leistungen in der Natur-

Less than a year later the same reviewer did receive a copy of Peale's text and wrote a comprehensive and sympathetic review, saying that Peale's work contained more information about the zoology of the South Pacific than any other work to date.[50]

A brief sarcastic comment in a letter from Charles Waterton to George Ord sheds some light on specific criticisms. It was a controversy between the thorough and well-read "closet naturalists" and the experienced field man:

> I am not at all surprised that our closet naturalists have pronounced Peale's bird and the Dodo to be pigeons. Neither would I be surprised if they were to declare their conviction that our cuckoo is not a bird because it has never been known to hatch its own eggs![51]

After having suppressed Peale's book, Wilkes and the Library Committee apparently first planned to have a supplement added to the illustrations which were to be published in an atlas. An unsuccessful attempt was made to get Dr. Griffith to prepare this. Then, in June, 1850, Drayton sought out John Cassin, with whom Wilkes had already had some slight contact. Drayton first reported, "Some of his family told me he went to Washington last week.... Now I make no doubt but that he has been spending some time in the Hall, has seen Peale, and if so he has 'spilled all his fat in the fire.'" After Drayton talked to Cassin, the former reported to Wilkes:

> He pointed out errors of Syntax.... Masculine terminations instead of feminine, and vice versi—showed several species, Marked Peale (Nov.) that seem as old as the hills, etc., etc., etc.—I put him on the track of adding an appendix to the atlas thus w^d make that part of the work at least complete, on which he brightened up like a Drummond light.... I can see, that additional to some compensation he feels he can do himself some good scientifically by undertaking the job.... He seems to be fearless, says, that as Mr. Peale has abandoned the work he don't know what he has got to do with Mr. P.[52]

In another context Cassin is described by a historian of natural sciences as a man "who tolerated neither rival nor neophyte." Cassin's star had been rising in Philadelphia during the years Peale was away. He had arranged and identified a large new collection which had been assembled by the Academy patron and later President, Dr. Thomas B. Wilson. Cassin was the closet naturalist, *par excellence*, the kind of man who was at his best when writing technical monographs or descriptions of new species in which he dealt with taxonomy, questions of synonymy and nomenclature. By 1848 a large number of his articles had appeared in scientific journals of the day. He represented the new, highly specialized scientist. Cassin received the constant support of Wilson in his work, and during the years of his ascendancy in the Academy of Natural Sciences in Philadelphia an outstanding reference library was built up.[53]

Wilkes and Drayton knew that the materials in Dr. Pickering's journal would supplement Peale's material and wanted to get these materials to Cassin. As the irreverent Drayton put it:

> Now about old Pick, the fact is that Cassin can do nothing without the d——d fool; I mean that the information that Pick could give him about all that is to be done, will make a good ending of this d——d department. Without Pick Cassin could do but little. No one knows as well as myself how greatly important this is to [a] satisfactory ending of the Ornithology.[54]

Negotiations with Cassin, who seems to have been a shrewd man and a hard bargainer, continued throughout 1850. Drayton was at times exasperated: "Now so far from desireing Mr. Cassin employed, I wish the d——d book with his d——d bad plates would be annihilated.... I must see him tomorrow and induce him to make the best offer I can."[55] On November 26, 1850, after Cassin had gone over some of Peale's materials with him, Drayton reported, "the cormorant [Cassin] wanted to show me that he had a bad bargain and thinks 'to do the thing up brown' he ought to have $2000 a year and five years given him to make the work what it should be."[56]

By February, 1850, Cassin had made his position clear. Drayton reported, "With respect to Mr. Cassin, you will see by his letter, that we cannot get him to finish Peale's atlas, or to do anything short of producing an entire new book."[57] Cassin probably suspected that Wilkes would be glad to see a new book produced. Spencer Baird, then at the Smithsonian, wrote to Cassin on March 1, 1851:

> Do you know that you will be playing directly into Wilkes hands by showing up Peales book. Nothing will delight him more. He has been bitterly opposed to Peale for many years, and is now opposing a claim of Peales for back services, on the ground that he was incompetent to his position in the expedition. Your [shot?] will enable him to prove what he perhaps finds it difficult to convince the committee of, and you may expose Peale seriously without doing aught but make Wilkes happy. Indeed I really think he is desirous of having you to do their work.[58]

Negotiations during 1851 and 1852 were on-again, off-again, and Cassin seems to have been officially appointed to do a new *Ornithology* in the summer of 1852. He was allowed five years to work on it.

geschichte der Vögel während des Jahres 1850, *Archiv für Naturgeschichte* **17**(2): 48, 1851.
[50] Hartlaub, G., R. Titian Peale's Vögel der "United States Exploring Expedition," in Auszuge mitgeheilt und mit Kritischen Anmerkungen, *Archiv für Naturgeschichte* **18**(1): 93–138, 1852.
[51] Charles Waterton to George Ord, Oct. 24, 1847, as quoted in Irwin, R. A., eds., *Letters of Charles Waterton*, 65.
[52] Drayton to Wilkes, June 17, 1850, MS, Wilkes Papers, Library of Congress.

[53] Stone, Witmer, John Cassin, *Dict. Amer. Biog.*
[54] Drayton to Wilkes, June 18, 1850, MS, Wilkes Papers, Library of Congress.
[55] *Ibid.*, June 30, 1850.
[56] *Ibid.*, Nov. 26, 1850.
[57] *Ibid.*, Feb. 16, 1851.
[58] Baird copy-press letter books, Chief Clerk's Office, Smithsonian Institution, as quoted in Haskell, *Bibliography*, 58.

Peale was helpless at the turn of events, and it is no wonder that, many years later, he still felt bitter about the manner in which, as it had appeared to him,

The materials forming our scientific stores, were peddled to authors, not so much to aid, but to supercede us: our positions held during the voyage were misrepresented, and higher salaries than ours offered, besides greater facilities to consult libraries, and other collections.[59]

Ord, who was becoming more and more of a recluse, tried to comfort and advise Peale from afar:

I am not surprised at the account of the treatment you have received with respect to your part of Wilkes' expedition. I have been long persuaded there was a plot concocted to defraud you of the produce of your labours; and from the circumstance of the powerful influence of the chief of the plot, I felt afraid that you would stand no chance of justice. Had you anything of the toad-eater in your composition, certain parties might have condescended to protect you; but your honesty and candour hardly comported with the views of those who sought to make you the tool of their designs. You have no remedy, at the present time, but submission: unless you choose to run the risk of losing your *bread*. Let me advise you to hold on to the sheet-anchor while the storm lasts. The winds will finally abate; and then you may be enabled to spread your sails to the favouring breeze. I have never seen any account of your book, nor have I beheld the book itself.... The time may come when you shall be enabled to hold up your head with the dignity of a man. These are the frank sentiments of one who respects you.[60]

In 1858 a new book, to replace Peale's and titled *Mammalogy and Ornithology,* Volume 8 of the official reports of the United States Exploring Expedition, was published. It was replete with a folio atlas of plates and was written by John Cassin. The classifications and names of the species are often different from those given by Peale, but on virtually every page large portions of Peale's field observations are quoted. At least these reports were not considered unreliable. The major difference is the addition of some material from Pickering's notes. Thirty-two out of fifty-two plates are by Peale. In the preface and in the text Cassin is careful to give credit to Peale where this is due, but this helped little to heal the wounds; Peale always felt he had been dealt with unjustly.

In a statement of his case, written in 1874, about five years after Cassin's death, Peale, still deeply hurt, wrote:

Cassin's report and mine are both in existence, and should they ever be multiplied sufficiently to be of any consequence, the world may judge between the rights of original observation, and closet philosophy;—what an observer says, and what others think he ought to say. I wrote under instructions from the joint Library Committee and attempted to explain by preface, (an author's privilege,) the rules observed in the work, in order to excuse what might otherwise appear negligent, in passing unobserved, the labors of other naturalists. The preface was suppressed and the report sent abroad without it. The illustrations by other persons, I have never seen. I made sketches from the living or fresh animals, which it was my wish and intention to finish, on return home, had I been allowed to do so. Having offended the agents of the committee, by a desire to see the contract engravings, my work was cut short, and the writer sought refuge in other pursuits—not so congenial, but more harmonious.[61]

Historians of natural science agree that in some ways Cassin's book, appearing at a later date, is more comprehensive. But they deal kindly with Peale. One of the most recent evaluations is that of Harley Harris Bartlett, in his excellent paper on "The Reports of the Wilkes Expedition, and the Work of the Specialists in Science," which was read at the Centenary Celebration of the Wilkes Exploring Expedition sponsored by the American Philosophical Society in 1940. He summarizes Peale's work, as compared with Cassin's, as follows:

He [Peale] was therefore not ill-prepared for his work as naturalist of the Expedition and his performance as an author would have held up well had he not had the competition of at least three men of extraordinary genius, namely, Dana, Hale, and Pickering. His talents were more in accord with those of the other gentlemen of the Expedition. After returning Peale was prompt in publishing his report, but unfortunately it met with disapproval of Wilkes, and after partial distribution (in accordance with the law) the remaining copies were destroyed, to be replaced by Cassin's substitute volume.

It is immediately apparent if one examines Peale's volume carefully that Peale was careless in such matters as agreement in gender between generic names and specific adjectives. Other little inconsistencies are to be found. He failed to utilize voluminous records of mammals and birds that had been made by Charles Pickering, the insertion of which made the chief difference between Peale's volume and Cassin's.

Only a professional ornithologist would be competent to say if Cassin's descriptions were really much superior to Peale's. Peale followed the good old tradition of a Latin diagnosis, in which he did not skimp. In fact, if latinity be any test of scholarliness, Peale's volume is the superior. The defects are obviously those of haste rather than of knowledge, of inexperience in editing and proofreading. After the lapse of a century it is easy to be more indulgent about Peale's faults than his contemporaries were. His book has blemishes to be sure, but not such serious ones that Wilkes or the country had any reason to be ashamed of it. However, it was a time when Americans were very sensitive about any scientific or literary shortcomings that they might have. Anything European was *a priori* good: anything American probably bad.[62]

. . . .

Elliott Coues termed Cassin "the only ornithologist this country has ever produced who was as familiar with the birds of the Old World as with those of America," yet, good as his work undoubtedly was, as judged by the standards of the careful workers of his time, it is perhaps open to question whether, in the light of the ideas of species that prevail today, Peale's less discriminating procedure might not have led him as near to the truth as Cassin's more laborious investigations.[63]

Bartlett prepared a careful list of the new names proposed by Peale, and compared this with the manner in which Cassin handled them. In his statement prefac-

[59] TRP, Surveying.
[60] George Ord to TRP, Jan. 27, 1852, MS, HSP.
[61] TRP, Surveying.
[62] Bartlett, Reports, 641–642.
[63] *Ibid.,* 645.

ing this appendix, Bartlett again stresses the point that he feels the more modern conception of geographic species might justify the reinstatement of some of Peale's species:

> The utility of the following notes will be indicated by the citation of the Mindanao hornbill. In recent works upon Philippine natural history, this bird appears under the name *Hydrocorax mindanensis* (Tweeddale), which was published much later than *Buceros obscurus* Peale. It should now be called *Hydrocorax obscurus* (Peale). Cassin considered that Peale's species was the same as *Buceros hydrocorax* Linn., now known in Philippine zoology as *Hydrocorax hydrocorax* (Linn.). In this, and probably in some other instances, Cassin went too far afield to find species to which Peale's might be reduced, and the more modern conception of geographic species might justify the reinstatement of others of Peale's species, as in the instance just cited. Some interested zoologist might do long-deferred justice to Peale by examining into the validity of all of his other proposals.[64]

Other critics have pointed out that Peale was at a tremendous disadvantage because he lacked so many vital references. Thus Witmer Stone has written:

> This report of Peale's is one of the rarest of books and its history is involved in obscurity. It has been claimed that he was not afforded opportunities to properly study and compare his specimens; but it would seem that at that time neither specimens nor books adequate for his work were to be found in this country. It was not until 1846 and 1847 that Dr. T. B. Wilson began to accumulate his great collection and library at the Philadelphia Academy and there was none elsewhere. At all events of 109 new birds described scarcely one third were really new.[65]

The comments of Frank L. Burns are in a similar vein:

> Apparently, upon the return of Titian R. Peale after nearly four years of travel and successful endeavor, similar invidious influences and controversies that overwhelmed John Townsend, were reenacted in the instance of another gentle soul, for others were placed in charge of his materials and he was hampered in many ways. . . .
> His official report, rather incongruously entitled *Mammalia and Ornithology*, published in 1848, included the descriptions of numerous species of birds supposedly new to science, for he had no means of ascertaining that many had been described, owing to the lack of essential works of reference. His inexperience in work of this nature counted heavily against him, for his contribution was deemed unworthy of the series in scientific value and was suppressed by Wilkes, who had retained command until the reports were completed. In 1852 [sic] the revised edition, *Mammalogy and Ornithology*, by John Cassin, appeared with Peale's folio volume of colored plates, denied the first edition. It is needless to state that Cassin through the liberality of a wealthy patron had the material and necessary works of reference and that the technical descriptions and synonymy were only matters of routine to that accomplished systematist.[66]

In passing, it should be noted that Peale was not the

only one of the scientists to have difficulties with Wilkes and the Library Committee, nor was Cassin the only stay-at-home scientist asked to write one of the texts. Criticisms were even raised about Dana's superb volume on *Zoophytes*, which Asa Gray and others were quick to quell.[67] Wilkes was anxious to keep on good terms with Pickering because he wanted the latter's materials for other reports, but in 1848 Wilkes wrote to Tappan: "Dr. Pickering is so slow. . . . I have lost my patience with him, and shall rejoice when I see him fairly out of sight."[68] Dr. A. A. Gould, who ended up doing the book on conchology, wrote after he had finished it in 1853:

> I am sorry to say that, like many of my predecessors I have had serious difficulties with Capt. Wilkes and the Library Committee, unfortunately I cannot find out exactly with which. I labored for nearly two years for which I can as yet get no compensation, and had it not been for the duties I owed to the scientific community, the work would have been left as Peale and Rich left their volumes. No consideration of personal reputation would ever have induced me to complete it, under the circumstances. It is a great shame that mere quibbles & a position of power should defraud a man of an equitable reward for his labors. Whatever may be the delinquencies on the part of others it shall not be said that I have been deficient on my part.[69]

Brackenridge, who also had difficulty with Latin nomenclature, finally finished his book in 1854. He too was "heartily sick" of the whole thing, and only prudence, he said, prevented him from taking "a *determined* stand against the wishes of a set of men, whose position—not knowledge . . . —would be sure to crush me."[70] Neither Rich nor Couthouy finished their works.

In the final list of twenty official volumes of the expedition, eleven authors did not participate in the four-year venture.[71] They were probably recruited as the most capable men to deal with the materials at hand; it was unfortunate in those cases in which the work of the others could be accomplished only at the expense of the men who had done the research in the field.

A victim of circumstances and his own temperament, and at a disadvantage in a phase of the work in which he had little experience and not as much skill as more brilliant contemporaries, Peale suffered a crushing professional defeat. In his own way, he had played a truly great part in advancing knowledge of the natural sciences during a pioneer period, yet his obvious and direct contributions to new knowledge are few. He supplied the selected raw materials with which others could build; his work supplemented and supported the work of those who stand in the first rank of the pioneers.

---

[64] *Ibid.*, 688–689.

[65] Stone, Witmer, Cassinia, *Proc. Del. Valley Ornithol. Club* **19**: 1–13, 1915.

[66] Burns, Frank L., *Wilson Bull.* **44**: 34, 1932.

[67] Haskell, *Bibliography*, 50.

[68] *Ibid.*, 65.

[69] Gould to Tappan, Dec. 22, 1853, MS, Tappan Papers **22**: as quoted in Haskell, *Bibliography*, 75.

[70] Haskell, *Bibliography*, 90.

[71] Meisel, **2**: 658.

XI

A Public Servant
And His Private Amusements

IN FULL middle age, in the years just before the half-way mark of the century, Titian Ramsay Peale began a new career, and shaped for himself a new pattern of life in the still new city of Washington. By 1850 Peale was established in his job at the Patent Office, and the very press of work that filled his working hours was undoubtedly a godsend, for it served to distract his mind from the painful memories of recent years.[1] He was to remain in the Patent Office for twenty-five years, from 1848 to 1873. For years he aspired to the position of Examiner, again enlisting the help of his Philadelphia friends, and at one time all the other Examiners signed a petition in his favor, which only served to arouse the ire of the Secretary of Interior.[2] Again, he created some of his own barriers with his proud and uncompromising behavior. He seems eventually to have achieved this position, and in his seventieth year he wrote to the President, offering himself as a candidate for Examiner in Chief, submitting only his long record of work, "without reproach," as testimony and asking for no outside recommendations.[3] It is not surprising to learn that his application was passed over once again. Despite these disappointments, the work at the Patent Office gave him a secure post, on a fixed if modest salary, and Peale appears to have fulfilled his duties in a competent and diligent manner. It was the sheet anchor which he needed and to which he clung. Though he could no longer add to the collections of a national museum, he assured his old friends that in his private amusements he would be sharing their interests.[4]

In the summer of 1850 he found a new marriage partner in Lucy MacMullen. She was a New Jersey woman of thirty-six, a maiden in possession of a small income. Peale's friends found her "well-qualified to promote his happiness."[5] Other family ties were still close. Franklin and Titian maintained a fairly regular correspondence until the former's death in 1870, and there was a fair amount of visiting back and forth. In the letters, too, there are always affectionate greetings to "our dear Lucy," and to the ailing daughter by Titian's first wife. Sybilla lived until 1861, but as early as 1850 Ord described her as being "in the last stage of the disease, which carried to the grave a sister and a mother—consumption."[6] The father had little control over his son, Francis Titian. In 1852 the boy seems to have been apprenticed in Philadelphia. He refused to return to his Uncle Franklin, with whom he may have lived for a time, and defiantly said he meant to do for himself and did not wish assistance from his father or his uncle. It is not surprising that the boy, who had been growing up during the years when his father was meeting defeat after defeat, lacked confidence in and respect for his father, who had been gone from home so long and so often. Young Titian was married in 1853 and little is known of him beyond his death date in 1869. His son, Louis T., the only grandchild of Titian Peale, seems to have lived with his grandfather in Washington during his teens, and the grandfather in turn, in later years, lived for a time with his grandson in Philadelphia.[7] To this grandson Titian Peale was to will his most valued possessions, symbols of his life:

---

[1] George Ord to Charles Waterton, May 5, 1850, MS; TRP to Coleman Sellers, Jan. 9, 1840, MS, Sellers Family Papers **3.**

[2] Letter to Alexander Stuart, Secretary of the Interior, signed by W. P. N. FitzGerald, Henry B. Renwick, L. D. Gale, J. H. Lane, and Sam Cooper, May 5, 1852, MS, Patent Office records, Dept. of Interior, National Archives, Washington, D. C.

[3] TRP to President of United States, March 12, 1869, MS, Patent Office records, Dept. of Interior, National Archives.

[4] George Ord to TRP, April 5, 1848, Sept. 2, 1848, Jan. 27,

1852, MSS, HSP. George Ord to Charles Waterton, Sept. 23, 1848, MS.

[5] George Ord to Charles Waterton, Oct. 6, 1850, MS; Sellers, *CWP* **2:** 421.

[6] George Ord to Charles Waterton, Oct. 6, 1850, MS.

[7] Franklin Peale to TRP, March 28, 1852; *Gopsill's Philadelphia Directory*, 1877 and 1878; Sellers, *CWP* **2:** 422.

I wish him to have my painting and drawing apparatus and materials, photographic apparatus and materials. My guns, pistols, fishing and sporting apparatus including my rifle with its inscriptions of when and where used and all my books on Natural History.[8]

Franklin and Titian corresponded about a variety of subjects of mutual interest. There were notes back and forth on experiments with electricity and magnets, and about Franklin's beloved collection of Stone Age implements. Franklin was always finding that the ancients had discovered mechanical principles which he thought to be new. Franklin also sent sketches of inventions he was working upon; once or twice he applied for patents, but usually he was just explaining his ideas and sharing his enthusiasms with Titian. In 1859 he explained a gadget he had developed to filter the drinking water from the Schuylkill; he did not wish to trouble with applying for a patent, inasmuch as, "My experiences in the Patent Line having already been pretty well *filtered* and well cooled."[9]

In 1854 Franklin was the center of a controversy in the Philadelphia Mint, where he was charged with misappropriation of funds. He was charged with over-extravagance in spending too much to improve the machinery of the Mint, and with employing the time of the workmen from the Mint in fixing things in his own home. If guilty, both were sins of exuberance and thoughtlessness rather than of guile. He resigned from his position, and Titian was able to suggest an opening in the Patent Office. Franklin kindly and tactfully refused, since he did not wish to have to ask for a job, and admitted to a certain laziness now that he had sufficient means to support himself. Franklin retired from any kind of employment for a few years, and then became president of a small railroad. With his wife, he was a leader in the Musical Fund Society for many years, and they regularly entertained outstanding musicians. He was to become a beloved figure in Philadelphia as a leader in similar social and civic endeavors.

Rembrandt Peale, with his lengthy lectures on Washington, had become a kind of grand old man of American art. Franklin and Titian were not above joking about becoming "as wordy as Rembrandt or a Philadelphia lawyer." Rubens, busy with gardening and painting on the farm in western Pennsylvania, kept in touch with his brothers through letters and family visits.[10]

A younger relative of whom Titian was particularly fond was his nephew, Coleman Sellers, the youngest son of Sophonisba Peale and Coleman Sellers. This nephew and Titian shared a common interest in the

new art of photography—a logical outgrowth of Titian's interest in achieving accurate and literal representations of nature. Back and forth went the letters discussing new experiments and procedures, and filled with little sketches of their equipment. Young Sellers developed a gadget for showing pictures to his family and friends; it was a device whereby the effect of motion was achieved through showing a series of photographs of related stages of action on a revolving drum. He enthusiastically sent it to his Uncle Titian to be shepherded through the Patent Office. The device was patented on February 6, 1861, and Titian is believed to have given it its name, the Kinematoscope. The family toy is now considered a machine "epochal in the annals of motion picture development" and as one of the most important forerunners of the present motion pictures. The word "cinema" has now long been a commonplace of the English language, and a variation of kinematoscope, the cinemascope, has attained a new eminence with the development of wide-screen motion pictures. The two serious amateurs could not know the future significance of this invention. They devoted their attention to a variety of problems, such as determining the proper nitrate bath for their precious negatives, or Titian's new way of removing hypo stains. Both were members of the original group of enthusiasts who formed the first photographic club in the United States—the Amateur Photographic Exchange Club founded in 1861. Oliver Wendell Holmes was among the twenty-two persons in this pioneering group.

When Sellers was named corresponding secretary for the club, his uncle cautioned him to check carefully all foreign publications before making any claims for new developments. The young man accepted the advice,

Fig. 42. Photograph by Titian R. Peale. "Inauguration of Pres Lincoln from our front Door G Street / T R Peale." Courtesy of Miss Jacqueline Hoffmire.

---

[8] TRP Will, Dec. 3, 1875, Probated March 21, 1885. Will ⅜ 504, 1885. Philadelphia County, Record of Wills, Philadelphia City Hall.

[9] Franklin Peale to TRP, March 15, 1859.

[10] Franklin Peale to TRP, March 9, 1855; March 27, 1855; April 11, 1863. See also an article which mentions Rembrandt Peale in *The Press* (Philadelphia), Oct. 26, 1858: 1; Rubens Peale to Anna [Peale], May 5, 1861, MS, Sellers Family Papers 4: 57; Sellers, *CWP* 2: 383.

FIG. 43. Photograph by Titian R. Peale. "View from George-town heights D.C." Courtesy of Miss Jacqueline Hoffmire.

FIG. 44. Photograph of Lucy MacMullen Peale, by Titian R. Peale. Courtesy of Miss Jacqueline Hoffmire.

and took every opportunity to give credit to his uncle for whatever new techniques the latter had introduced. As testimony of Peale's devotion to the new art, one finds among his effects many boxes of early photographs—views of Washington churches, interior studies of practically every room in the houses on G and K streets where they lived, family pictures, pictures of

friends and associates, studies of the Presidential Mansion, as the White House was then called, views of Delaware Water Gap and of Rock Creek Park in Washington, and pictures of soldiers and Civil War camps in the Washington area.[11]

The Civil War did not greatly disturb the life of the Peales. Prices were higher, making it hard to meet expenses on a fixed salary, and preventing Titian from indulging as much as he would have liked to in photographic experiments. Others in the family worried about their safety in Washington, but Titian and his wife remained unharmed. Both Franklin and Titian were more spectators than participants in the events that swirled around them, though Titian wrote with feeling:

It will take a long time, however, to forget the long line of ambulances we daily see entering this city freighted with the maimed.[12]

To judge by photographs, calling cards, and other fragments of evidence, the Peales led a fairly active social life during their twenty-five years in Washington, and enjoyed the friendship of a wide circle of friends. Secretary of State Seward and his family and the family of Professor Joseph Henry of the Smithsonian seem to have been good friends. One finds among the calling cards a full roster of important people of the age: the Secretary of War and Mrs. Belknap, the Postmaster General and his wife, Mr. and Mrs. John Sherman, Hannibal Hamlin, General and Mrs. Grant, General and Mrs. W. T. Sherman, General and Mrs. Burnside, Secretary of War Edwin M. Stanton, General and Mrs. Frémont and Miss Frémont, Mr. and Mrs. Stephen A. Douglas of Illinois, Secretary of the Treasury Hugh McCulloch and Mrs. McCulloch, and General Montgomery C. Meigs and his wife, to name but a few. The Peales attended at least one Presidential reception, for the names of Mr. and Mrs. T. R. Peale and the Misses Clara and Mary Peale (Rubens' granddaughter and daughter) are listed in a newspaper account as being among the guests at Mrs. Grant's first reception of the season, on January 11, 1871.[13]

Several of the names just listed recur in a list of seventeen men who a few years before the Civil War, formed an informal club that held regular Saturday night meetings. They called it the "Saturday Club." Without by-laws, constitution or officers, they were a

[11] Coleman Sellers to TRP, Aug. 19, 1860; Sept. 19, 1860; Nov. 1, 1860; Feb. 3, 1861; Feb. 13, 1861; Feb. 17, 1861; March 10, 1861; Oct. 20, 1861; Feb. 9, 1862; May 29, 1862, MSS, Sellers Family Papers 4. See also TRP to Coleman Sellers, May 26, 1864.
McCosker, M. J., Philadelphia and the genesis of the motion picture, *Penna. Mag. Hist. and Biog.* 65: 401–419, 1941; Jacqueline Hoffmire Collection; and Coleman Sellers, An old photographic club, *Anthony's Photographic Bulletin,* 1–17, New York, 1888.
[12] TRP to Coleman Sellers, Mar. 28, 1864.
[13] Jacqueline Hoffmire Collection; *Washington Daily Evening Chronicle,* Jan. 11, 1871: 1, in Coleman Sellers Mills Collection.

group of like-minded men who discussed questions of scientific or public interest at their meetings; afterwards they had a sociable supper. M. C. Meigs, Hugh McCulloch, Joseph Henry, and Titian Peale were among the members. It was said of them:

> ...all of them were interesting men, all well known to each other, and some of them to the public, by their scientific and literary attainments; there was not one who would not have been distinguished in any literary and scientific club in this country or in any other; there was not a money-worshipper or time-server among them all.[14]

In 1870 the club members, then numbering forty-three, asked Professor Henry to preside over the founding of a new society devoted to the free exchange of views on scientific subjects and to the promotion of scientific inquiry. This group became the Philosophical Society of Washington, and Titian R. Peale was one of its founding members.[15]

Peale's scientific and artistic interests continued to occupy his out-of-office hours for the rest of his life. During this period of his life he wrote a few short but competent articles, several referring back to his Long Expedition notes, one dealing with methods of preserving Lepidoptera, and another reporting his own findings of Indian remains in the vicinity of Washington.[16] A draft of a letter, dated October 6, 1859, among Peale's papers appears to be in response to a request from the Smithsonian to write an essay concerning preservation and natural history displays. A dozen years had failed to heal the wounds suffered after the Wilkes Expedition, and in his draft he declined the offer:

> I felt it was a great misfortune to be obliged to abandon the experience of a life devoted to what I still believe was a good cause. And now to write on the subject solicited would arouse painful memmory of hopes long deferred and gone. I am willing that the world of visitors to public Museums shall gape at rampant, grinning remnants and other monstrocities prepared for their inspection by some bungling laborer, or mechanic who may not be able to gain a living by his legitimate labors, if they were satisfied. But for my part, I retire from such collections with a feeling of disappointment that the beauties of nature can be so tortured and the torture tolerated. I was ready in 1846 but in 1859 there has been too many racks in the block.[17]

Despite the disavowal, he did write an article on the methods of preserving Lepidoptera, already mentioned, which appeared in the 1863 *Annual Report* of the Smithsonian Institution.

[14] Hugh McCulloch, 1863, as quoted in A. C. Peale, TRP, *Bull. Philos. Soc. Wash.* **14**: 317, 1905.

[15] A. C. Peale, TRP, *Bull. Philos. Soc. Wash.* **14**: 317, 1905.

[16] Articles by TRP in this period, all in the *Annual Report of the Board of Regents of the Smithsonian Institution*, are, in chronological order, as follows: Ancient mounds at St. Louis, Missouri, in 1819, 386–391, 1862; Method of preserving Lepidoptera, 404–406, 1863; On the uses of the brain and marrow of animals among the Indians of North America, 390–391, 1871; and Prehistoric remains found in the vicinity of the city of Washington, D. C., 430–432, 1873.

[17] TRP to "My dear Sir," Oct. 6, 1859, MS.

FIG. 45. Family group photograph taken by Titian R. Peale: Anna Peale (daughter of Franklin Peale), Louis Peale (grandson of Titian R. Peale), Lucy MacMullen Peale (Mrs. Titian R. Peale), and Titian R. Peale. Caption reads, "Anna Louis Lucy TRP. Photog^r / Back door 1321 K Street Washington July 4th 1870." Courtesy of Miss Jacqueline Hoffmire.

Most of the oil paintings by Peale so far located date from 1850 onwards. He appears to have done them chiefly for his private pleasure, though occasionally for profit. Many are nostalgic in theme. He dipped into his long closed Long Expedition sketchbooks and reworked the subjects recorded there.

One of the most ambitious of Peale's paintings of Western themes is a large, 54″ × 42″, canvas, the *Bison Herd*, painted in 1854, and now at the American Museum of Natural History in New York. It is not clear whether this oil was painted for pleasure by the civil servant, Peale, or whether there was an expectation that it might be sold. The painting (fig. 46) was given to the American Museum of Natural History by a close relative of Titian Peale's second wife. Nostalgia for his own experiences in the West, and the widespread interest in the West which by the fifties had been stimulated by the literary efforts of men like Washington Irving and Cooper, and explorers' accounts such as those of Frémont, may well have stimulated Peale to turn to western subjects as a source of artistic inspiration. The *Bison Herd* is almost photographic in its realism, and a greater sense of organic form is to be seen in these animals than was apparent in earlier ani-

FIG. 46. Oil painting. Bison Herd, 1854. Courtesy of the American Museum of Natural History.

mal studies. It is the West as Peale must have known it, and as it is still seen in the mind's eye of many an American.

Twice in his lifetime Titian Ramsay Peale spent time in the American West. When little more than a youth he had journeyed with other members of Long's Expedition across the wide expanses of the American prairies and the "desert" area in what is now Colorado. At that time the most westward areas they traversed and the interior areas away from the river systems were still largely unexplored by white men; they encountered Indians who had never before seen white men. Even along the great river highways such as the Missouri River there were few settlers and traders; one of their festive occasions was graced by the presence of the first white woman said to have lived in the area. Again, in his mature middle years, while a member of the Wilkes Expedition, Titian Peale traveled overland across the West Coast area from the mouth of the Co-

lumbia to the port of San Francisco. By that time, 1841, a few hardy settlers had pushed into the Willamette Valley, but the great rush of settlers and, in California, of seekers for gold, was still a thing of the future. Peale saw these areas before they were to capture and inflame the enthusiasm of America—enthusiasm for a dream of great gardens, of agricultural utopias and Eldoradoes. He knew them in fact rather than in fancy. In both cases he traveled with a vanguard of scouts who saw it as their duty to report facts. Their reports added much to the texture of fact and fancy that characterized the average American's picture of the West in the years to come.

A *Buffalo Hunt* and a *Buffalo Kill* are the subjects of two oil paintings dated 1873. The first is a reworking of the theme of the lithographs of the 1830's (figs. 47 and 48); the second is clearly taken from the 1819–1820 sketchbook. Both bring to mind, in fresh colors

FIG. 47. Oil painting. 1873. Buffalo Hunt on the River Platte. Courtesy of Carl Schaefer Dentzel.

FIG. 48. Oil painting. 1873. Buffalo Kill. Courtesy of Carl Schaefer Dentzel.

Fig. 49. Oil painting. 1877. The men of the *Vincennes* gambolling on an "ice island" in the Antarctic. Copied from the engraving in Wilkes, *Narrative* **2**, opp. p. 325. Courtesy of Western Americana Collection, Yale University Library.

and crisp lines, the West Peale knew.[18] Objective, literally minded, he did not embroider his subjects.

A letter to a Philadelphia relative written in 1870 indicates that at that time Titian Peale was painting with some hope and expectation of selling his canvases:

I am glad you are pleased with the Elks, and did not expect much admiration of the mountain Sheep. Franklin wrote me he had authorized the framing of the first named in hopes it could be on exhibition in time for the Xmas holidays. You are both so kind that we cannot divide our gratitude. The days are now too short, for me to touch a brush, outside of office hours: In the spring we may perhaps begin again, as there is a drawing of antelopes on a canvas, but I fear there are but few people having a fancy for such pictures, and it is not to my fancy to make fakes. . . .[19]

Peale would have been pleased to sell a painting occasionally, and selected from his repertoire Western subjects that would have some popular appeal, but as

a scientifically oriented man and as one who was brought up to feel that one of the highest aims in art was honestly and realistically to imitate nature, he would not indulge in any sort of romantic distortion for artistic effect. It was not his fancy to depict "fakes." In truth, he was not a particularly good painter.

One of the most amusing of Peale's paintings, if utterly lacking in artistic merit, is an oil painted in 1877 and done after a Wilkes sketch published in the narrative report (fig. 49). The explorers are shown having a gambol on an "ice island." Here the *Vincennes* men had obtained geological specimens from the boulders, sand, and gravel imbedded in the ice, as well as a supply of delicious fresh water from a small pond. And, as depicted in the painting, "the men amused themselves to their hearts' content in sliding."[20]

One of the most satisfying of Peale's paintings is a small landscape painted in 1873 (fig. 50). To those who have spent time on the wide expanses of sandy beach in New Jersey, it evokes a familiar picture of winds, scrawny vegetation, and sand dunes. There is a stark,

---

[18] I am grateful to Miss Doris Creer for notes on measurements and colors. She examined the canvases for me in Los Angeles in December, 1955.

[19] TRP to Mary (very possibly Mary Jane Peale, Rubens' daughter), January 3, 1870, MS.

[20] Wilkes, *Narrative* **2**: 325.

FIG. 50. Oil painting. 1873. Sand Dunes, New Jersey. Courtesy of Miss Jacqueline Hoffmire.

dramatic quality to the outlines of the dead and barren limbs in the foreground. It was a familiar scene to Titian Peale, who often had come here since a child to study waterfowl, and he painted it with clarity and feeling. The colors are the tans, grays, blues, and blacks of the shore. In the left foreground is a small mass of glittering particles of real sand stuck to the canvas, almost unnoticeable, but adding to the effect of visual reality. It is there not because of an aesthete's interest in surface texture, but as a contribution to as complete an interpretation of visual verisimilitude as possible, upon which Peale, in the tradition of the artist-naturalist, put great value.

His home, with its photographic paraphenalia, easels and painting equipment, rows upon rows of neatly arranged specimens of butterflies, and guns (still used on shorter excursions), must have seemed like his father's old painting- or work-room, with its painting equipment, turning lathe, and small kiln. Private amusements that sometimes produced important results, but that always satisfied the active curiosity of the mind, constitute a *leit-motif* in the history of the Peale family, and Titian followed the family pattern.

When Franklin Peale died in 1870, Titian acquired many of their father's letterbooks, manuscript autobiography, and other papers from him. These had

been in Titian's possession immediately after his father's death and appear to have been in his or Franklin's possession during most of the intervening years. Franklin had just begun a memorial, or biography, of their father. Titian, the last living member of C. W. Peale's large family, and his wife, Lucy, now undertook to complete the task. They wrote to other members of the family for other papers, and, with the aid of Titian's nephew, brought to virtual completion the prodigious work of organizing, copying, and editing the vast corpus of material. Some members of the family suggested that Titian and Franklin, in their earlier years, may have destroyed some of the still missing papers of C. W. Peale. Lucy avowed for Titian that this had never been so, and that the latter was an exceedingly provident person who never destroyed a thing. This problem can never be solved, but one should note that there is enough that is derogatory about the boys still among the papers—details of Franklin's unhappy early marriage and episodes recording Titian's obstinacy—that, had they chosen to destroy papers, they might have disposed of some of these. The biography—actually a cutting and editing of the papers as they existed rather than a newly written text—still exists in manuscript, two fat volumes numbering over one thousand pages. The dedi-

FIG. 51. Photograph of Franklin Peale, by Titian R. Peale. Courtesy of Miss Jacqueline Hoffmire.

FIG. 52. Photograph of Titian R. Peale. Caption reads, "By Mr. Walker 1860." Courtesy of Miss Jacqueline Hoffmire.

cation to the father with whom the spirited sons had clashed from time to time is nonetheless sincere:

To our Father—A tribute of affection—An offering of gratitude for his noble example, and Honor, for his pure elevated character.[21]

At least a full century separates the years which Charles Willson Peale's papers first record and the years when his youngest son poured over the manuscripts. The events in the lives of father and son spanned two wars on the North American continent, the War of Independence and the Civil War, and each had known some of the war heroes of his own day. During this span of time America had changed from the simple, agricultural economy that C. W. Peale had known in Maryland to the industrial economy based on some of the new inventions which Titian studied and passed upon at the rate of one thousand or more each year. The manuscript was ready in 1873 and the well-known historian, Dr. Benson J. Lossing, agreed to take charge of further editing and publishing of it as a memoir.

Funds were never found for the publication of this biography, and it remained for a later descendant of Charles Willson Peale—Charles Coleman Sellers—to complete the task first undertaken by Titian Peale.[22] In September, 1871, Titian Peale had been invited to become a member of the Historical Society of Pennsylvania, a tribute to his interest in history. Before his death he gave some of the family papers to this organization.[23]

A letter written by Titian Peale to Dr. Lossing reveals that the former was as energetic as his father had been at this age. Moreover, the son's sentiments on the need for absorbing work and the desire to see the pleasanter side of things echo the philosophy of his father:

You say you have "uninterrupted good health at the age of 68." I say, may you long continue to enjoy it, and continue as you always have been,—a *working man*, for good works like yours, are the foundation of a good society. As for *leisure*, it is a synonym for idleness, the "root of all evil," and can't be enjoyed by a person constituted as we know you are. That's my opinion.

Now at the age of 81, I feel blessed by good health, and not oppressed by poverty or wealth,—but must have something to be at besides *bread & butter* or I would be in mischief. I cannot feel, but a little unpatriotic, at times to find myself and wife afloat in the world, after spending the best half of my life in the service of the government, helping to found a bureau of *Hydrography*, a *National Museum*,

[21] TRP, Biography of Charles Willson Peale, MS.

[22] Lucy Peale to Coleman Sellers, July 6, 1870, MS.; TRP letter, undated, addressee not given; TRP to John A. McAllister, Sept. 27, 1871, MS, Library Company of Philadelphia; TRP to James Shrigley, Sept. 27, 1871, MS, HSP; George Escol Sellers to H. W. Sellers, Dec. 28, 1896, in George Escol Sellers Memoirs, typescript copy, Book V, 3, MS.

[23] TRP to John McAllister, Sept. 27, 1871 and Dec. 14, 1872, MS, Library Company of Philadelphia; TRP to James Shrigley, Sept. 27, 1871, MS, HSP; TRP to Dr. P. Wroth, Nov. 3, 1873, MS, HSP; Notes and Queries, *Penna. Mag. Hist. and Biog.* 1: 223, 1877; 9: 121–125, 1885.

a *Botanic Garden*, and an *Astronomical Observatory*, at Washington, the proceeds of the expeditions:—besides exploring the way to a vast interior, and a west coast for our people who followed there, and now count by millions.

I feel now left to shrink like a caterpillar into its pupa state; unnoticed until my time comes, to take wings like my butterflies, and cease to require *pap* from the Demagogues: But so it is.

Excuse this growl, I can't help a little squerm now and then but feel better when it has past—my egotism must [be] attributed to age, my hearing is not so good as formerly—as for sight, that reaches both ways, forward & backwards. I try and I think you do—to keep my eyes on the pleasant views.[24]

The work on American butterflies, begun so many years earlier, in the 1830's, remained a preoccupation of Titian Peale throughout the Washington years, and it was to this work that he devoted most of his efforts after he retired from the Patent Office in 1873 and returned to his home city, Philadelphia. He had been constantly hampered by lack of books since there was no good library of natural history in the District of Columbia. He had done what he could, studying and adding to his collections whenever possible, but it was rarely that he had found persons who shared his particular interest. He had felt rewarded whenever some notice was taken of his work, but had made little progress and at one time regretfully admitted that his project was still chiefly good intentions.[25]

When he returned to Philadelphia, however, he began working anew on his book to be entitled "The Butterflies of North America." Parts of it had to be revised, as some specimens to which he had given names had now been described by others, and he had to try to incorporate their work into his. He collected and observed conscientiously, and continued carefully to execute his figures in oil on thin cardboard. He enriched many of his paintings with fine details of beautiful foliage and flowers. In his introduction, he pleaded the cause of the importance of field observation:

In compiling a history of the Butterflies of North America, I will endeavor to prove the truth of these remarks, but expect to commit many errors, as it is very difficult to collect reliable original matter—few persons with time and means are willing to devote themselves to the labor of careful observation; most Entomologists being satisfied when they find a new species and give it a *name*, which fills the catalogues and cabinets and leaves us without further useful information. Thus many a marvelous history is lost. It is like bad mining and leaves much "rubbish" to contend with.

His standards for illustration before had been so high that the printing of his book had been impossible. Now he decided to abandon these standards in order to have the work go ahead. His hope was to create a volume significant for providing a rich body of observed data:

In this work I have not aimed to make new species, but rather to reduce the number described and give more information about those named but not known. I commenced collecting the material for this work about half a century since, but received no encouragement to publish on account of the expense of illustration, without which I have thought such a book would be of little practical use; and now my object is to divest the subject as far as possible of all technicality, and illustrate by the cheapest possible mode of doing in passable justice to the beauties of our subjects.[26]

The rich, carefully executed drawings belie his stated willingness to abandon these standards. He cut and rearranged his drawings, and probably reworked some of them (figs. 53 and 54). But a haunting poverty made the publication of his book impossible. It was destined to remain unpublished. It had become a kind of life-long preoccupation and companion, and, with the break in his professional career, he could perhaps never quite hope to catch up with the latest literature and at the same time to include all the data gained from first-hand observation. It remains today a voluminous manuscript which, like the edited version of his father's papers, never reached the press. Some of the content has become obsolete. The best of the figures, which are varied in quality, testify to his love for his subject and his careful and painstaking concern for accuracy and honesty.

From the little evidence available one has the feeling that his friends and acquaintances treated the bearded and silver-haired old gentleman with a mixture of admiration, pity, and indulgence. They admired him for his early achievements and youthful exploits, for his part in the pioneering days of the study of natural history, and for his steadfastness of purpose, the gentleness, good humor, and lively curiosity which he still displayed. They pitied him for the genteel poverty in which he was forced to live, and for the personal defeats which had blighted his life. They indulged him because of these mixed emotions, and because they had learned to love and respect him.

He and his wife, Lucy, were forced to live with relatives and occasionally in a boarding house in order to meet expenses.[27] Franklin's wife had left them a small sum of money and a small trust fund, but this barely carried them through.[28] From time to time Titian was able to sell a painting which helped in a small way, but one senses the struggle was always there.

The men at the Academy of Natural Sciences for a time provided him with a room in which to work and with a room for his collections. Here his wife came every day and sat with him as he worked on his paintings and on his manuscript. In the manuscript there

[24] TRP to Benson J. Lossing, May 21, 1881, MS, Harry Peale Haldt Collection.

[25] TRP to Prof. T. W. Harris, Jan. 12, 1854, and TRP to Baron R. Osten-Sacker, Dec. 4, 1862, microfilm from Museum of Comparative Zoology at Harvard.

[26] TRP, Butterflies of North America, MS, AMNH.

[27] Copies of *Gopsill's Philadelphia Directory*, for 1877, 1878, 1879, 1880, 1881 and 1885, show various residential listings, sometimes with his grandson, for a time with James B. Peale, physician, and then in a residence on Girard Street; TRP to John Cropper, Nov. 8, 1884, MS, New York Public Library.

[28] Will of Caroline E. Girard Peale, May 13, 1870, probated Oct. 12, 1875. Will ⚹ 804, 1875, Will Book 85, 404, Philadelphia County, Record of Wills, City Hall.

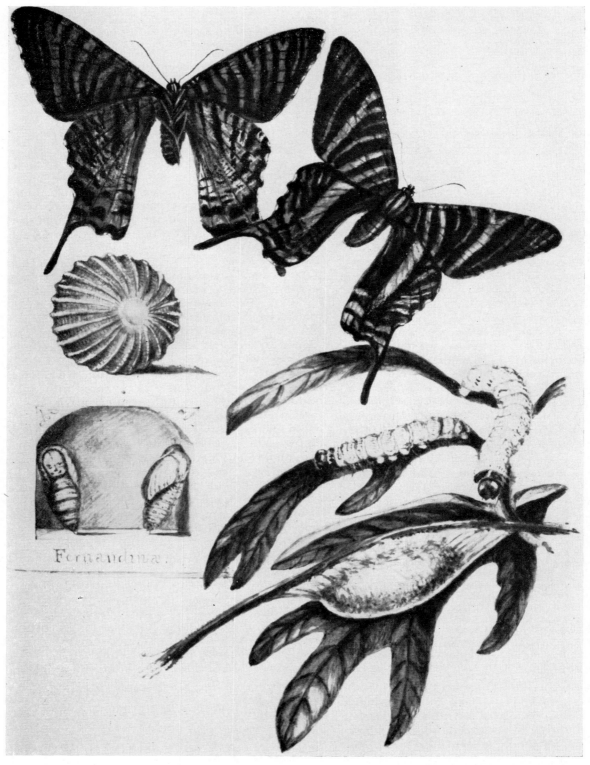

Fig. 53. Water color. *Herperidae Urania Fernandinae*, Plate CXXVI for Peale's unpublished "Butterflies of North America." Courtesy of the American Museum of Natural History

FIG. 54. Oil painting on cardboard. *Nymphalidae Pyrameis Huntera*, Plate LXXVI, for Peale's unpublished "Butterflies of North America." Courtesy of the American Museum of Natural History.

are many pieces of highly readable description that reflect his earlier experiences and his life-long love of observing butterflies. He makes mention of traveling on foot in California in 1841, or of a remembered experience along the Magdalena River in South America, or of a specimen given him by a member of a foreign delegation in Washington. He writes with love of his subject, and one knows he observed with the eye of an artist as well as that of a naturalist:

Although not strikingly rich in color, this insect [*Papilio phaon*] requires all the force of the painter's pallet to represent it, also much force of language to describe it, because all the rays of the spectrum are reflected in its wings com-

bined more or less according to the angle of light in which it is seen.[29]

. . . .

In warm and moist forests, or close bushes, where the winds seldom move the dense foliage, we find these delicate creatures [*Heliconidae heliconia diaphana*], flitting like animated soap bubbles with an undulatory motion, amongst the low herbage, seldom above the level of the human head. As they pass the eye in fragmentary sun-beams they glitter with all the brilliance of the most precious gems by reflected or diffracted light—then become almost invisible by the

---

[29] TRP, The Butterflies of North America, Plate XXII, *Papilio Phaon*, MS, AMNH.

FIG. 55. Oil painting. 1884. Pair of Quail. Courtesy of Mrs.
    Joseph Carson.

transparency of their glass-like wings—the small foliage being distinctly visible through them.

This species is peculiarly sylvan, they are subject to some
variation in different localities, and the species is but illy
determined by Entomologists. I have never found them but
in the deepest shade—there, Fairy-like they spend their lives;
hence we know nothing of their transformations in early
life.[30]

Peale's entire collection of butterflies and insects, together with his catalogue of it, was bequeathed to the
Academy in 1899 and, thanks to his meticulous and
excellent methods of mounting and preservation, it is
essentially intact today. The collection includes specimens collected as early as the 1830's and as late as November, 1882; geographically it includes specimens
found near Philadelphia as well as some found in
more remote areas such as St. Catherine's Island in
Brazil and those given him by the Maclearys in Australia.[31]

The old man, trained in the traditions of his father,
of William Bartram, of Alexander Wilson, and of
Thomas Say, continued to work as an artist and as a
naturalist. At times the younger men liked to hear him
reminisce about the old days. On May 18, 1881, the
members of the United Bowmen, some of them not
much younger than Titian Peale, honored him with
a special party to which they invited over one hundred
of his personal friends. He responded to their toasts
with a brief account of his life, and his words were recorded in the Minute Book:

I do not consider myself superanuated but some of you
may doubt my antiquity when I tell you of my birth in the
Philosophical Hall on Independence Square ¼ of a century
after the Declaration of Independence. There I imbibed the
spirit which then prevailed and has lasted till now. . . . There
I imbibed a taste for *Nature.* . . .

He recalled for them his election to the Academy of
Natural Sciences in 1817 and the Florida and Rocky
Mountain trips.

It took two years to reach a place now known as "Colorado" and to return, now done in two weeks.

Afterwards, I spent one year on the Magdalena River, in
New Granada, amongst other things finding the best material for making bows—Pehewy Palm.[32] See the Bow after 50
years. Use the one marked [here Peale's symbol of the circled
snake swallowing its tail was drawn. In the Minutes of the
United Bowmen the members were usually referred to only
by their symbols.] [It] is still reflexed after throwing thousands of arrows, and winning many prizes from the Bowl
down to the leather medal.

This did not extinguish the exploring Mania, the Antarctic Expedition culminated after ten years labor. . . . We
did not reach the South pole because an unknown *Continent* stopped our Progress. That Continent is still sleeping
in the Glacial period. . . . We can't say much about the
Geology or the future usefulness of the land down there.
Then we visited New Zealand, the Fiji and other Canibal
Islands and prepared them for civilization. After this we
were directed to Explore the Western Coast of this Continent, . . . and ascertain where the boundaries should be
north and south, and also if the few hundred inhabitants
were worthy of notice. Our report gave rise to the "fifty-
four-forty or fight" question with England. . . . The Southern Boundary was left unexplored because we lost the U. S.
Ship Peacock at the Mouth of the Columbia River. The
final result of that expedition and exploration has been the
addition of several rich and flourishing States to our Union
with Millions of inhabitants where we found but a few hundred trappers & adventurers.

The Sum total of that South Sea "Surveying and Exploring Expedition" has been the collection of materials sufficient to found a Hydrographical Bureau, a Natural History
Museum, Botanical Garden, and Astronomical Observatory
in Washington and has served in a general way to elevate
our country in the rank of Civilized nations.

Now I find myself here surrounded by good and kind
friends after a wandering life, years of which were spent
amongst Savages, canibal epicures and other isolated varieties of the human race, including official demagogues in
Washington.[33]

Ten days later they gave still another party in
honor of their oldest and only remaining founding
member. This time there were no speeches, but a few
congenial hours were spent at a table placed "for our
Venerable friend [Peale's symbol was drawn in] and
some of the elder guests, under the care of a distinguished Medical director of the Navy with a Bottle
of Whiskey at hand to be used in case of emergency."[34]

His next few years were quiet ones during which
the healthy and alert old gentleman occupied his time
with his books and his papers, his photography, writing, and painting. An oil painting of a pair of quails
(fig. 55), done for one of his friends in the United

[30] *Ibid.,* Plate LIV, *Heliconidae Heliconia Diaphana.*
[31] This collection is to be described in detail in a forthcoming
article by Maurice Phillips in the *Entomological News.*

[32] According to a note from Dr. Armando Dugard of Barran-
quilla, Colombia, the Pehewy Palm referred to by Peale is probably an English phonetic rendering of the Spanish "Pijiquay." It
is listed in his Palmas de Colombia, *Caldasia* 1: 63 and 81, Dec.
1940, under *Guilielma gasipaës* (HKB) Bailey. According to him
the name pijiguay is used mostly in the lower (northern) part of
the Atrato Valley, and especially in the Sinú Valley of north-
western Colombia.
[33] Minutes, May 18, 1881, MS, United Bowman Collection, HSP.
[34] *Ibid.,* May 28, 1881.

Bowmen, is one example of his continued productivity during the very last year of his life.[35]

Titian Ramsay Peale died on March 13, 1885, after only a day's illness.[36] At the funeral, his friends from the United Bowmen and the Academy of Natural Sciences were among those who mourned his passing. They and surviving relatives remembered him as a careful observer whose experiences in all parts of the world helped to make him an agreeable companion. His low-voiced conversation, full of anecdotes and stories which had taken them back over three-quarters of a century, now continued only in their memories.[37]

The body of Titian R. Peale lies buried in an unmarked grave in the plot belonging to the estate of his brother Franklin in Philadelphia's Laurel Hill Cemetery.[38] There are other more tangible and fitting memorials to the man: a mountain on the Colorado-Utah border and an island near Wake in the South Pacific bear his name. They are memorials to a man who went to the far corners of the earth to seek and record knowledge so that others might learn; they are memorials to a man who in his own way sought to serve truth and beauty.

[35] Canceled check in collection of Mrs. Joseph Carson, dated April 1, 1884; Minutes, MS, United Bowmen Collection, HSP.
[36] Chas. H. Gibson to Chas. P. Hayes, March 13, 1885, MS, HSP.
[37] A. C. Peale, TRP, *Bull. Philos. Soc. Wash.* 14: 325–326, 1905.

[38] According to Laurel Hill Cemetery Records, Philadelphia, Pennsylvania, T. R. Peale was interred March 16, 1885; according to the records of Bringhurst Undertakers, Philadelphia, Pennsylvania, TRP's death occurred on March 13, and there were five carriages used for the funeral.

Fig. 56. Drawing. "Brig Porpoise & Schooner Flying fish / Antarctic Expl. Exped. by TRP."

Part Two

PEALE'S JOURNALS
OF THE
WILKES EXPEDITION

I

Introduction

The officers and members of the Scientific Corps of the Wilkes Expedition were ordered to keep daily journals so that there would be a complete and accurate record of all that the members of the expedition observed. This had initially been recommended by the American Philosophical Society and was incorporated into the General Instructions issued by the Navy. Even though the order was fairly specific, Wilkes felt it necessary to explain it further to the men of the *Vincennes* after the squadron was underway. He stressed, first of all, the responsibilities which the expedition had to the general public to accumulate accurate and verifiable information:

> The duties devolving upon all the officers of this Expedition are altogether of a public nature, and it is incumbent on me to say, require of them to bestow their constant and devoted attention to all incidents, facts, or occurrences, . . . in order that hereafter they may (if necessary) verify or confirm by their testimony any information in relation to the same, and thereby place the evidence beyond a doubt. This can only be effected by keeping full and complete memoranda of all observations, made at the time, and entered in the journals.[1]

He wanted more from them than would ordinarily be recorded in a log-book, and encouraged his officers to record their opinions on all observations that would be of interest to the public:

> The kind of journal required is not a mere copy of the log-board, but it is a diary, in which will be noticed all that relates to public information, being a record of all objects of interest, however small, which may take place during the cruise, in the scientific or any other department: and the views of the officer ought to be briefly expressed concerning things that may come under his notice. The very record that *nothing* has transpired during the day, may be of use; but it is believed that this will be of rare occurrence.
> The whole will form a mass of evidence for the use of the government on our return, which will tend to illustrate and make clear the transactions and occurrences that may have taken place, as well as the habits, manners, customs, etc., of the natives, and the positions, descriptions, and character of such places as we may visit.[2]

Further, he made it clear to his officers that he intended to examine the journals from time to time and to make use of them in the reports to be written after the return of the squadron:

> I wish particularly to avail myself of the results and observations of all, to avoid the possibility of passing over any subject without full examination and remark.
> A casual memorandum or observation, believed at the time of little importance, may lead to important and satisfactory results. These journals, therefore, will become a useful medium of communication between the officers and myself, relative to the scientific and other duties in progress.[3]

At the same time he stressed the fact that private affairs and opinions of events of a private nature should have no place in the journals:

> I trust I need not remark that the above relates entirely to public transactions. With private affairs I have nothing to do: they are, and always should be deemed sacred, and, consequently, will form no part of the records.[4]

These orders shaped the nature of the journals which the officers and men of the Scientific Corps kept while on the expedition. The journals of each man inevitably bear the individual stamp of their author, but one is conscious of a certain restraint; these are not lively private journals kept solely for the writer's own pleasure or for the interest and pleasure of family or close friends. These men tried to record facts and to make their observations as objective as possible. They had in mind a wider, and scientifically-minded, audience. At times it seems as if Captain Wilkes was looking over their shoulders. Lieutenant Colvocoresses later published parts of his own journal and in his preface specifically stated that his journal had been inspected at several intervals during the voyage:

> It may be proper to observe, as affording some guarantee for the correctness of the information contained in this Volume, that it has been compiled from a Journal . . . which the author kept in obedience to a "General Order" from the Navy Department, and that the Journal in question

---

[1] Wilkes to First Lt. Thomas T. Craven, Sept. 13, 1838, in Wilkes, *Narrative* 1: 367–368.
[2] *Ibid.*

[3] *Ibid.*
[4] *Ibid.*

was frequently submitted to the Commander-in-Chief of the Expedition for his inspection and perusal.[5]

Though Peale's journals share with those of the other men a certain lack of intimacy because of the aforementioned restraints, he did not hesitate to record righteously his objections to Wilkes' policies from time to time. If journals of a public nature were to be required, he was to record, even as was requested, his own opinions on certain events and policies. No doubt Wilkes was irritated by several of Peale's comments concerning the commander.

Five of the seven or more journals which Peale kept while on the expedition are printed in their entirety in the subsequent pages. The originals are in the Library of Congress and are numbered and dated as follows:

No. 1 Dated August 1, 1838, to April 7, 1839.

No. 2 Dated April 12, 1839, to October 10, 1839.

No. 3 Dated September [sic] 24, 1839, to June 13, 1840.

No. 5 Dated January 1, 1841, to July 18, 1841.

No. 7 Dated September 22, 1841, to February 19, 1842.

It is possible that Journal No. 4 was lost in the shipwreck of the *Peacock*. Journal No. 6, as Peale himself recorded, was lost on September 22, 1841, while on the overland trip from Oregon to California. In his first journal Peale noted that he kept a special notebook while in Rio de Janeiro and this too has not been located. It is not clear whether he kept an eighth journal for the final leg of the voyage, that is, from their departure from Singapore to their arrival in New York, during which time they made several stops including one at the Cape of Good Hope and one at St. Helena. Since most of the expedition's official tasks of surveying and exploring ended at Singapore, and since most of the time after this was spent at sea, it is possible that Peale did not keep a journal for this final period.

Despite a certain impersonality and lack of intimacy which the official purposes of the journals engendered, much of Peale's journals make interesting reading. South American gardens and churches, Fiji Island warriors, Australian ranches, the missions of California and Philippine cigar manufactories are alike observed and noted. The many descriptive pages about the South Pacific islands provide a contemporary picture of these areas and their people during the strategic years of the mid-nineteenth century when the influences of Western Europe and America were first beginning to be felt, and hence are of special interest to those interested in the history of the South Pacific.

For those who enjoy stories of the sea, the account of the thrust into the Antarctic as well as the descriptions of the frequently difficult landings provides vicarious adventure. In reading the journals one also shares with Peale in the little events that break up the long monotonous days at sea, especially during the first year, a year which was a kind of slow prelude to the busier and more varied subsequent years. There are the religious services, endured with a certain stoicism on a swaying deck; there are the efforts to catch specimens of the few birds to be seen; there are the welcome stops at ports in Madeira and in South America; occasionally there are comments about the cleaning and scrubbing of the decks or the dancing and play-acting of the crew which helped to while away the time.

Peale's notes and observations hold a special interest for the historically minded naturalist, especially the ornithologist. However, these constitute only a part of his records. Equally important were the specimens he collected and the numerous detailed drawings he made en route. Many of the former were carelessly handled before his return from the expedition and many drawings as well as specimens went down with the ship, the *Peacock*, on July 18, 1841. The Historical Society of Pennsylvania has an old card listing a "Catalogue of Birds, etc." of Peale among its manuscript collections but has not been able to find this in recent years; it may have been a Wilkes Expedition record. A "Catalogue of the Specimens of Mammalia and Birds collected by the South Sea Surveying & Exploring Expedition During the years 1838, 39, 40, 41, 42" among the Peale manuscripts at the American Museum of Natural History is chiefly a numerical listing of specimens collected, with few additional notes. The serious student of the history of zoology should, of course, consult Peale's 1848 publication, *Mammalia and Ornithology* **8**, U. S. Exploring Expedition, for the summation of his findings.

Ethnologists and practitioners of other sciences may also find useful information in these journals. If some of the observations seem inadequate by present-day standards, the journals are perhaps significant for providing us with a picture of the way in which a nineteenth-century scientific person went about his task, the observations he deemed important, the kinds of equipment he used, and for a picture of the limitations and handicaps under which he worked.

A portion of Journal No. 7, that covering the overland journey from Oregon to California, has been published in an attractive little book of limited circulation edited by Clifford Merril Drury and with an introduction by Carl Dentzel, titled *Diary of Titian Ramsay Peale* and published by Glen Dawson of Los Angeles in 1957. Otherwise, except for occasional excerpts of a paragraph or two, the journals have never before been published.

The text of the journals as here recorded is essentially as it is in the longhand notebooks. There are no omissions. There is always the problem of trying to read longhand notes, but Peale's handwriting, though extremely small, is reasonably legible. As far as possible within this limitation the spellings and capitalizations of words are as he wrote them. His spelling is reasonably good and not sufficiently awkward to be

---

[5] Colvocoresses, George M., *Four years in a government exploring expedition,* Intro., New York, 1852.

quaint or difficult for the reader. He often spelled place names several different ways. Occasionally there are apparent omissions of words and occasionally he repeats the same word twice. These errors are recorded exactly as they occur in the text. Peale was careless about terminating sentences, often running two or three together, separating them by a colon, a semi-colon, a dash or a combination of these. At times he used periods but began the new sentence with a small letter. In the interests of clarity, periods and capital letters have been substituted for these in as accurate a manner as has seemed possible. Otherwise the punctuation is Peale's. The words or phrases which Peale underlined in his journals are printed in italics here. He did not underline the scientific names of various species mentioned. The scientific terminology is Peale's own and, of course, of the period. No attempt has been made to correct or change this.

From time to time Peale added supplementary comments on the usually blank left-hand page of his notebook. Sometimes these are specific notes or explanations, and in the printed text which follows they are inserted as footnotes with asterisks. At other times he recorded three or four pages of additional comment in continuous narrative on these opposite pages. He did this, for example, after he had left Santiago, Chile. In these cases I have separated Peale's supplementary text from the daily journal by three centered asterisks at the beginning and end of the supplement and inserted it in what seems the appropriate sequential order.

A map of the world, on which Peale's movements (mostly on the *Peacock*) are traced, is shown on the inside of the back cover (map 2). Peale usually wrote the location, the month, and year at the top of each journal page, and a similar practice has been followed here. In order to provide logical subdivisions for the reader, I have divided the text into several major geographical sections. These divisions were not in Peale's text but will not, I trust, in any way interrupt the flow of the original narrative.

Numbered footnotes are mine, and these are few. In the preceding chapters I have tried to provide a brief but general summary of the years on the Wilkes Expedition which will, I hope, help the reader to read Peale's diaries in context. Some of his observations, including zoological and geographical notes, are admittedly incomplete and vague. However, to identify or elaborate in detail upon these would be an undertaking of considerably larger scope than has seemed appropriate for this study. The information for most of the notes which I have added has been drawn from Wilkes' five-volume *Narrative,* and the reader who wishes to pursue any fact or observation further is referred to this and to the special scientific publications which resulted from the expedition.

II

The Atlantic

No. 1

JOURNAL,

BY

T. R. PEALE

PHILADELPHIA   1838   AUGUST

On the 1st of August I recd orders from the Navy Department to report myself for duty in the Scientific Corps of U S Surveying and Exploring Expedition, to Lt Comanding Charles Wilkes on board the Ship Vincennes at Norfolk Virga previous to the 5th. On my arrival in Norfolk found the Vincennes, Ships Peacock and Relief in a rapid state of preparation for sailing —on the 7th dropped down to Hampton roads (17 miles) where we were subsequently joined by the Brig Porpoise and Schooners Sea Gull and Flying fish— making in all six sail. The Scientific Corps were divided among the squadron as follows.

Dr. Pickering, Itchst	Vincennes
Mr. Couthouy, Mallg	Ward room
J. Drayton, Draughtm	
T R Peale, Natst	Peacock
J. D. Dana, Minst	Ward
Hale, Philolst	room
Mr. Rich Botanist	Relief
Mr. Agate Draughtm	

In addition to whom there was a gardener on board the Vincennes.*

17th In the afternoon were notified by signal of the Vincennes (flag ship) that the Squadron was under sailing orders, consequently we all had to remain on board impatient to start on an enterprise for which many of us have been prepared for the last 12 months.

*   *   *

LIST OF OFFICERS

Vincennes

Comdr Charles Wilkes Jr
1 Lt Thomas T Craven

---

* Brackenridge

Flag Lt Overton Carr
2d Lt Robt E Johnson
3 Lt James Alden Jr
4 Lt Wm L Maury
Actg Master James H North
   " Surgeon Edd Gilchrist
Asst   "   John L Fox
   "   "   John S Whittle
Purser R R Waldron
Chaplain Mr Elliott
Passd Midshipman Totten
   "   "   Reynolds
   "   "   May
   "   "   Josh P San[d]ford
Midshipmn Geo M Clark
Astg do Saml Elliott
Boatswain Wm Smith
Gunner W Bright
Carpenter Wm M Lai[gh]ton
Sail Maker S W Hawkins
Pilot Benjn Vanderford
Pursers Stewart, R P Robinson.
     122 Men including 15 Marines & 2 boys.
[Along side margin:]

Scientific Corps

Joseph P Couthouy	Boston	Joseph Drayton	Phila
C Pickering	Philada	J G Brown	repairer of instruments

LIST OF OFFICERS

Peacock

Lt Comg Wm L Hudson
1st Lt S P Lee
2d " Wm M Walker
3d " Geo F Emmons
4th " Oliver H Perry
Acting Master Tho A Budd
Surgeon J F Sickels
Asst do Silas Holmes
Purser Wm Speiden
Passed Mids. J B Lewis

124

" " H Gans[e]voort
" " G W Harrison
" " Henry Eld
Midsmⁿ Wilkes Henry
" Henry [William H.] Hudson
Boatswain Tho G Bell
Gunner J D Anderson
Carpenter Jonas Dibble
Sailmaker J. D. Freeman
Pursers Stew^t W H Insley

Scientific Corps

T R Peale Phil^a
Hor^o E Hale Boston
James D Dana N Haven
Seamen 17. O. seamen 26, Landsmen 4
Boys 2. Marines 11. Total 93.

LIST OF OFFICERS

U S Ship Relief

Lt Com^g A K Long
1st Lieut Rob F Pinckney
2^d " A L Case
3^d " J A Underwood
Act Master G T Sinclair
" Surgeon J C Palmer
Pass^d Mids. A B Davis
" " Thom^s W Cumming[s]
Capt^{ns} Clerk J R Howison
Boatswain J Black

Scientific Corps

Rich D C
Alfred Agate N Y
Brackenridge.
Midsh. James L Blair.

LIST OF OFFICERS

U S Brig Porpoise

Lt Com^g C Ringold
1st Lieut. M J L Claiborne
2^d " H J Hartstein
3^d " J B Dale
Act^g Surgeon Ch T B Guillou
" Master A S Baldwin
Pass^d Mids S F Blunt
" " Geo Colvŏcoressis
Capt^s Clerk T W Waldron
Boatswain Oliver Nelson
Carpenter Amos Cheeks [Chick]
Sail Maker John Joines
Pursers Stewart W H Morse.

LIST OF OFFICERS

U S Pilot boat Sea Gull

Pass^d Midsⁿ J W E Reid Com^g
" " F A Bacon 2^d

Pilot Isaac Percival

11 Men

U S Pilot boat Flying fish

Pass^d Mids. Saml R. Knox Com^g
Midsⁿ G W Ham[m]ersly
Clerk R Ellis. [Ellice]

* * *

18th Sailed from Hampton roads with a light breeze towards the Capes, in sight of which we remained at 10 oclock next morning having parted with our Pilots at midnight, a light wind and smooth Sea gave favourable opportunity for trials of the sailing properties of the different vessels composing the squadron which was not lost.—a few Stormy Petrels (Pr. Wilsonii) were the only Birds visible and the water was altogether so pleasant that few were seasick and all at the tolling of the bell, joined in divine Service on the quarter deck. Captⁿ Hudson read the service and prayers in a very impressive manner, the Vincennes only being provided with a Chaplain (Mr. Elliott).

23^d Thursday Nothing worthy of remark has occured since Sunday, the wind has been against us, many have been sea sick, I amongst them and little was to be seen although the weather has been clear & pleasant on deck but too warm to be comfortable below, air 80–2, water 78–81. Lat 34° 38′ Long.—we lost sight of the Procelarii Wilsonii in the Gulf Stream and have not seen any other except one solitary bird of a larger species of Procelaria it was mottled black & white. Flying fish have not been infrequent & saw a solitary Dolphin yesterday. And this morning was surprised by a beautiful crab making for some sea weed which I soon recognised in Desmarest's[1] figure of Lupa pelagica; last

---

[1] Peale and the other members of the Scientific Corps had a small working library aboard ship. It is not clear whether these were part of the expedition's equipment or whether they were the personal libraries of the men involved. Peale had some of his own books on board, all of which were lost in the wreck of the *Peacock*. The American Philosophical Society, in its recommendations to the Secretary of the Navy in 1836, prepared the following list of books which it suggested be taken on the expedition:

Lord Anson's Voyage round the World in H.M.S. Centurian [*sic*]. (1740.)
Beechey's Narrative of A voyage to the Pacific and Beerings Straits &c (1828.)
Bougainville's Voyage round the World (Forster's translation), 1769.
Ellis's Polynesian Researches, 1829.
Freycinet's Narrative of a Voyage round the World. 1820.
Kotsbue [*sic*] Voyage of Discovery: in the South Sea.
Morrell's Narrative.
Parry's Journals in search of N. W. Passage.
Peron's Voyage de decouvertes aux terre Australes.
Porter's Narrative.
Yate's New Zealand, 1835.
Bennett's Wanderings in N. South Wales &c. 1834.
Tyerman's Journal of Voyages and Travels &c (South Sea Islands, China and India, 1831.
Weddell's Voyage towards the South Pole, 1825.
Adanson's Senegal.

evening the Vincennes made signal to follow her action and immediately put about, and stood for the relief which was almost out sight astern, on reaching her at night they boarded her in a boat, and per procedure [?] gave her instructions to meet us at Rio janairo, as we then made sail on our course and soon left her out of sight, on which we all rejoiced as she had not been able to keep company, although we have been under half our sails waiting for her.

24th Friday Lat 36° 37', Lon 71° 30' 35"

Calm all the squadron within visiting distance and the opportunity not lost; a few birds in sight, one a swallow, and a Petrel. The only ones near enough to distinguish; a Butterfly* came on board, probably from a chrysalis brought in one of the ships with wood. Dolphins were playing around [?]. One I caught besides a few smaller fish caught in hand nets from a boat which was lowered for us to inspect the drifts of Sea weed & by which we found a few crustacea, etc.

Tuesday 28th Late 38° 13'. Longe 60° 35'

Since Saty last the scene has been greatly changed all the bright faces, which were so delighted in the cabin were changed by the storm which followed, a gale accompanied by heavy rain set in from the southward our decks leaked into our berths from above and the water shiped rolled about at its leisure beneath our feet. Bedding, Books, crockery and all that was not *well* secured pitched together in fellowship; no piping to divine service on Sunday, and on Monday when it had cleared off cool from the N W none of our fleet were visible, a tremendous Sea was running and our ship continued to *scudd* but with such reduced sail, that they were not sufficient to steady her, & we rocked in a very uncomfortable manner until yesterday when

Bennett's New South Wales.
Chronological History of discoveries in the South Sea by Capt. Burney, R. N.
Desmarest's Mammalogie.
Cuvier's Animal Kingdom.
do Dentes de Mammiferes.
Traite d' Ornithologie par R. P. Lesson.
Cuvier's Histoire et Anatomie des Mollusques.
Dillwyms Catalogue of Shells.
Lumark's [Lamarck's] des Animaux sans vertebres.
Latrielle's Histoire Naturl des Crustaces et des Insectes.
De la Beche's Geological Manual.
De la Beche's Theoretical Researches.
De la Beche's How to observe Geology.
Lyell's Principles of Geology.
Humbolt's [Humboldt's] Works.
McCulloch's Classification of Rocks.
Dr. Danberry on Volcanos. [*sic*]
Von Buck's Work upon Volcanos. [*sic*]
Elie de Baumont.
Transactions of the Geological Society of London.
Article, Geology in the Encyclopedia Metropolitana.
Besides the Standard Works on Mineralogy.
In Silliman's Journal, Vol. 1st, page 71, and Vol. 3rd, page 249 useful instructions are to be seen relative to the choice and preservation of Geological Specimens.

* Vanessa cardui.

the sea began to abate, and Captn Hudson giving up all hope of meeting our consorts made sail on our course, and we glided along cheerfully from 6 to 10 knots. A few of Mother Careys* chickens kept us company and two Tropic Birds (Boatswains of the sailors, from the pointd tail like a marling spike) were seen; with a few exceptions no Mollusca have been visible since the gale, I have observed but one Physalia; but although few of the deep sea Molluscs are visible to the naked eye multitudes constantly fill the ocean around us, the water is luminous with them under our bows at night and sparkles with them during the day, most of them microscopic. We are now out of the Gulf Stream the temperature of the sea is 75° air 80°. Sea weed still abounding but in small detached pieces; there appears generally to be a difference of about 3 degrees in the temperature as indicated by 2 thermometers one being placed on deck and the other at the main topmost head.

Sunday Sept. 2d A calm and pleasant day with the wind from the N W but very light, a sail in sight ahead, standing to the South. All the men dressed for muster and divine service, Captn Hudson officiating in a very impressive manner, on these occasions. I cannot but feel that our government has done us injustice in not assigning a nominal rank to the members of the Scientific Corps; while all appear in their respective places & dress, we alone are left as idle spectators by courtesy only being considered officers without grade, subject to the usual etiquette of a man of war without any privileges.

Our ships also have been constructed without any design for their future opperations, and are totally unfitted for the service, it is true state rooms on the gun deck have been constructed for our accomedation, they are wet and dark,—where neither drawings or preparations of specimens can be made. The captns Cabin is the only place on board where such oppurations could be carried on & there only at the sacrifice of his private convenience; the Relief is the only vessel in the squadron at all fitted for the Service and she is such a miserably bad sailor, as to be unfitted on that account. Her comfortable poop cabin is the only place in the whole fleet which could be used in any but the most calm weather at sea for Scientific investigation. The usual Naval etiquette prevents our working on deck and the want of light and air below!

A pretty little species of Physalia has been floating past us this morning, they are about an inch in length and the same height of crest with blue tentacula. I presume it to be a distinct species from the uniform size, being less highly cold and without the long proboscis like process of Phs Perrinii.

We have had nightly rains and squalls for the last week, but the wind having been mostly from the West has been fair, the winds during the day variable.

This afternoon overhauled the Brigantine "Joven

* Procelaria Wilsonii.

Emilia" of Malaga from Porto-rico for St Ander. She is the first vessel we have spoken since we parted company of the Vincennes and such is the dearth of antics to interest the voyager, that it created quite an excitement.

Friday 7th Since the 2^d the wind has been more favorable and more of it so that we are getting quite comfortably on our course with a moderate sea, but get no more fish or Mollusca, neither do we see as many birds, a few Procellaria at so great a distance that I could not recognize the species were all that have been seen. Flying fish are also more scarse: the weather pleasant, therm^r 80° in the water 76°.

Sat^y 8th Lat 38° 12' Long^e 31° 29' 30" Saw a Spermacitia Whale, and a number of Procelaria Leachii followed us. They are the first we have seen near enough to feel certain of the species on account of the forked tail. We were all very anxiously looking out for the Land expecting to make the peak of Pico (Island of Fayal) in the night, but were disappointed as we did not see it until the afternoon of

Sunday 9th In the morning had prayers as usual, in addition to which Captn Hudson read a sermon; we sailed along the south side of Fayal, but a heavy bank of clouds effectualy obscured the land untill the afternoon when we had gone so far to the S E that the peak of Pico only was visible for a short time, a snipe flew round the ship for a while, and a quanty of Salpa passed us. Some of them were united in masses and others free.

Tuesday 11th Found us between the Islands of St. Michael & St. Mary; the former presenting to us a cheerful prospect of highly cultivated lands with neat white dwellings, but the latter presenting quite another aspect being quite barren & dreary with bare volcanic rocks rising abruptly from the sea, though on the south side I understand is quite fertile presenting an agreeable slope from the Mountains to the Sea; considerable quantities of ashes and pummice stone were floating on the surface of the sea, some of which we procured in our nets, and as the pieces of pummice were much worn our conclusion was that it had been washed from the gullies in the Islands by some recent heavy rains. But few birds were in sight and no fish or Mollusca; the weather being pleasant and storms anticipated from the appearance of the clouds it was considered prudent to have the chain cables brought from below onto the gun deck to have them inspected and put in order for use, their additional weight so high up in the vessel made her ride uncomfortably and sail much worse besides destroying our promenade and smoking parties which are confined (the smoking part) to this deck forward of the "bitts," I have therefore been obliged to amuse myself in painting a design for the back board of "Dingy" (the smallest boat in the ship) on which I have designed an Eagle resting on the striped shield, spreading his wings over and protecting the *Peacock* (our ship) with the united constellation over & around. The Dingy is the boat

FIG. 57. Sketch. "North end of St. Michael's, bearing 08."

which I have selected as the most likely to be best for my shooting excursions up creeks etc. being calculated for but two oarsmen, and very light [fig. 57].

Sunday 16th Morning hazy with a heavy sea a few Boobys around us, made the Island of Madeira on our lee bow to the S of us, and Porto Santo on the N. We passed round to the E. of Madeira between it and the desertas, which are high rocks rising abruptly from the sea and much broken on their surfaces. At the north end of one there is a remarkable detached rock looking like a col^mn several hundred feet from the Island, numbers of Boobies and gulls were flying about them and from appearances I should suppose it to be a favourite breeding place for them as well as other oceanic birds. Madeira is equally high and precipitous at the E end but shows more traces of fertility, and as we rounded to the south side it appeared through a glass to be a perfect garden, the hills being terrased with stone walls and cultivated to their summits, with a respectable portion white plastered stone houses distributed over the whole; on nearing the city of Faneshall which we could not succeed in doing untill late in the day* owing to the want of wind, we discovered the rest of our squadron lying at anchor, the Vincennes and one of the Sch^s having arrived last evening and the Porpoise and the other this morning, indeed we saw a Brig & schooner to windward of us which we took for them, but for the fact of their not ans^g our signals. Landed towards evening and found that a party composed of Dr. Pickering, Mr Drayton, Mr Couthouy, and Brackenridge the gardener had started in the morning overland to the other side of the Island to be gone some days and that another party had gone to take the altitudes of the peaks barometrically, and what pleased us all a Brig was loading to sail for N York on Thursday next; a walk and abundance of fruit contributed much to the pleasures of the evening.

Tuesday 18th Was detained untill late in on board in order to pay a visit of ceremony to the Governor, which turned out rather a stupid affair; we were ushered into a spacious hall of the castle which was hung round with portraits of the different Governors of the Island and four historic paintings representing the dis-

————
* of Monday.

covery settlement and population, all miserably executed, but not devoid of interest. On the Civil Governor's reception of us he requested all to be seated, and conversed a few minutes with Captn Wilkes in English, he appeared dull with but little curiosity and was apparently glad when we took leave in order to pay our respects to the Commandant who spoke through one of his aids as interprter, and kindly gave an order that we should be allowed to go to and from our ships at any hour of the night; the gates being usually closed at 8 oclock in the evening. They were both pleased to dispense with the ceremony of firing salutes, from the liability of damage to our instruments. These matters being over Dr. Sickel and myself made a visit on horseback to the gardens of the late Conde Joannes Carvalhalius who died a few months since. Our road led to the eastward of the town over a well paved way along several of the Mountain ridges along which were planted many chesnut trees now covered with unripe fruits, we passed numbers of both men and women carry^g burthens on the heads steadied by a strap across the forehead precisely analagous to those used by the natives on the cordilleras of the Andes, the men carried mostly wine in goat skins, the women coal, wood, Hay, etc. The most remarkable feature of these people is the enormously thick legs of the women, and their small conical caps which are worn by both Sexes alike, these caps are called "carapusa" or crapusa, and are the same shape as those now worn by some of the natives of the interior of Africa, also represented in Champolin's Egypt^n antiquities on the heads of their African prisoners the material only is different, these are of blue cloth lined with red, while the africans are mostly of wove grass. Carvalhalius's gardens are very extensive and tastefully laid out and abound with exotic plants and but few of the Island among many Americans it was gratifying to me to recognize the Coreopsis tinctoria* which I had the pleasure of introducing first at the botanic garden attached to the University of Penn^a and the scarlet sage (the latter I am uncertain of) but the former it appears has become common in Europe & was introduced here from France. Among the birds introduced into this garden the Silver Pheasant of China was the most remarkable & thrives well: as also the Fallow Deer. The pavements are wide and beautifully laid, being composed of small pebbles of various colours which strike the atten^n of every visitor accusto^{md} to our gravel walks, they are far more beautiful and here more durable, but would not stand the frosts of our climate.

We are here just in the height of the vintage and hourly meet parties of the peasants bringing their wine into town on their backs in goat skins; the grapes are trodden to pulp in wooden vats and pressed in the same with a wooden screw and lever. The juice finding its way out by a wooden spout into tubs, the quality of the wine depending in a measure on the degree of pressure applied. Small yellowish grapes make the sweetest wines (Malmsy) blue grapes hard pressed Tinto (common). It is barreled and prepared by the merchants in town.

The abundant ravines and mountain streams afford great facilities in water power for mills, which are of the simplest construction, flutter wheels with a shaft direct to the stones (of Lava) in a simple square box above, with a hopper, the flour is scooped out of the box and *sifted* through a sieve made of cane into another box, and carried in bags on jackasses to market; of course it is brown and much filled with husks. The mills are usually about 12 feet square, built of stone with thatch or tile roof.

My next Journey was to the Coural (or Corral) a remarkable gorge leading to the centre of the Island. The road was intricate and apparently very dangerous over and along precipices of about 2000 feet (a stone of about 1 pound required 7″ to fall about $\frac{2}{3}$rds the way down), the scenery was of the most stupendous and beautiful, and consequently could approximately be described by the pencil only, the grapes and oranges do not thrive beyond an altitude of about 1500 feet as they then are liable to mildew before they ripen potatoes do well. Eye sketches of complicated mountain scenery are nearly always too inaccurate to be useful. I therefore solicited the company of Lt Perry and returned on a second occasion to the summit of the Coural mountains, armed with a camera lucida & table, etc. On hiring horses for these Journeys it is customary for a driver & guide to go with the horse, he goes on foot, there are generally "geHo" fellows— cary a cudgle in one hand and whack the horse with the other (look out for your legs) a good horse and accomplished rider sometimes escape this oppuration but not entirely, a gallop of 6 or 7 miles does not seem to render the driver the less vigilent, he is always at your horses tail and clings to you like the old man in Sinbad the Sailor. There is no tire in them, not even in exertion. Every man, woman & child after you leave the town which is sufficiently infested begs, and from the time you come in sight the little children with clasped hands are *singing* "almas por corina."* or something which sounds like it, when if your driver has any mercy for you, he whacks his (your?) horse with a yell of Capra-ca-a. The roads are 4 to 8 feet wide well paved with pieces of lava, walls on the side, with a gutter on top leading water to the vineyards, wine casks are drawn, as well as water for the shipping on sleds (a kind of boot) by a small breed of crooked horned mild looking oxen. Goats are brought into town to be milked at the doors; the market for fruit, fish, etc. are seperate enclosures, with small "square" sheds with shutters which are rented out. Churches

---

* Mr. Nuttall described in the Journal of the Acad^y of Nat^l Sciences a number of Plants which he claims the credit of introducing but does the great injustice of claiming plants which were growing from seeds brought by Col. Long and myself and placed in charge of Mr. Dick in the Universities garden.

---

* coz-i-ma or cour-i-na.

numerous but tasteless in ornament, excepting some of the waxen saints which are well executed; the Padres were very polite but oddly dressed, red stockings, breeches and coat black; wide & cocked hat & gold tassels, but other grades of rank differently. The clanging of bells less incessant than I have heard them for prayers in South Ame[a].

The prisons have their inmates pretty much in common. Many carry on their trades of button & shoe making, etc. and hand their manufactures on poles through the grated windows, while others spend their time in hailing and begging of the passers by, and when in the 2[d] Story lowering strings with bags affixed to them to receive the alms.

The soldiers are well dressed and look comfortable & contented, don't beg and on the whole are the best of the people, the officers gentlemanly & courteous, their music excellent. The females of this Island excepting some Indians which I have been among are the furthest from beautiful of any I have seen, their legs and ankles are monstrously enlarged (either by the early habit of carrying loads on their heads or the mountain roads) and their features coarse and masculine, but from the number of children about the houses on the roadsides I would infer they are good mothers.*

Our Consul J. H. Marsh is absent in England where he has resided some time but Mr. Burden one the partners of the firm has filled his place in a most flattering manner and kept open house to all our officers, to his kind assistance we owe many obligations which we hope long to remember.

The birds, Quadrapeds and Butterflies bear a very close analogy to those of the southern parts of Europe, among them I observed the:

Rabbits—Lepus cuniculus
Red legged Partridge   Perdix montana?
Dove
Yellow Wagtail   Motacilla Boarula
Swift—Cypsclus murarias
Titlark   Anthus pratensis
Gold finch   Cardueli commanis
Canary   Fringilla canaria**
Kistril   Falco Tinunculas
Blue thrush   Turdus cyaneus
Brambling   Fringilla montifrugilla***

Besides Blackbirds but in cages, but whether they are natives of the Island I had no means of ascertaining.

Monday 24th Left the Island in the afternoon with a moderate breeze from the N.E. My time be much occupied in taking care of my specimens and drawings, is much more pleasant than before; the sea in these regions does not afford that abundance of the larger

Mollusca which abound in our harbours, but the smaller species are equally abundant, no birds or fish.

*   *   *

Spermacetti whales often appear off the town, and one which a boat was pursueing gave the opportunity of ascertaining the intervals of respiration; it was 25–30 seconds the average short of 30″.

*   *   *

Thursday 27th The weather thus far has been remarkably pleasant, and the vessels have been able to keep close together, the Peacock as she is now trimm[d] sailing the best; today we were close enough to converse and the whole having been painted while at Funchal present a fine appearance. We brought two bullocks from the Island, one was killed yesterday and the other this afternoon, a shark made his appearance soon after the garbage was thrown overboard but soon left us; a Bonita was caught in the stomach of which we found some interesting crustacae and a squid.

Friday 28th Winds still light and a smooth sea, our vessels close enough to exchange visits. Capt. Hudson dined with Capt Wilkes in the Vincennes and such was the proximity of the two ships at one time that some apprehension was expressed that might be entangled; Dr. Pickering, Chaplain Elliot and Lt. Johnson paid us a visit and a shore bird came aboard but left us again before I saw it.

Sat[y] 29th The water today has a remarkably green appearance as though we were on soundings but 140 fathoms of line did not reach bottom; the squadron in close comp[y] and the Sea Gull alongside of us; today like Saturday on shore has been one of general scrubbing and holystoning all the gang way ladders down besides the hub-bub of buckets and swabs, these scrapers which are unknown on shore are found to be capital things to destroy paint and fancy work.

Sunday 30th After prayers this morning Capt Hudson read us an excellent sermon, which was objectionable in one respect only, that was its length or rather not its length but the length of time we had to stand uncovered, for when these sermons were written it was for a shore congregation, who it was intended should all be *comfortably seat[d]*; not so with us, we stand and balance ourselves to the motions of the ship which becomes rather tiresome. The same green water today, but no bottom with 280 fathoms of line. Two flying fish came on board of us. At 11 oclock P.M. the Vincennes hove too, and burned two blue lights which was a signal previous agreed on for all the squad[n] to do the same in order to wait until day light to search for some rock said to have been seen about this position and marked so in some of the charts.

Monday Oct[r] 1st Lat   19 26 45
                          Long 20 43 . .
The same green water but no soundings. A Noddy (Sterna stolida) near us but no other indications of proximity to land. Examined the water under a micro-

---

* No Negros are found on the Island and our ward room servents were looked upon quite as curiosities.
** about the town alighting on the house tops.
*** on the mountains where there was trees, only.

scope but did not discover sufficient mollusca to warrent the assertion that they give colour to the sea, on the contrary they, the larger ones at all events, are less numerous than we have generally observed them in blue water.

Tuesday 2ᵈ The weather pleasant with a moderate breeze from the N. E. but a very sensible raise of temperature both in the air and water: air 80 water 82° Captⁿ Wilkes Lt. Johnson and Mr. Drayton came aboard from the Vincennes. Lt Lee and myself returned the visit to dine with Capt. W. and were accompanied aboard by Purser Speiden and Mr. Eld & so spent a merry afternoon with the ward room officers.

Wednesday 3ᵈ Laid too last night and spent today in search of the Bonita Shoals without success. The vessels were spaced so as to embrace the widest space within signal distance (at least 16 miles) and by tacking several times it could hardly be possible should a shoal or rock exist, for it to escape our notice, the only birds seen today were a couple of Mother Cary Chickens (Procellaria Leachii).

Thursday 4ᵗʰ Still the same pleasant weather but warm Thermʳ 82°: in the evening the Vincennes sailed so close with us that quite an animated conversation was held between our two commanders, and a bugler having been discovered on board the Vinˢ he was directed to contribute to our entertainment;—rather a failure, and not so good as one of the crew tinkling on a mandolin on the forward deck. They saw the land of Mayo today. We did not make untill next morning; passed it and came close into St. Iago in the afternoon but as we found it impossible to get into the harbour (or anchorage) of Porto Praya before night, it was concluded to stand off and on untill morning when we entered and landed about 11 oclock. We have arrived just at the termination of the rainy season and the Island appears remarkably verdent both hills and valleys are covered with abundant grass and other vegetation. Birds and butterflies I found in my excursion in plenty, in fact having no assistant I obtained many more interesting and beautiful species than was in my power to retain for the weather being excessively warm in the valleys my birds spoiled before I found time to finish my notes & drawings. Quails were very abundant and afforded good sport had we been so disposed or had the time, their notes (Per-wet-wet-) indicated their presence everywhere. Their food I found on dissection was principally caterpillars and five which I shot all proved to be males with their testes much enlarged from which I infer that it is the commencement of the breeding season. Sparrows were numerous and of a variety of species, some with rather pleasing notes, one in particular interesting from its mode of constructing a covered nest or thorn bushes from 5 to 10 feet from the ground. Crows are numerous and appear to be new and I saw one Raven whose voice is totally unlike that of N. Amᵃ. Its habits and general appearance the same. The most numberous species of Butterfly was Papᵃ Bolivia of Livˢ. They are smaller than those of Java

or N. Holland. On the whole there is a fine field at the present season for the naturalist on these Islᵈˢ, however sterile they may be at any other. The people are 19/20ᵗʰ black with sundry grades of admixture with the Portuguese and the different tribes of the West Coast of Africa; are poorly clad, the climate requiring but little, and miserably improvident in other respects. Goats & jackasses abound, and appear to thrive well, the cattle were also in good order from the abundant pasturage. Oranges Bananas Plantains, etc. were plenty, cheap and good. Our Consul* received the officers very hospitably and entertained about 20 at dinner: he has lately lost his wife: Our instructions requiring us to be on board at sunset, our visits had to be flying ones, the landing is difficult, a point of rocks some distance from the town to the east (¼ᵗʰ of a mile) is the only place, and there it is necessary to watch the receding of the surf and jump from one point of the rock to another before the next wave returns.

Our Store Ship Relief has not been here, but her absence does not alarm us, because her being a bad sailor and probably fallen to leeward, she may have shaped her course to Rio Janairo in preference to beating up again to the rendezvous at a sacrifice of time.

Sunday 7ᵗʰ Underway before breakfast on our course for Rio Janairo; in the afternoon had a heavy shower of rain with some thunder & lightning which obliged us to have the hatches covered and consequently from the excessive heat, upwards of 80° found it very uncomfortable working at my preparation of bird skins, etc. as they were rapidly decomposing. Capt. H. as usual read prayers and a sermon, after which the Chaplain Mr. Elliott came on board, but did not submit us to a second service as we were somewhat fearful he might the sun being too powerful to admit of our standing for more than an hour in its rays uncovered.

Monday 8ᵗʰ Discovered a large ship Standing northwesterly, bore away to speak her and found she was the Conquerer from Bombay for Liverpool, and the opportunity of communicating home being so good, she was detained about two hours untill our letters were prepared and entrusted to her. Recᵈ two general orders from Captⁿ Wilkes, one against wearing mostacios which most of the officers have been cultivating and the other directing the members of the Scientific to wear the undress uniform of the officers with whom they are messᵈ.

The sea for the last few evenings has been remarkably luminous from the vast quantities of Mollusca contained in it, so much so that there was quite a brilliant reflection from the ship's bottom, last night particularly.

Tuesday 9ᵗʰ Lat 11° 19′ 54″ Longᵉ 24° 14′ 30″. A swallow came on board today appearing to be much exausted, as we didᵗ succeed in taking it I could not

---

* Mr. Gardiner.

determine the species. A butterfly (Apatura bolivia?) was caught on board, it is the same species which I saw at Porto Praya, and has probably kept us company from the Cape de Verdi. Light winds in the early part of the day, with showers in sight at night calm and oppressively warm & humid thermom.ʳ 83.

Wednesday 10ᵗʰ Calm and sultry all day the night oppressive; Purser Waldron and some of the officers of the Vincennes paid us a visit.

Thursday 11ᵗʰ This morning the Swallow which came on board before yesterday was brought to me nearly dead, it had escaped all efforts to capture it, but perished from hunger. Contrary to my expectations it proved to be the Chimney Swallow of Europe (Hirundo rustica of Pliny). We had the upper half of the ports taken out in each of our State rooms today, which is really a luxury; to enjoy both light and air at the same time is more than we have had since we left the Chesapeake. My joy was but of short duration. I had written thus far when a puff of wind blew my light out, it was almost a perfect calm but one minute before, and my room being on the lee side made it somewhat singular, but all was soon accounted for by the ship's being taken aback by a brisk wind from the opposite quarter, all the ports were ordered closed, and my joy turned into the discomfort of a hot night in a close room.

Friday 12ᵗʰ Inspection day as usual when all the men and officers appear on deck, and as the roll is called the men pass forward in front of the latter as each man's name is called. A parcel of small sharks followed us but would not take the hook. Another swallow followed us but did not come on board.

Sunday 14ᵗʰ Our religious service was more than usually comfortable from the circumstance of the awning being spread, and seats provided. A sail in sight to the southward, one of the schooners ordered to speak her, but from the continued calm she was recalled before dark without effectᵍ our object. The weather continues calm and sultry. We scarcely move through the water but glean sundry mollusca with the greater ease.

Tuesday 16ᵗʰ Yesterday experienced very heavy rain, the hatches & ports having to be closed we suffered for want of ventilation and light, at night parted company with the rest of the squadron.

I have often been amused at seeing the marine drills, the various attempts to keep in a line while the ship was rolling was always amusing, but when the sailors turn came to exercise with small arms it afforded a fund of amusement us idlers. Jack has no idea of soldiering, and won't understand military language; "Keep on the beam," "and *lay* further aft" pay attention and no skylarking or I'll flog you like h——"; were the first commands, the rest suited the case in much the same manner, notwithstanding which sundry toes felt their neighbours muskets, and the marine sargeant seemed to suffer great agony. Sailors are perfect children, and have to be governed by the same rules, if

Fig. 58. Water color made by Titian R. Peale while on the Wilkes Expedition. "No. 13. ♂ / At Sea. Latᵉ 6° 50′ / Longᵉ 21° 38′ / Octʳ 19ᵗʰ 1838. T R Peale." Courtesy of Miss Ida Edelson.

you reason with them it must be after their own fashion.

Thursday 18ᵗʰ The same continued calm interrupted by rain & slight squalls, we have seen but few birds or fish. A Noddy came near us yesterday, a few Petrels are about us today and two small sharks of about 3 feet long have followed us for several days. They get plenty of food from the ship and cannot be induced to take a hook and keep too deep for the Harpoon; Porpoises are but seldom seen. The thermometer gives (owing to the hygromatic state of the atmosphere?) but a poor indication of the sensible state of the temperature; the average is about 81 degrees while the sensible heat is quite as great as it was previous to our leaving the U.S. when it ranged above 90°; a heavy misty atmosphere seems to hang round the horizon and the water at night is generally about 2 degrees warmer than the air.

Friday 19ᵗʰ An unpleasant rainy day, the wind so light as not to save us from being carried to the north by the currents. Large quantities of Velella passed us which were almost all dead, in all probability killed by the heavy rains. A Warbler (Saxicola) came on board, it was much exhausted and was soon taken; it bears a close resemblence to some of the European species but appears distinct (See drawing Bird, No. 13) our Latitude at noon was 6° 50′ Longᵉ 21° 38′. Another swallow (Hirundo rustica) was taken yesterday.

20 Satʸ Free from rain but still cloudy but being Holy stone day we are not free from wet decks etc. Another swallow flew into the cabin.

Tuesday 23 Nothing material has occured. Since the 20ᵗʰ only one sail, seen yesterday. We have been searching for sundry shoals found on the charts, but not in the ocean; we have now got into the S.E. trade winds, and are moving quite lively. Lat 5° 40 N, Long^e—At daylight saw a ship which when first seen was taken for the Vincennes, but on bearing away towards her she hoisted the Dutch ensign. She is bound to Batavia. Another ship showing American colours excited much greater interest, we gave chase in hopes of some news from home, she showed no disposition to wait for us, and when a musket was fired for her to heave too it passed unnoticed, but No. 1 second division seemed better understood. The topsails were backed and Lieut^t Perry was sent on board, he bro't us a few newspers but not much in them. The ship was the "Cowper" of Boston for Batavia, 49 days out: A Dove came on board but sundry unsuccessful attempts having been made to catch it, it took its alarm and started off east towards the coast of Africa.

Thursday 25th Our position yesterday was such as to give every encouragement for the complete refutation to the position of one of the shoals* we have been in search of. Today our lat^e is 4° 14', Long^e 20° 17', 15". The weather is sensibly cooler, 75 to 81. In the afternoon boarded the British ship, Earl of Durham, bound to Sydney N. South Wales.[2] She was filled with emigrants, both male and female. They furnished us three newspapers (quite a treat) but not much of interest in them for us.

Sunday 28th We have been repeatedly flattering ourselves that we struck the S E trade winds ("the trades") but each day there has been a disappoint^t as we have now got a south west wind with unsettled weather, rained all the morning with squalls; had our divine service on the gun deck, but finished abruptly on account of a squall of wind. Yesterday had an unusual number of Procellaria round us. I tried catching them with a fishing line but did not succeed untill we prepared a light thread line without a hook, with that we caught four in a short time, by their flying against the thread and becoming entangled from its lightness. They varied considerably in size, were all males and of the same species common on the coast of the U.S. Thalasidroma Wilsonii of Bonaparte. Our lat 3° 17' and longitude 17° 53'. It is somewhat remarkable that we have no fish around us, nor with the exception of the Petrels, any birds.

Monday 29th A shoal of Porpoises and a few Bonitas under our bows, but no success in taking them. In the evening at 9 oclock had an exhibition of *Aurora Borealis.* The rays of light were not col^d, arose in the N.W. central above the horizon, and passed the zenith, were constantly changing, and appeared to me in one or two instances to be below the clouds, which were nebulous, and abundant, in this however I may have been deceived, but others agreed with me that it was so. Our
Lat^e D. R. 2° 16' 36" N.

* French shoal.
2 Australia.

Long　　　17° 07' 45" W.
Temperature of air 81
Water　　"　　" 80. The atmosphere very moist and the wind blowing and all sail breeze from the S W.

We have seen a few birds, but with the exception of the Petrels (Th^a Wilsonii) they have all kept too far from us to listing [?] with the species. All the marine animals we have been able to obtain have been of diminutive size, and a large proportion of them crustaceous and microscopic, a few of them we have satisfactorily ascertained emit a phosphoric light, but still the luminous masses appear to be mollusca, the Pyronomae being the most brilliant.

Thursday 1st We are now about 30 miles north of the equator with a fine breese from the S W—directly ahead for us and on the "Triton bank"—a shoal thirty miles south of the line has to be sought after before proceeding for "Rio," we anticipate a long passage having already been 25 days from Porto Praya. A very large shark and a spermacetti whale were seen to day but at a respectful distance from us.

Monday 5th Crossed the equator on Friday and have been searching until today for the Triton bank, without success, and I think have certainly searched enough to prove it does not exist short of 100 fathoms below the surface of the sea. One Bonita is the amount of our capture among fish, a Noddy, among birds besides a small Hawk which I shot but falling into the sea when we were making rapid headway we had left it too far astern to clear a boat in time to pick it up. This morning while fishing for Bonitas from the end of the bow sprit, I saw two quids of tobacco, a few chips and a bunch of oakum directly in the ships course. If the ship had not been going at the rate of 5 knots through the water it would not have been remarkable, but as such was the case it was curious that on the broad surface of the ocean we should so exactly hit the track of some other vessel not then in sight although the air was remarkably clear.

Friday 9th The whole of this week we have been enabled to lay our course with a fine S E breese for "Rio" the weather clear and pleasant, temp^e 75–80. Our headway too great for catching fish or in fact seeing them, being 8 knots per hour, excepting flying fish which we *"flush"* in shoals sometimes of a hundred or more. At times too we meet great quantities of vellela and Physalia and have passed some sepia of several feet in length. We lost sight of the Procellarie* on the line in Long^e 18°.

Sunday 11th Lat 12° 29' South
Long. 30 50 West

Untill today our wind has been steady and strong from the S E but now it has slackened and shifted north of East. Consequently we are going before it with all the inconveniences of the rocking motion of the ship. The Stormy Petrels have not entirely disappeared as noted on the 9th. The Magellanis clouds

* Thalasidroma Wilsonii

were first seen a few nights since with some disappointment as the imagination is apt to figure a c[e]lestial phenom[a]—as noted as they are as something striking. Whereas, a mere whitish spot, a fragment of the "Milky Way" as it were, would never be observed were it not stationary and to be seen only in one hemisphere.

Tuesday 13th The anniversary of the "Meteoric Shower" was watched last night with some diligence, but there appears some difference in the opinions of the observers, some making the numbers visible greater than usual, others the contrary, as suited a preconceived theory. Those who have not been the continued habit of observing meteoric phenomena I have always remarked, discover what they consider something wonderful and arrive at hasty conclusions until sober experience sets them to rights.

Still plungeing and rolling gaily on our course before the wind with *all* studder sails set, like a bird spreading its mighty wings and playing over the water for the shore.—All hands "a scrubbing," holy stoning and sluicing the ship, preparatory to painting—everything is in much the same state things might be of a Sunday morning in a country town; all studying appearance and trying to forget the work of the week by working twice as hard.

(*Wednesday 14th*)

(Lat 15° 38′ S. Long[e] 35° 18′ 30″)

Thursday 15th A Moth (Erebus) flew on board yesterday afternoon, the weather lowering and squally, several sails in sight in the course of the day, thus at 4 found ourselves between two carrying lights, on which we supposed ourselves in our squad[n] again, but on hoisting our night signal and burning a blue light without receiving an answer, we stood on our course. A continued squally weather, rain with some lightning, and a heavy cross sea.

Friday 16th Early part of the morning cloudy but it cleared off before noon, passed in sight of six sails of fishing vessels on the Abrolhos banks. Kept constantly sounding and found bottom at from 24 to 40 fathoms, coral and broken shells. Obtained one perfect specimen of Caryophillae and some minute shells in the crossing of the lead. Two Boobies (Sula fusca) and a Tropic bird with one or two Petrels (P. Wilsonii) were the only birds seen.

18th A rainy Sunday. Service on the gun deck, little or no wind; high broken land in sight for a short time in the morning, but so covered by clouds and mist as to make it questionable. A Bat (Molossus) and three moths came on board, the water unusually blue, being of quite an intense indigo colour. Had we kept the fine N E wind which we had part of last night we should have arrived at our port today, but as it is we all feel sorely disap[d].

III

Eastern South America

20th Tuesday Arrived in the harbour of Rio de Janeiro, anchoring abreast of the town too late in the afternoon to land but on the following morning Messrs Dana, Hale and myself took up our quarters on shore; they at the Hotel Pharoux and I at the Hotel du Nord where I engaged a room at "one mil reis" per day.

— DESCRIPTIONS IN RIO —
— POCKET BOOK[3] —

Sunday Jany 6th 1839 Having completed our stores and refitted *all* the vessels we once more weighed anchor and beat out of the harbour against the sea breeze, but it dying away just as we cleared the sugar loaf we had again to anchor outside. In passing the U.S. Ship Independence they maned the rigging and gave us three cheers, which promptly returned. After coming to an anchor the Schooner Flying-fish returned into port to recover some of our deserters but was not very successful. Two however were obtained by boarding a slaver bound out. One of them a *negro*!! who received his dozen lashes with the Cats (all that the law allows) with the regrets of Captn Hudson, that it was out of his power to give more. On Monday afternoon Lt. Walker and myself with my assistant Alfred Jacquinot landed for a short time on the Is^d do Rouy on the north side of the Harbour mouth. After adjusting Lt. Walker at the Camera lucida stand to make a view of the entrance to the harbour I made the circuit of the Island, which is a solid mass of granite rock, bare on the steep sides but covered with vegetation on the summit and in the ravines, where I found a number of birds and lizards—a remarkable line of Barnacles & Serpula surrounds the Island at high water mark but is not more than 4 feet in width, affording a good foot hold where the rock is too steep to be traversed without its aid.

---

[3] Unfortunately, this notebook has not been located and may have been lost.

After collecting a few birds & shells we discov^d a signal had been made for us to return on board which we succeeded in doing as the Squadron were getting "under way." The wind was light but fair and by Tuesday night we had lost sight of the coast of Brazil.

Sunday—13th The wind has been steady from the N & East, and our course for the week about SSW with pleasant weather, the thermometer ranging about 75°. This morning was calm for a short time after 6 oclock but then it commenced to blow quite a gale from the S E with a heavy Sea, the gun deck and my room was very wet, my room particularly had to be baled several times in the course of the morning. Had prayers while under reefed topsails, but no sermon. We have seen a variety of Mollusca and but few birds, of the latter we have seen only Procellariae. Of the former we have seen a beautiful species of Cestuna about two feet long, a variety of Physalia, etc. The thermometer fell to 65° and we were glad to put on some of our Cloth Clothing. The rain fell in torrents during the morning but by evening it had cleared off again.

The Exploring clothes furnished by the government were distributed during the week to the men, but a portion of it, the overcoats particularly, proved to be of but indifferent quality, from the swindling propensities of the contractors. The coats which cost the Exped^n 16$ were certainly no better than others purchased by Individuals for 10.

Wednesday 16th Our passage south to the present time has been pleasant, with mod^e winds and clear atmosphere therm^r about 68°. This morning observed the water to be filled with minute animalculi. Large quantities of Porpoises and "Black fish" were playing about. The Porpoises were about 4 feet long, of a darker lead color above and white beneath, and were very active and playful leaping sometimes in pairs five or six feet clear of the water. The "Black fish" were ten or twelve feet long, Jet black above and pale beneath, having a white spot just behind the dorsal fin. They appeared to belong to the subgenus *globicephalus* and closely resembling the figure of the *deductor* represented in the 6th vol. of the Naturalists library[4] which however is without the conspicuous white spot on the back of those seen today. Two species of Procellaria were flying near us, one appears to be the Thalasidromia Wilsonii, the other appears to belong to LaCepedes genus Prion, and ∴ probably the Pr. caerulea discovered by Fonten in immature plumage as these are sooty brown above & white beneath. They have been quite silent while near us.

Thursday 17th This morning we passed through patches of a greenish substance which the sailors call Whale Spawn. It as well as some which we saw yesterday must have covered several acres in extent. On examining some which we procured in a bucket, I found it to consist of small bundles of fine fibers about 1/20th of an inch long, each fiber as measured by a micrometer 1/2000th of an inch in diameter, and were without animation appearing to be fragments of some animal or vegetable matter. Possibly it may be excrementicious & left by the whales or Porpoises of which there was large "shoals" in the vicinity.

Spoke a Whale Ship which reported that they had been six months cruising, had taken 300 barrels of oil, and intended going to Pornambuco in two weeks, from thense to the U.S. All the Squadron sent letters on board. Like mine, most of them must have been short on acct of short notice.

In the evening spoke a Brig from the LaPlata bound to the Falkland Islands.

Friday 18th This morning a shoal of several hundred Porpoises passed on their way to the S.E. They moved with astonishing velosity. There was more than a hundred of them in company, leaping entirely *over* the waves & were out of sight in a few minutes. It was the species described by Lesson, the Phocaena bivittatus as figured in the Naturalists library,[5] which is a very characteristic plate of it. Passed several spots or lines in the ocean of a yellowish green colour, the largest ½ a mile long and onbout [about?] 50 or 100 yards wide, on examination it proved to be the same substance which coloured it that was observed yesterday. (Bundles of minute tubes, which did not appear to possess animation) when examined by the unassisted eye they looked like minute yellow spiculae, but under the microscope they were found to be in bundles of various numbers & size about the 1/20th of an inch long like those of yesterday and about the same thickness (1/2000th of an inch) the largest measured 1/1000 of an inch.

Saty 19th A raw & unpleasant mist & at times so dense a fog that the Vincennes fired guns every half hour to keep the squadron together. Several whales were passed during the night & a whale ship. We feel

the cold very sensibly although the thermometer has not been below 58°.

Sunday 20th Had prayers & a long sermon on the spar deck as formerly, during which we passed a number of Seals, some of which moved with great rapidity and sometimes leapt entirely out of the sea to the height of 3 or 4 feet. They were of various sizes (Young?) but were generally about 3 feet long and while in the water appeared entirely black.

Monday 21st Calm most of the day, sent a report to Captn Wilkes which I had written yesterday, and exchangd some shot with the Vincennes in order to be ready to land on the Coast of Patagonia at the Rio Negro which we now understand to be our first port. A few Albatross and Cape Pigions around us, and quantities of "Kelp" consisting of two species of Fucus, on which we obtained an abundance of Anatifer and minute Crustacea. Several visits paid & returned with the Vincennes.

Tuesday 22d Nothing remarkable occurred today but the weather being pleast and dry, without wind, induced most of us to get our fowling pieces in order and make sundry other arrangements against the game before we land. A whale was within half a mile of us but being alarmed by crossing the wake of the Brig I was not enabled to get a distinct view of it further than to see it had a dorsal fin,* & was not more than 30 or 40 feet in length at most, and quite black. Two species of the Albatross about us, one a dusky black, and about 4 feet in extent, the other white with a dark back, and about 6 feet across.

Friday 25th Yesterday was calm at noon but as usual for the last few days the wind sprung up towards evening from the eastwards—(Sea breeze) and this morning a low and almost level shore was in sight notwithstanding a heavy atmosphere, numbers of Libelulae and other Insects came aboard. Calm again at noon, but about 5 oclock a gale attended with lightning and rain came from the N.W., and considerable sand blew on board although we are 10–15 miles off. Anchored untill the gale passed and then stood in towards the land untill after night and again anchored in 10½ fathoms sandy bottom. Had several lines out, but caught no fish. Gales are prevalent on the coast at this season. From their blowing across the Pampas they are called "Pamparos" and are at times very violent. The only Birds seen were the sooty Albatross, a Procellaria larger than the Cape Pigion, and a flock of Terns.

Sat. 26th Last night the Schooner Sea Gull got ashore, and made signals for assistance on received which she got off without damage, leaving her anchors untill today. A signal from Capt Wilkes called all the members of the Scientific Corps on board the Vincennes to receive general instructions. We were then transferred to the Schooner Flying Fish to be landed in the Rio Negro, Capt. W. accompanying us himself. Struck on the bar in crossing and were obliged to an-

---

[4] The reference is to William Jardine, *The Naturalist Library*, Edinburgh, 1833 ff., of which 17 volumes had been issued by 1837.
[5] *Ibid.*

* Placed very near the tail

chor until the rising of the tide when we floated off and returned to meet the S^c Sea Gull, and were again transferred on board of her. Capt Wilkes returning in the Flying fish to his ship, but directing us to preceed up the River whenever the tide should be sufficiently high, but in attempting it although the bar had been previously sounded, we again struck and were in quite a perrilous situation for several hours momentarily expecting the mast to go over board, we threw up several rockets and burned blew lights for assistance. Lt. Johnson with a boats crew came in time, and by the rising tide we continued to beat untill finaly at 8 oclock we found ourselves in safety inside of the rivers mouth, and anchored in five fathoms water, the part of the bar we beat over affording but 7 feet and the schooner drawing 9½ feet. Had she gone to pieces, which at one time was probable our chance of safety was small for we were half a mile from the shore with continued breakers to it.

Several horsemen were on the sand hills reconoitering while we were aground & we were hailed from the shore after dark requesting us to send a boat which we did, being fully armed, we explored the sand hills for some time and found a house near a signal staff arms and a cartridge box filled with ball cartridges were found near the door but for some time no poeple.

Finaly two Pilots (English and French) made their appearance, they told us that they had supposed our squadron to be french and as this port is under the Buenosayres flag, we had given considerable alarm, made arrangements with the pilots to take us to the Town (Puebla de Carmen) which is 21 miles up the river. Our party marched back, all delighted with the novelty of the adventure, and on getting on board all (fifteen) slept soundly on the floor lockers etc. in the Cabins.

Sunday 27th Landed early for a hunt, and on going to the pilots house to deposit our coats etc. intending to sleep there we found a guard of lancers had arrived in the night with orders from the Governor to take the pilots away. They appeared to be in great alarm, but Capt. Ringold of the Porpoise and Lt. Perry determined to go also, besides Purser Waldron. Horses were obtained from the soldiers and a guide. Along the sea shore and mouth of the river are long ranges of sand hills—formed of White Sand and broken Shells, covered in spots with rank grass and aromatic plants among which abound a species of Bustard (Pedrix) Deer, Patagonia—Cavy's (called Hares) and a small species of Armadillo in abundance, besides now and then, a family of ostriches. Drs. Fox & Holmes wandered with me over the sand hills towards the sea to the north and besides a number of birds, killed a fine Buck which we were desirous of conveying to our friends whole, but found the task a most laborious one. We had several miles to carry it on our backs in an excessively hot sun, the country around not affording any trees. On arriving at the Pilots house we found it necessary from the suspicions of the guard to send

my asst. Jacquinot on board the Sch^n as he cannot speak english & his french exposed us all to the suspicion of belonging to this country, the Navy of which have commensed active warfare. Soon after Dr. Fox and I carried the Deer down to the landing in order to send the venison to the officers and the skin to my asst; but we made signal in vain for an hour and a half when I skined the animal intending to leave the carcase on the beach, when Pas^d Mid^n Bacon, the 2^d officer of the schooner came to us in a surveying boat and reported to us that Captn Ringold had left orders that no boat should be sent to us untill were were to leave the River. Consequently upon this uncivil treatment the venison was left on the beach and we returned to the pampas hunting. Our situation was very uncomfortable as we could get no provisions and had to drink brackish water. The thermometer being at 87°. I was very successful in obtaining many singular birds, but from the heat of the weather, and seperated as I was from Jacquinot who had the materials, most of them spoiled. I replaced such as I could find.

Monday 28th Mr. Hale returned last night from Puebla de Carmen whither he had gone with Purser Waldron, and brought an order from Captn Ringold for us to be on board by nine oclock this morning, when he intended to leave the River. We all went to the beach as soon as we saw his horses on the opposite side of the River and made signal for a boat, *but waited all day in vane, none were sent.* Dr. Fox left us and walked to the mouth of the river where the Schooner flying fish was laying. He there found Captn Hudson who sent a boat for us and we returned on board the Sea Gull previous to going to the Flying fish in order to get some meat of a number of Beeves just slaughtered to Capt Ringold detained us.

Last night in sleeping on shore, or in trying to do so, we were submitted to perfect torture innumerable fleas on the floor, bushes & earth all appeared the same, so that we greeted the return of day as a blessing. Dr. Fox and I sallying at once to the sand hills and breakfasting on a "Partridge" (Bustard) killed on the way.

Slept soundly on the cabin floor in field beds of blankets, coats, flags, and every thing the Schooner afforded; some few on deck under the sails.

Tuesday 29th Remained on board the Schooner all the morning, the tide being unfavourable until noon; the commandants nephews, from Puebla de Carmen, breakfasted with us. They are fine active looking young men in the picturesque dress of the country. Dr. Ducatel of Baltimore was one one of their party, has been here several years and adopted the customs of the country, has been quite successful in the practice of medicine but not so much so in recovering his mony. In cross^g the bar out we found 16 feet of water in the shallowest part. The pilots state the bar to be a shifting one subject to be changed by every gale of wind from seaward or freshet from the river.

Were taken on board the Vincennes first, thense to

the Flying fish and finaly on board the Peacock late in the afternoon, having reported the conduct of Captn Ringold to Captn Wilkes while on board the Vincennes.

Wednesday 30th A dense fog all day, a few boats having started before it came on to Survey were caught out. The Vincennes continued firing every half hour to guide them, but the current being too strong for them to regain their own ship, Lt^s Maury & Johnson came aboard of ours for the night. Two guns in quick succession being the signal of their safety were fired and we all turned in after a merry evening. In the morning

Thursday 31st it commenced blowing a gale from the SE directly on shore, we were within half a mile of a shoal directly on our and the tide run over 2½ knots.—We had to slip our cable and put to sea, leaving six men on shore who belonged to the Vincennes. For the space of half an hour our ship was in a most perrilous situation. The breakers Close under our lee, and a very heavy sea setting us right on thence by promptly setting sail and slipping our cable depended our salvation. At noon the gale had ceased, and the Sea began to moderate, so that the Squadron put about to recover the Anchors. The Brig Porpoise also having slipped hers with 75 fathoms of cable.

Friday, Feb. 1st Searched all the morning in vain for our bouy, but found it in the afternoon adrift, it having chafed from the anchor. The Vincennes boats land^d and recovered the men besides sundry armadillos and young ostriches, etc.

Sat^y 2^d Reported the conduct of Lt Ringold to Captn Wilkes in writing from a consciousness that an early understanding is absolutely requisite to our future comfort and success. At two bid a final adieu to the Rio Negro and lost sight of its sand hills in a couple of hours under single reefed top sails.

Monday 4th Great quantities of birds were seen in flocks sitting on the water around us; among them were a few Terns & gulls, but the greater part appeared to consist of two or three species of Procellaria, etc. In the evening a severe gale commenced from the SW with a heavy sea, it was in fact the most violent of any that we have yet experienced. It was indicated by the fall of the barometer, as most of the changes have been since we have been on this coast. The thermometer also fell about 20°*, producing a change of feeling by no means pleasant. In this instance as in many others I have remarked that sudden changes of temperature while the thermometer ranged above 32° when attended with much humidity occasioned a greater sense of cold than the same changes have when below that point. The cheerless swash of water too, over the floor of my State room might have made me feel the comfortlessness of a ship in a storm when

table lamps, bureaus, and every thing which was not well secured were dashed from one side of the ship to the other.

Thursday 7th Until last evening, when the wind had died away calm we have hardly been able to get our acustomed exercise from the heavy pitching of the ship. The wind then changed from S.W. to N.N.W. which now enables us to lay our course. The thermometer is now rising, being 55° while yesterday it was down to 49° in the evening the Barom^r fell to 49 75/100 and a dense fog came on which was supposed to indicate a gale, but the night was clear and starlight with a moderate wind.

But few birds have appeared around us today, those few were mostly procellariae, and one of them about the size of Thalasadromia Wilsonii had a white breast!! No fish, seals or porpoises seen but now and then masses of fucus most of which appeared to have been eaten from the Stems. A shell dredger which I had begged was sent from the Vincennes.

Monday, 11th But little has occured worthy of record. We occasionally pass masses of Fucus, which has apparently been detach^d from the shores. The birds we see are few in number and variety (Procellariae, now and than an Albatross) and today a shoal of Porpoises amused us for a while but we were unsuccessful in taking them. The weather is pleas^t but changeable, the therm^r indicating a range of temperature from 48° to 56.

Wednesd^y 13th. Yesterday we had quite a gale from the S.W. but unaccompanied with bad weather otherwise. Temp^e 50°. In the morning passed an immense quantity of birds in flocks, sitting on the water. They were but little larger than the Sterna minuta and somewhat like them in colour, they have however rather more of a swallow like action on the wing, but did not come near enough to the ship to let us see more. Today the wind moderated, became fair and allowed us to set all sail again. The Sooty Albatross is quite abundant and comes very close to the ship, but does not seem inclined to take a hook which is the usual mode of taking them. A small flycatcher came on board this afternoon which I caught, but in the attempt to take it previously one of the men had pulled out its tail, in consequence of which I gave it its liberty without determining the species.

Thursday 14th On turning out this morning found the ship before a brisk N.W. wind with studding sails set and the land of "Terra del fuego" on our Starboard beam, & Staten Island[6] on our larboard bow, the first high and undulating, the later mountainous and very much broken into irregular peaks of various fantastic figures of a dark sombre gray colour, with here and there a brilliant white patch of snow. Our passage through the Str^ts of LeMairo from having a strong current in our favour as well as a brisk wind, was very rapid, scarcely affording time to make sketches of the

---

* to 49°, which is the lowest we have yet had it. The two schooners were ordered by signal to make the rest of their way to the port of destination which they promptly obeyed and were soon lost sight of.

---

[6] Staten Land.

various headlands. In the bay of good success we saw a small schooner getting under way and standing along the land to the west. We supposed her to be the Sea Gull, but the Vincennes kept her signal to come within hail flying for several hours with now and then a gun to call attention, but without avail, she kept away from us. The land as we rounded Cape St. Vincent was high, broken, covered with a sombre verdure in the vallies, the summits of the hills & mountains being mostly naked, with small spots of snow, some of the rocks decidedly volcanic in colour and figure while others looked like a decomposing granite, a few bearing a chalky aspect. In some of the ravines we, by the aid of our glasses, could see streams of water and *timber*. When opposite to Valentyns bay (today is Valentine's day!) the wind increased to a gale, obliging us to close reef'd top sails, immediately after which it suddenly changed to the opposite direction (SE) making a lee shore for us, at night, however, it died away calm, leaving a heavy sea. We saw two swallows with white breasts and a few ducks, the only land birds, but of the marine species a few black and other Albatross, besides a small procellaria much resembling Wilson's.

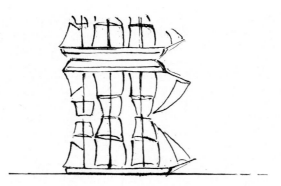

+ Vincennes as seen off between Cape Horn and Nassau bay. Feb: 17th

Reflected land, Cape Horn Feb: 17th

FIG. 59

Friday 15th Found us within sight of the landmarks of last evening with a S W wind, a few fitful showers of rain fell during the night and one flash of lightning was seen. We were nearly all day about 5–6 miles to the south of the Vincennes, the weather cool but not unpleasant, 54°—the lowest termperature we have yet experienced being 44° a few nights past. A few Albatross floated past us in the evening when we were nearly becalmed. They sit very lightly on the water with the tails higher than their bodies, and appear quite unsuspicious of danger from fire arms. In the evening Staten Land was just in sight, bearing NNE. And Cape Horn also in sight bearing SW by W. At night the Vincennes and Porpoise were just in sight to the W and Northward of us around Cape Horn.

Day breaks at ½ past 2 in the morning, and the twilight continues until ½ past 8 PM.

Sunday 17th The wind was directly ahead for us to work round Hermits Isd and Cape Horn. We have now the long heavy and even swell said to be peculiar to the Pacific Ocean. All the mountains of Terra del fuego are covered with snow and present at the distance of 15 or 20 miles from the coast a desolate appearance. Large patches of floating fucus (Kelp) of several different species were constantly passed among some of which we found a few shells, etc. but the most remarkable phenomena witnessed was the "Mirage" the Vincennes & Brig were about 10 miles to the north & east of us & were each presented to us in three images; two being upright and one inverted [fig. 59]. The headlands being similarly reflected besides two vessels (a Ship and Brig) to the southward, and beyond the visible horizon. The thermometers during this phenomena indicating the anomaly of a higher temperature in the upper regions, than that which existed below, that at our main top mast brace being at 65 degrees while that on deck was at 50, thus making the remarkable difference of 15° in so short a distance. At this period (4 PM) it must be remarked that such was the point at which the real and reflected image of the Vincennes met, that ∴ in the top gallant sails were merged; but in a short time the reflecting surface raised and the images were distinct, as represented in the lower view of a hill on the left of the opposite view.

Tuesday 19th All yesterday was lost by head winds or calms. It was not untill near night that a favourable wind enabled us to enter Nassau Bay, a rocket and blue light was answered by the Vincennes from Orange harbor where she had entered in the morning by it and a beacon light on an island we were enabled to anchor also untill this morning when we removed further in, soon after which some of us landed and I succeeded in killing 3 species of geese and a few smaller birds on the hills. The store ship Relief has been here since the 29th of January, having visited Good Success Bay and one or two points on the coast previous to entering this harbour.

IV

The Antarctic

Monday 25th The Brig Porpoise with Captn Wilkes on board & her tender Sea Gull got under way for her voyage South. Cheers were exchanged from all the vessels with good wishes, and they steered east of Hermits Island out of the Bay. Soon after which our ship (the Peacock) and the Flying fish as her tender also made sail out, leaving the Vincennes and Relief only behind. The former to remain untill our return the other to circumnavigate Terra del fuego, and finish the surveys of some unexplored channels.

Messrs Hale, Dana, Pickering, and my assist Jacquinot were temporarily transfered to the Relief besides Dr. Gilchrist to assist in her scientc duties, while sundry other changes have been made among the officers.

Lt. Johnson has received the command of the Sea Gull (tender to the Brig Porpoise) and Lt Walker the Flying fish (tender to the Peacock), Lt Pinkney to first Lt. of the Peacock in the place of Lt. Lee (suspended and sent on board the Relief), Lt. Maury to the P————[7] in place of Lt. Walker, transferred to the Flying fish, etc., etc. Mr. Couthouy & Mr. Drayton are to remain in the Vincennes leaving myself as the only remaining member of the Scientific Corps to go south, for which I have conceived it a duty to volunteer, although the product in Natural history may be small yet be it what it may, it will be looked for with interest.

We had not reached the entrance of Nassau Bay when it commenced to blow a gale from the SW in consequence of which we run back to the entrance of orange harbr again for shelter, and anchored fast before night.

Tuesday 26th Stood out of the Bay again with a fair wind in the afternoon passed the Diego Ramurez Islands and at night had lost all land astern, but a severe gale came on from the NW with a tremendous gale which obliged our tender to lay too, consequently we had to follow her example in order [to] wait for her, many of the officers were made sick by the extravagant

---

[7] *Porpoise.*

motions of the ship, and as my room was flooded as a last resourse I took to my cot too, not only to keep dry, but warm; as I find that most of us experience the cold quite as much with the thermometer at 43° in rainy and wet weather with damp clothing and no fire, as we should with the thermomt much lower & dry weather.

Wednesday 27th Still lay to for our tender of which we have lost sight, a very heavy sea, with fierce rain squalls, which continued until

Thursday 28 when the weather moderated, and several guns were fired for the Flying fish, but as we did not get sight of her we stood on our course alone. The wind changeable and squally from the SW and in the evening some hail. A few birds following us consisting of two small species of Procellaria and a few Albatross. Temperature 43.

Saty March 2d Still the same variable weather with misty rains and squalls with a tempe varying less than might be expected from the changes of wind being generally 40–5°. We feel the cold more sensibly from the highly saturated state of the atmosphere, and from our not having yet put up our stoves.

Wednesday 6th Today it became necessary to put up our stove on the gun deck in order to enable the sail makers to work which was otherwise impossible from the unyielding state of the ropes. We had a slight sprinkle of snow with the thermometer at 35. The Sea continues to be too heavy to carry much sail and the wind variable and squally, principally from the westward in consequence of which we are much further east then we hoped to be Lat. 62. Long

We have had several whales and two "shoals" of Porpoises around us, the former not near enough to designate species, the latter appeared from the wonderful celerity of motion and two broad white lateral lines connected by one or two white bars to be "Pernetty's Dolphin."

A very pretty species of Petrels has been following us for some days, its voice, size and habits are the same as Wilson's, but it is white beneath from the neck down, the underparts of the wings white with a dark bar in the middle: about the bill is red (the bill itself?) Breast black.

Another species about the same size is of a pale lead colour above, with a dark col^d bar on the wings, & all white beneath. Its actions are more sprightly and swallow like, it flyes around the Ship but does not so constantly follow her wake as the others do.

There are a few larger Petrels and Terns now and then about us but *all* differing from those seen near Cape Horn, the Albatross's being the only ones which might be supposed the same. The sea and wind have both been too violent to allow a successful issue to my attempts to take them with fishing lines, or to get them if shot.

Our gun deck notwithstanding all our care proves to be so wet and cold that all the men were today ordered to sleep on the berth deck. The gun deck has been constantly afloat since we left Orange Bay, even my room and the Pursers opposite to it, and furthest forward of the cabins, have been almost untenantable, the floor being all the time covered and swashing as the ship rolls, and as we cannot any longer bear the remedy of a windsail, everything partakes of the accumulated humidity and darkness, a "bulls eye" barely enables me to dispense with a candle.

Sat. 9th Lat 62° 51' Long^e 77° 4' D R

This morning Lt. Perry awoke me when he left the midwatch (4 AM) with a large snow ball in his hand, from the first which has fallen in sufficient quantities for so merry a purpose, the rising sun however dispatched all that remained on our decks although the sun itself was invisble to us on acc^t of the dull and heavy clouds which filled the air; a drisling rain and hail succeeded without wind to steady the ship in a tremendously heavy cross sea, in the afternoon in attempting to reef the maintopsail, one of the men (Stewart) was precipitated from the yard into the sea, striking the main rigging in his fall, he lay insensible in the water supported feet up by his large "exploring Boots" over which a bowline was thrown by which he was dexterously drawn on board again, a boat could hardly have lived, had it been lowered so that his recovery was almost miraculous, his recovery is doubtful still as far as regards the injuries rec^d.

We have passed and been followed by several flocks of Penguins*, but have seen no seals.

Monday 11th Yesterday a large "shoal" of *Blackfish* followed us, but on my firing one ball at one of them the whole left us, they were of the same species with those seen off the La Plata, the old ones *all* having the same white spot posterior to the dorsal fin, the young were without it untill about 6 feet in length, the largest of the old ones we saw was about 14 feet long.

Today was passed a large iceberg, it being the first created quite a [sensation?], even the sailors left their

---
* Jackass Penguins, Aptenodytes demersa.

breakfast to have a look at it, its elevation appeared to be about 100 feet.

Tuesday 12th Stewart the seaman who fell from the main topsail yard on Sat^y last died last night, his lungs having become gorged with blood from the violence of the concussion. His remains were committed to the deep with the usual ceremonies this morn^g, Capt Hudson taking the occasion to address the men on the uncertainties of life, previous to reading the funeral service.

Two Icebergs were passed laying to the northward of our course, one was more than 100 feet in elevation.

Friday 15th Night before last we had a fall of snow, follow^d by rain, some of the snow hung to our rigging and sails most of the day, but the sun appearing enabled us to determine our position to be Lat 64° 17 S. Long^e 86.52 W. I shot 2 Albatrosses, of a species I believe undescribed, they are of an ash color with sooty heads. A boat was lowered but only one of them obtained on the return of the boat in hoisting her in one of the bolts drew out and she was stove in the fall out, fortunately the men had left her.

To day we passed 14 icebergs, one of which was about 200 feet in elevation. They are all of them of a pure untarnised white with delicate blue shaddows on their declivities and destitute of all living things.

The thermometer stands generally about 33° the vicinity of the ice not seem^g to affect it. This evening another slight snow.

Three species of Albatross fly around and follow the ship besides the 3 or four species of Petrel already mentioned and Pintadoes (Procellaria Capensis) now seen in considerable numbers for the first time, our general course about SSW.

Sat 16th Snow and rain all night with an uncomfortably high sea. Last night had a faint exhibition of Aurora australis. It was cloudy, but a faint white light was visible to the south in the few interstices between the clouds & horizon. A heavy gale of wind obliged us to lay too on

Sunday 17th Notwithstanding which we had Service and a sermon, the sea being so high that the men had to lay on the deck and hold on by whatever was near. We shipped several seas and the vessel rolled so as to bring the water up into the lee gangway on the spar deck. The whole of the gun deck was afloat including my room by which I suffered severe losses in drawing paper books, basons, etc. The ship was covered with a sheet of ice to windward and had her head rigging completely loaded, making it necessary to beat the ropes and sails every few minutes. The thermometer fell to 24° in the air and 32 in the sea.

Monday 18th The gale still continued with a tremendous sea, the ship laying to, but towards evening it moderated so as to enable us to make sail again. Numerous Cape Pigeons, or Pintados (Procellaria Capensis) followed the ship beside the Sooty headed Albatross and three species of Procellaria unknown to

FIG. 60. Oil painting. Inscription on back reads, "Schooner, 'Flying Fish,' USN. Lt. Walker, at her *ne plus ultra*, 70° 14′ south latitude. March 1839. Painted on board the US ship 'Peacock' by T. R. Peale, Scientific Corps, U.S. South Sea Surveying & Exploring Expedition. From a sketch by Lt. Walker." Courtesy of the American Museum of Natural History.

me and a Sheath bill (Vaginalis alba. Gm.). We caught a Blue Petrel (P: cyane. Less.) and a Cape Pigion but were unable to take any of the others although I tried to shoot them as they passed to windward of us hoping they would fall on board, as the sea was too high to lower a boat.

Thursday 19th Last night was nearly clear and we had a beautiful display of the Aurora australis. Distinct pencils of light ascended from the South East portions of the horison nearly to the zenith. A continued *twilight* seemed to exist in the south and about Midnight the cercuscations were observed delicately colored with red and pale blue. Numerous icebergs surroundd our course during the day, some of which we estimated to be over two hundred feet high. Some Penguins were seen.

Wednesday 20th This morning I was roused early to make drawings of some of the icebergs which we were passing. The wind was from the northwestward and we made rapid progress south, but were soon surprised by numerous ice floes on every side of us, and had

eleven icebergs in sight at one time, when a fog coming on we were obliged to heave too, and wait for the weather to clear. The sea was so smooth that we were enabled to ascertain the magnetic dip to be 78°. Our instruments being balanced on the gambles of an old compass which by adding a pendulum to the bottom and supporting it on a bottomless stand is made to answer the purpose perfectly when the sea is not too high.

Two whales, some sheath bills and a few Petrels were near us during the day. The fog cleared somewhat before night when finding ourselves in too close proximity to the ice to lay during the night, we made sail to the north untill we got more sea room and laid too again for the night as usual since we have been among the icebergs.

A trial was made to day to get the temperature of the sea at the depth of 400 or more fathoms with a self registering thermometer & a brass "marine diver" but the wire used in place of a line which was of copper, broke—the instruments consequently lost.

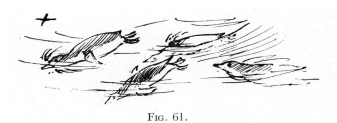

FIG. 61.

Thursday 21st A NW wind and dense fog, the consequence of which was that we had to lay idle all day. We found a current of about the third of a mile northwardly per hour. Shot 3 species of Petrels, one the Cyaneus of Lesson, the others probably new. A small whale pass'd near the ship, and one or two others seen "blowing" in the distance.

Friday 22d Was aroused this morning in order to shoot at some sheath bills, a flock of five or six having hovered around the ship, but was on deck too late as the wind (Still NW) was freshening and several large icebergs were seen through the fog close under our lee, to avoid which we had to make sail & stand to the N.E. to avoid them; but our difficulties increased as the wind rose for we soon found that were were surrounded by them and detatched floes; at one time there was about 30 of enormous size, which seemed to say "thus far shalt thou come, and no further."—so our ship was turned southward again. We had to keep under easy sail to prevent the ship from drifting on them—a thick fog and drizling rain rendered our situation very perilous.

A whale, and a flock of Terns passed near us, the latter bore a close resemblance to S. Arctica in voice as well as size and shape.—The water is below the freezing point (31°) yet is slightly phosphorescent and contains many minute crustacea, which I find in the stomachs of Petrels.

Sat^y 23d A Sunday we had snow, rain and sleet, with thick weather and a heavy sea, the wind still at N W and many ice bergs around us. We had our service on Sunday as usual between decks, Captn Hudson reading us a long and salutory sermon, the men in the meanwhile sitting or laying on the deck to prevent their being thrown from side to side by the sundry heavy lurches of the ship.

Monday 25th The weather somewhat milder in the morning, caught two Cape Pigeons (Pr: Capensis), numerous fin back whales* playing around us some of which came within a short distance of the Ship. Three seals also floated past us on small ice floes, one of them I shot, but it disappeared. Shortly afterwards in the vicinity of some large icebergs to the south of us we discovered the Schooner Sea Gull and fired a gun to attract her attention to us. She soon joined us and a boat was sent aboard of her for Lt. Walker. He informed us that he had penetrated as far south as he

---

* Baleanopterus Australis

could, being stopped by an impenetrable barrier of field and floe ice, with innumerable "bergs" in which he was twice embayed and escaped with difficulty, and was obliged to put about and run north as new ice had commenced forming, his Lat^e 70° 14 S Long^e 105 west. Our Lat 68 06 S Long^e 95° west.

Capt Hudson on the recei^t of this unfavourable information called all the officers in the Cabin to give their opinions of the probabilities of further success at this late season of the year: when it was unanimously recommended that further attempts to go south should be abandoned untill a more suitable season of the year, the winter having now set in. The men were called on the quarter deck and the determination announced to them, and sail was made to the north sorely against our will but by the dictates of common prudence. Considerable snow fell and the wind increased to a gale.

Friday 29th Until yesterday we have been enabled to lay on our proper course north but slowly on account of the few icebergs which we still encounter, with but one gale of wind in the four days, it has however been cloudy since Monday, with rain, snow and fogs. The latter was so thick yesterday that we were obliged to keep blowing a horn at intervals which was answered by the Schooner in like manner, notwithstanding which we were parted in the latter part of the midwatch last night. A cannonade and blue lights were fired but this morning the fog was still to thick to see but a short distance and nothing could be heard from hers. It was calm all day with a moderately rolling sea. Temp^e 35°, no sun or clear sky to enable us to get an observation, but we believe ourselves from the dead reckoning to be about on the Antarctic circle.

No animals have come near us except^g a few small Petrels and Penguins. The latter swim more rapidly *under* the water than they do on the surface, and always retreat from us with motions precisely like small Porpoises, most frequently leaping entirely out of water when coming up to respire [fig. 61].

Sat^y 30th Last evening the fog dispersed for a few minutes and showed us a clear horizon, and a large ice berg under our lee, and the moon was seen, but showing a pale and sickly light. At midnight we were thrown in considerable alarm by a dense smoke issuing out of the main hatch. The crew were turned to quarters and the usual preparations made to drown the magazine & spirit rooms, but prompt movements were made to discover and extinguish the fire. It was found to proceed from a bag of coffee which had been burnt in the afternoon and put into a bag and placed in the hold for safety. The bag & coffee were consumed, and but little damage done to the other stores or ship, though the excitement for the time necessary to ascertain the extent of the danger was such as can readily be imagined when the remote situation in which we are is taken into consideration with the weather we should have to encounter even should we all be enabled to get into the boats, which in itself would be a questionable matter. Drizzling rain and slight spurts of snow, temp^e 37 at noon. A few little spots at intervals of clear sky. Course NNW with a light breeze.

Monday April 1st A blue light was descried this morning at about 4 oclock to the North east of us, which was promptly answered by burning another and day light enabled us to discover the Schooner Flying fish having born away to meet the signal. We have been running at a rapid rate with a strong south wind since yesterday morning and a heavy sea, which as we run before the wind occasioned us to roll very unpleasantly as it was difficult to keep our feet under us. A new jib was compleated by our sailmaker for the Schooner, and sent on board of her in the evening with dispatches for the rest of the squadron at Orange Bay. The rigging was manned and we parted with three cheers, and this morning

Tuesday 2^d she was no longer in sight. Our Lat^e at noon was 57° 41′ Long^e 84′ 15. The weather clear *to us* although it would be considered cloudy by those who had not experienced as much "dirty weather" as we have. A number of Pinttados (Cape Pigeons) are still following us. Yesterday I shot a gigantic Petrel, and today two sooty Albatrosses followed us. The small Petrels have all left us.

Sunday 7th Laying to in a heavy gale of wind and tremendous sea. Lat 53 37 Long 85 16. Surrounded by birds, some of which we succeeded in catching with fishing lines. 12 species of Diomaedae exulans, 7 of D: chlororhymos, and one Petrel). The usual service and a sermon was read in the morning and afterwards the gale abating we stood on or near our course. A large ship passed astern of us heading E. but at too great a distance to distinguish her colours. The stomachs of the albatrosses were filled with the remains of cuttle fish, but for the circumstance of their following the ship I should infer that they prefer *dead* food to living.

NOTES

No. 2

T. R. PEALE

PACIFIC O.   1839   APRIL

Friday April 12th Since Sunday last we have had several clear days and favourable winds, our Lat at noon 44° 45′ Long^e 79° 38′. We were able today for the first since leaving Orange bay to open some of the gun deck ports and air the ship. Many Albatrosses follow us, among which are an unusual number of the "exulans" in all states of plumage; the young birds of the first season are brown, in which state they are described as a distinct species, then follows a change of colour, more or less mottled untill the adults exhibit a pure white excepting the primaris & secondaries which remain black; the very old birds are even destitute of the small pencilled lines crossing the plumage of the back. In all stages the bill remains of a flesh colour. *It is never black*, as described in Diomaedea

Spadicea Latr. in Lessons manual. A few specimens of the Sooty Albatross are seen now and then. They are some of them almost plumeless on the back, the front of the head nearly black with a light margin on the neck.

Several parties of Porpoises have come under our bow, one of which we struck with a harpoon today but owing to the great headway of the ship it was draged off the iron. All are of one species which was first made known by the Nat^{sts} of the Coquile (Delphinapterus Peronii).

This ocean has been anything but what its name implies, Pacific, since we have been in it, today being almost the first in which we could sit on a chair without first getting some security by our hands or feet. The floor of my stateroom (on the gundeck) has been so long soaking that now it has become slimy from the decomposition of the wood. Fortunately a vacant space in the wardroom admits of my sleeping there to escape the effects of the damp which shows itself on the opposite page of this book although it has been kept in India rubber in the dryest part of my wardrobe.

Sunday 14th A delightfully clear and pleas^t day, temp^e—which has made it so like a clear fall or spring sunday at home that with one accord all the officers were seen doffing their rusty overcoats and caps to appear once more in their usual undress uniform— even the men did not wait for the order through the Boatswain "all hands dress yourselves in your blue jackets & trowsers with black hats" but were seen getting ready for it. The ports were open on the gun deck and everyone seemed smilingly to enjoy our first clear and mild weather since leaving Orange Bay. Prayers and a sermon read on the gun deck, fires not lighted. The [wind] is regular from the SSE and from the settled appearance of the clouds we presume ourselves to be in the "trades" running before it at the rate of 5–6 knots. Numbers of Albatrosses and two or three other species of Petrels around.

Monday 15th A perfectly clear and cloudless day, a fair wind and all studding sails set. Everyone on board occupied in cleaning up as we expect to reach Valparaiso by Thursday. A small land bird (Orpheus) came on board but again left us.

Tuesday 16th Wind ahead and not a great deal of it, calm part of the day & evening, and cloudy but no rain. The sea at night was unusually luminous with Molluscs in large shoals resembling luminous clouds, a few Medusa and some kelp passed.

Wednesday 17th Numbers of Whales were playing around us last night and today, some of them came so near the ship that I was tempted to shoot a musket ball into one of them. It was not more than 40 yeards off, and although the ball entered between the spiracle and pectoral fin, it seemed to make but little impression further than to prevent it again approaching so near.

These Whales appear to belong to the genus Rorqualas, but are different from the "australis" seen within the antarctic circle in having the spiracle further forward and in having a shorter head; the pectoral fins under parts of the body and tail are white, the lips, head and fins were covered with barnacles. They were about 40 feet long.

Light winds from the N & Eastward, a ship was discovered some distance to windward of us. She bore down to speak us, and her Captⁿ came aboard just before night. He commands the ship Frances of New Bedford, has been out Whaling 28 months, has sent home 900 barrels of oil, and has now 400 on board. He left Talcajuana the day before yesterday and is in want of men.

Thursday 18th Almost a dead calm, the sea almost perfectly smooth, except a undulating sea which raises the ship so gradually as almost to be unfelt by us. Number of Mollusca around and among them a species of Rhyzophyso, resembling long threads, red and one end and blue at the other. Our Whaling friend in the ship Frances gave a number of Island lances and shells to a party of officers who visited him today. He has visited a number of Islands and is now going to Valparaiso.

Friday 19th Calms and head winds. Made the land as we stood east on both bows but at too great a distance (from 10 to 30 miles) to distinguish much of its characters. Lost sight of our friend the Whaler.

Sat 20th Found on arising this morning that the wind had changed to SSW and we were going directly before it with all the studding sails set and a long range of the Andes covered with snow in sight, the lower mountains near the coast being scarsely discernable, the weather beautifully clear and all hands in the full tide of rubbing, scrubbing, holy stoning and brushing, etc.

Sunday 21st The dawn of day was one of the most beautiful I have ever witnessed. All the snow capt mountains in the distance were edged with a beautiful "pink" tinsel-like tinge, while those nearer the coast formed a deep shadow, ridges only catching the beautiful rays of light; as the sun rose the effect changed but the scene lost but little of its sublimity. Arrived in the harbour of Valparaiso about noon and had the pleasure of receiving my first letters from home, a gratification which required to be experienced before it can be appreciated. My latest dates were on the 19th of Nov^r/38, all well.

V

Western South America

Found the Relief had arrived about a week before us and a store ship the Mariposa from N York with stores for us about the same time. The Ship Relief was not able to enter the Straits of Magellan on acct of tempestuous weather, she was very near being lost at Cape Noir where she was almost on the rocks when the wind changed and she was enabled to get clear with the loss of all her anchors and cables. The service on which she was ordered had to be abandoned, and on her arrival here she was unable to enter the port untill the British sloop of war Fly sent an anchor on board.

The City of Valparaiso presents but a poor appearance from the anchorage, being built at the base of a range of hills of 1500 feet in elevation which at this season are very barren and destitute of verdure. The houses are one and two stories high in one narrow street along the shore, or perched irregularly on level ground to be found or made in the various quebradas or ravines in which places they cannot be dignified with any other name than huts, built of sun dried bricks (the best) or wattled and plastered with mud; tile roofs to the best, the others thatched with wide projecting eves. The population of the quebradas seems to contain a large proportion of females who wear red "Bayettas, and black eyes with such an easy grace that few sailors leave the port without empty pockets, and a high estimation of their hospitalities. The higher classes of females are reported virtuous and estimable in the domestic circle, but I cannot add as far my observation has gone that they are beautiful, they have pretty feet, a graceful carriage and dress their hair with great pains and taste, but in general terms they would lose by a fair comparison with the Ladies of my own country. The fashions of dress etc. are french, with the exception of the bonnet which they are just beginning to wear. The proportion of foreigners met in Valparaiso is large and there are few stores where the English language is not understood. The advance of civilization being decidedly more rapid here than in any other of the South American republics, the natives are more polite, intelligent, and hospitable, the ladies of the higher classes more virtuous and were it not for the harrassing wars of their neighbours it would be a desirable commercial residence for such as like an equable and cool climate. The *Custom house* is the *finest building in the port* (an exception to all Spanish American cities) well built, convenient, and ornamental. The harbour however can hardly be dignified with the name, being unprotected from the Sea during all the winter months when it is much exposed to the effects of "northers" and is then dangerous. They are most violent in June & July. The gales do not blow home, but the sea is so heavy as to cut off communication with the shore, the only landing being at a wooden mole which is not sufficient to resist its effects. Three balls were given during our stay, one to the President (Prieto) in honor of the recent victory at Yugai, over the Peruvians, the others by the citizens and foreigners, to all which the officers of the Squadron were invited. They were all got up and conducted in a manner that would have been considered creditable in any part of the world.

A review of the millitia took place on the plaiancia one Sunday, which to us had one remarkable feature, in being attended by a number of the most respectable ladies of the place who with the President & his daughter march^d down the line of review, and afterwards danced with the officers on the field in the presence of the soldiers.

All the South Americans are inveterate dancers, the Chileans taking the lead at the ball given on the 30th ult^o the parties did not break off untill sunrise, and then numbers escorted the President & party home to the governors house where the dance was renewed until 12 oclock M. The taste for music is general, but al-

145

though there is a number of National airs only one to my knowledge has been printed, all in common are being imported as well as the instruments, Pianos being almost as general as in the United States. A fondness for flowers is also general, but gardens are not generally cultivated with any care. There are but two in the City, they are on the Almendral, closely walled in, and kept in tolerable repair. In them great pains is taken with forcing plants & flowers, among which are some which I assisted to introduce from the prairies of the Arkansas, in 1822—Coreopsis tinctoria. Centaurea Americana etc., & which are now common all over the civilized world.

I made two visits to the Capital City Santiago, about 100 miles east of Valparaiso. The usual mode of conveyance is on horseback or in "birlochos" (gigs) drawn by one horse in the shafts, a postillion rides another on the left side, sometimes a second on the right, whose horses are fastened by strips of hide connecting the vehicle to their saddles. On descending declivities a "lasso" is fastened to the hind part and held back by the extra or right hand "birlochero" the first retaining his place, and keeping the reins of the shaft horse in his hand. A relay drove of 8 or 10 horses are driven by a third rider, to replace those riders and in the shafts every 5 or 6 miles.

Thus prepared the two passengers have nothing to do but keep their seats with as much composure as they can muster, while the vehicle is driven pell mell over hill and dale at a smart gallop. The numerous lashings of raw hide in various parts of the crazy machines showing that a "break down" is not unusual. The roads are kept in repair by convicts, and in some places are very good, over the quertas or ridges being laid out with considerable ingenuity. We started from Valparaiso about five in the afternoon, slept in Casa blanca, a pueblo of 5 or 6000 inhabitants, it is situated in a very fertile valley, where we saw the only small tract of woodland found in this part of Chile—it is about 1000 feet above the level of the sea. The following morning we crossed the "querta de Zupata," stopped at Curacavi, situated in another fertile valley of the same name, after which we crossed the "querta de prada" a very steep ridge of about 1200 feet elevation. It is so steep that the the road makes between thirty and forty zigzags to attain the summit from which there is one of the most sublime views imaginable.

* * *

On arriving in Santiago, we immediately called on Mr. Pollard, U.S. Charge des affairs, who received us with the greatest courtesy, and treated us with great attention. He entertained us liberally, and introduced us to the best society—Senʳᵃ Alexandre the wife of an Hatian merchant gave several "Turtulios" on our acctᵗ where every exertion was made to please and entertain. At one of them, a little girl seven years of age danced the "Cachucha" of Andelusia for us in a most exquisitely graceful manner, such indeed as I have not seen surpassed any where.

* * *

Looking NE you have the extensive plains and valley of the Mayjo stretched out before you with here and there a conic mountain standing in solitary grandeur. The distance being composed of the lofty range of Andes clothed in eternal snows, the plains of the Mayjo have at this season a dreary and desolate aspect being like the mountains almost without vegetation. A few mimosas and Cacti being the most conspicuous, the latter rising in high clustering cylinders with scarlet flowers, but desolate as it now appears, the aspect must be otherwise in summer, the numerous and extensive thorn hedges, enclosing what are the no doubt fertile pastures, growing sufficiently to prove the value of land.

This being almost the only road for wheel carriages in the country, nearly all the merchandise is brought over it for every part of the state in ox carts of enormous dimentions, the wooden engraved axles of which may be heard for miles before you meet the team. The wheels are without tires, top wattled cane, covered with bull hides: drawn by 6 or 8 oxen, the food for which is cut straw alone, carried in a net on the top of the cart to be used wherever they tire on the road without reference to any particular stages.

Santiago is built on a plain at an elevation of 2500 feet above the Sea. The mountain stream of Maypocho running through one portion of the city and supplying it with water which is conducted through all the principal streets, running down the center, assisting much but not superceding the necessity of scavengers. The city, however, is generally very clean and presents a remarkably neat appearance from the circumstance of the laws obliging every one to whitewash their houses outside once every year, the roofs being all of red tile adds much to the neat appearance.

I hired a birlocho to take Mr. Drayton & myself to the mountains to hunt Guanacos and started at dawn of day on a clear frosty morning. We found some of the little brooks and puddles frozen. After going about 10 miles we had to abandon the birlocho and take the horses and a guide to ascend the Cordillera, reaching the snow after a laborious ascent about noon. Found a single herd of Guanacos in the afternoon several miles from where I had to abandon the horses, and Mr. Drayton, the mountains being too steep for their further progress. The animals were very shy and frequent only the most inaccessible summits never leaving the vicinity of the snow. I could not succeed in approaching nearer than 200 yards, but after wounding several killed a very fine one. While butchering it a Condor afforded me a beautiful rifle shot, but pitching obliquely over a precipice of several thousand feet my time was too short to descend after it, sunset leaving me barely time to descend from my lofty pinacle to a place of safety.*

The Guanacos frequent particular little spots for shelter in storms and feed on several small thorny herbs which impart a flavour to their flesh and excrement which may be smelt immediately on entering one of these places of resort. The animal killed measured 9 feet from the nose to the end of its tail, stood about 4½ feet high and carried the tail usually quite erect, uttering when alarmed a sound like that emitted by the species of gryllus known in the U States as the "Catydid." The bezoar often found in the stomach is highly prized as a "remedia" for sundry complaints, also as a gum. The animal is never hunted for the market, although the flesh is good, but is not considered a delicacy.

Wolves are found abundantly in the mountains, and foxes, two of which we killed, but no other large animals that I could hear of. The lower lands abounds in birds and small animals & but few insects. Several species of land shells (Bulimii) abound among the wrecks of the numerous cylindrical cacti.

No tidings have been received of the Schooner Sea Gull, the last seen of her was off Cape Horn during a heavy gale when she parted company with the Schooner Flying fish which sought a harbour untill the gale abated, but the Sea Gull keeping at Sea, and not having been seen since, we fear she is lost with all her officers & crew.[8] Lt. Craven it was concluded should wait for her, and the rest of the squadron sailed for Callao.

*   *   *

The public buildings of Santiago are generally on a great scale, and well designed but nearly all have suffered more or less from the destructive effects of earthquakes.

The Government House and Cathedral as usual are fronting on the plaza in the center of which there is a fountain most elaborately executed in marble. The Cathedral is plain in its exterior, but internally from its great extent and massy structure very imposing. The side Altars however are much disfigured by the horid taste exercised in ornamenting with jewels etc. some relics of saints.

The mint has never been finished and has been much injured by earthquakes, so that it [is] probable it never will be. The process of coining is the same as practised in Europe during the last century, the machinery being very clumsy. A modern form press has been imported but from the stupidity of the labourers was soon put out of order and there is not a sufficiency of

ingenuity to make the requisite repairs, consequently the whole of the new machinery lays idle.

The climate of the city is very delightful, rarely any snow in winter although always in sight on the cordillera. There are few or no negros, consequently the lower classes have more the appearance of industrious contentment than I have seen any where else in South Am^a. Fruit and vegetables are abund^t and of excellent quallity, grapes and peaches particuly are of the finest quallity. Apples are also plenty but no pains have been taken to secure a good quallity of them. Cabages, Beets and Cauliflowers are the largest and finest I have ever seen.

Horses & Cattle are proverbialy fine, the beef excellent, also mutton. The average price of horses about 12 dollars.

*   *   *

It is not fair to quit Valparaiso without noting among other hospitalities, the polite attentions of Mr. Hobson, U S Consul. Everything in his power was done to obtain information for us, and whatever assistance he could think of.

He is a gentleman who is respected by all parties, and just such as every American must feel will do credit to his country. I only regret that the office is such under our government that few of this worth can be holding it abroad.

*   *   *

June 6, 1839 When we sailed the wind was fair with pleasant weather, but the next day it changed to NW and blew a gale with a heavy and uncomfortable sea. As usual my room was all the time full of water taken in at the ports or very wet from the effects of such misshaps.

The gale lasted several days and we parted company with the rest of the Squadron. The weather was then pleasant and we proceeded alone, meeting little that was unusual. We saw a number of whales, spoke one whale ship.

June 19th Arrived at Callao. The Vincennes arrived on the day following. All the squadron moved down to the Island of San Lorenzo which is 7 miles from the castle of Callao, where we remained untill all the stores were removed from the Relief and numerous changes made among the officers & men of the squadron.[9] All

---

* One of the most remarkable effects of the jaunt was the reflection of the suns rays from the snow, notwithstanding the water under the snow was frozen in some places strong enough to bear my weight, and kept my wet feet very cold, yet my face and hands were blistered by the suns heat and became very sore, particularly my lips and nose.

[8] She was never heard from again and was lost at sea.

[9] "On receiving the reports of the commanders of the different vessels, active operations were at once begun to refit, replenish our stores, and complete our duties. The necessary changes in officers and men were made, in consequence of my determination to send the Relief home. This I resolved to do on several accounts. I have stated that from the first I found her ill-adapted to the service; her sailing I saw would retard all my operations, and be a constant source of anxiety to me; . . . The expense was another consideration, which I conceived myself unauthorized to subject the government to, particularly as I found on calculations, that for one-tenth of the sum it would cost to keep her, I could send our stores and provisions to any part of the Pacific." Wilkes, *Narrative* 1: 231.

Fig. 62.

Fig. 63. Facsimile signature from Peale's notebook.

the invalids were sent on board the Relief, her officers & men were taken mostly to the Vincennes, & preparations made to send her home after leaving supplies for us at the Sandwich Island and Sydney, New South Wales.[10]

The only conspicuous object in Callao is its castle and fort, so cellebrated for the obstinate defense it made under Gen¹ Rodil, and for the quantities of blood spilt in the vicinity at various periods. It has now in a measure been dismantled and in a fair way of going to ruin. The walls are very strongly built of sun dried bricks faced in parts with stone. The most interesting objects are of a melancholy nature, being the ruins of the old city of Callao destroyed by the earthquake of 1768? when a part of the Island of San Lorenzo was sunk into the sea opposite the city; and the city itself submerged; the waves destroying what was not already destroyed by being shook to pieces. The very foundations of some of the houses appear to have been turned over while others are covered with pebbles thrown up by the surge. The present City is about ½ a mile east of where the old one stood. A wooden mole gives harbour and affords a good landing for boats. The most imposing house is a two story one directly in front of the mole with a large sign on the end: "Billiards" the great amusement of Callao at all times unless Monte is excepted, etc.

Lima is not more than 6 miles to the east, and most of the respectable merchants reside there. Stages run twice a day; the road is quite straight, about 60 feet wide, and in tolerable condition being without gullies as it never rains here, but the dust is quite an equiva-

[10] Hawaiian Islands, and Sydney, Australia.

lent. The approach to the city of Lima has been realy beautiful, but is at present much out of repair. There is a double row of willow trees, and a stream of water on each side of the road enclosed by a wall with seats, etc. The city itself abounds with Churches and the remains of the most extravagant luxury, but at present it suffers in a measure from the recent contest with Chile. The cathedral is a beautiful build^g from its size and lavish ornament, but much of its decoration is in bad taste, the great altar is composed of silver but the work has been so bad, and it is now so dirty that few would suspect it of being other than pewter. It is surmounted by a dome, the collumns of which are encased with silver. In a room on one side of the church is a collection of the portraits of all the ArchBishops of Peru, some of them well painted, but most of them very indifferent. There is but one vacancy which was not filled in consequence of the last Arch Bishop being friendly to the Spanish cause during the revolution previous to independence. In vaults under the great altar all their bodies excepting his are interred in nitches of the side walls. Many of the coffins are open, exposing the dried up remains, of which the Sextons made no difficulty about disposing for a small compensation, "if I give you a dollar will you allow me to take that skull? como no" says the sexton, the consequence was that in place of one being taken, two at least are now tossing over the waves of the Pacific towards the Islands, where probably they will receive the company of some equally honored canibal, "sic transit gloria mundi"—There is more beautiful carving about the choir of the cathedral than I have ever seen in any one building; but the organ is small and harsh toned, the great dependence being placed on portable instruments. There is a Hospital attached to the church which I did not choose to enter, but from which the dead were brought to be buried in a cart with two tiers of drawers which were taken out to answer the purpose of temporary coffins [fig. 62].

The Monastry of San Francisco was however the most impressing building. It is said to cover several acres of ground. Where all that wealth, luxury or taste could suggest was expended in the construction of courts, gardens and chappels. A Museum was founded in 1836 but is much neglected it contains however some interesting remains of the Incas.

* * *

At the hall of "Cabildos" are to be seen some of the archives of the City of Lima, kept in tolerably regular order until recently. Many signatures of the old Vice Roys and "Mayors" are quite curious, among others that of Pizarro; he could not write but like many of his contemporary officers only "made his mark."

Facsimile, Francisco Pizarro 1535.

It was customary for the clerk to write the name & the person placed his thumb on it, and made the mark each side.

The Expedition left Callao on the *13th of July, Saty* We now consist of the Vincennes, Peacock, Porpoise & Flying fish; the Relief being detached and to go home after leaving some stores for us at the Sandwich Islands and Sydney. The Sea Gull not heard from since she left Cape Horn.

The weather was pleasant and wind fair, nothing of importance occuring while Monday 15th when a case of small pox gave us some uneasiness. All the men and officers were vaccinated and the patient kept under proper covering on deck away from the rest of the men. This is the second case, one having occured at Callao (one of our best boys, Joseph—who was shiped at Rio Janeiro) he was landed and left to the care of the Consul. A Shark was caught measuring 9 feet 1½ inches, but such is the detestation of the sailors, that the specimen was spoiled as soon as it reached the deck. Flying fish were first seen on the 20th in Lat. 13° 30′ 20″ Longe 89° 25′, they being the only ones observed since we left the Atlantic. The Cape Pigeons (Procellaria Capensis) quitted us here, a few gannets seen.

Sunday 28th Our weather thus far has been pleasant with a strong trade wind about E varying a few points. We have had a few showers of rain but they were of short duration day before yesterday in Lat 15° 52′ 5 Longe 105° 55′ 15″. Saw the first tropic birds since which we occasionally see them and a few Petrels the latter flying close over the surface of the water but at too great a distance to distinguish the species. The Tropic birds have a voice like Terns, not quite so harsh but similarly uttered when they cross over the ship. Two whales past us today going at the rate of five or six knots, they had dorsal fins.

Thursday August 1st Today the squadron spread as wide as possible to be within signal distance in order to discover if possible an Island laid down in Lat. Long . We estimated our visual scope to be near forty miles, our distance apart was estimated by firing guns to measure by sound.

We have seen within a few days several shoals of Black fish, which were about 15–20 feet in length entirely black, with a dorsal fin, and a keel like process anterior to the tail, amounting almost to a second dorsal fin. The anterior fin much curved and the snout very obtuse. A second species came around us today, having a very acute snout, of an olive color above and bluish white beneath, with one or two lateral lines of the same colour. A dorsal fin much curved and placed very far back. They were about 20 feet in length, raised their heads quite out of water to breathe, which they did with very little noise and without ejecting water or spray.

Another species still larger, entirely black and rounder in form passed us a few days back with a dorsal nearly straight and of great length, being at least 6 or 8 feet out of water. I cannot identify either of the 3 species with any described by Cuvier, Boneterre or Demarest.

Yesterday I killed one of the Tropic birds which have now and then been seen for the last few days, it proved to be Phactor phanicarus, but one other species of bird, apparently a Petrel has been seen within the last week, and no fish excepting a few flying fish. The winds moderate and generally about SE, now and then a shower of rain. The crew are generally healthy and our small pox patient nearly well. The men are rehearsing a play and making dresses and other preparations for its performance. The sea sufficiently smooth for Mr. Agate and myself to be occupied in finishing up some of our paintings & Sketches. The Vincennes carried away her main royal mast this morning but soon had it replaced by another.

Sunday 4th The weather has now become very warm (thermr 81°) with moderate breezes and a smooth sea, so that we are enabled to draw, paint, etc. with our ports open without being endangered from having our rooms filled with salt water. A "Frigate" (Tachypetes aquilus) came and reconoitered the ships from above their masts today, it was alone, and the only we have seen since leaving the harbour of Rio de Janeiro. Our Late was 17° 58′ 10″ S, Longe 121° 5′ 15″. I thought it probable that it might be a harbinger of land and had a man sent to the mast head to look in the direction it took in a strait line to the south, but no land was visible although the horizon was perfectly clear.

Tuesday 6th We have the same unchangeable weather, with a clear sky and moderate and variable winds from the eastward. A very few flying fish are occasionally seen, and a few Tropic birds, but no others.

Wednesday 7th Dead calm nearly all day, many of the officers and men in bathing, notwithstanding 3 sharks had been seen a short time before. Sounded with 375 fathoms of line for the temperature which was found to be 46° at that depth, 77° at the surface & the air 80°. For several days I have observed *insects* swimming around the ship, on taking one today found it to be a genus closely allied to Nepa. They are very active in swimming on the surface but sometimes dive under, about ¼ of an inch long and of a pearly-blue colour with black legs, only two pair of which are used in locomotion, the other pair used like the prolegs of the mantis, the structure being analogous. One Tropic bird seen.

Saty 10th Yesterday and today the wind strong from the eastward with a high sea. The ship going before it is uncomfortable from the excessive wallowing motion, the ports necessarily kept shut. Thermr 80 with but little variation at night. At 10 last night hove to and lowered a thermr 400 fathoms when it registered 49°, at the surface 77′s°.—We have been required to keep a meteorological watch for the 8th, 9th, 10th to register "falling stars" etc. but for the two nights past their appearance has not been unusual, as to numbers or brillianty.

Few birds consisting of two species only have been seen. One Frigate at a great height, and a few Procellaria at too great a distance to recognize. No fish.

VI

The South Pacific

Sunday 11th Last night we had an exceedingly heavy fall of rain with much lightening and thunder. Today the atmosphere clear with a temperature of 78°. Saw Tropic birds feeding on small fish which were taken by plunging from a considerable height. Directly after church "land ho" was called from the mast head, but it proved to be a bank of clouds stretching along the horizon to the south of us.

Tuesday 10th Almost calm. The Island of Clermont Tonnere was discovered directly ahead, but the wind was too light to make it before night. It is very low in appearance, the trees being distinguished first. A few Terns seen. At 8 p.m. hove to; sounded with 1140 fathoms of line without finding bottom. It was about 10 miles from the Island. Temperature of the surface 77½°, at greatest depth 44¼.

Wednesday 14th Commenced a running survey of the Island with the ships with a pleasant easterly wind. A few natives armed with long spears appeared on the shore as if waiting for us to land. No canoes were visible and as we made no attempt to land, we learned no more about them or their islands than was visible through our spy glasses. The number of natives seen was not more than 12 or 15 who showed no hostile dispositions. A few of them appeared to be partialy clothed. No houses were visible. The land was a very narrow strip of apparently coral rocks, enclosing a lagoon of about five miles in diameter with here and there a cluster of trees among which cocoa nuts were conspicuous. It is a sorry business that our government should have sent a Scientific Corps to collect information and make a "survey" (in the present day this term includes all the Natl Sciences) of the countries we may visit, when the officer under whose charge it has been placed should consider it quite unnecessary to appropriate a single boat out of the whole squadron for their use, in consequence of which we must remain on board admiring through our spy glasses that which it is utterly out of our power to avail ourselves of. I hope in the next twenty four hours he may see his error, and retrieve the credit of his country and the expedition by allowing us to work as well as himself.

This island has been surveyed by the French in the "Coquile" and subsequently by the English in the "Blossom," (Capt. Beechey) but its internal examination remains for further voyagers who may consider the resources of a land of equal importance with its hydrographic position. Sounded with 500 fathoms of line about 2/4ths of a mile from the E point of the island. Coral bottom in dead fragments.

Thursday 15th Last evening ran off, and lay to for the night to the NE of the land, at sunrise it was not in sight, but a moderate breese soon placed us in a situation to continue the survey. In measuring distance by sound it was necessary to wait in one position some time in order to allow the schooner to change her position, in one [of] these intervals three sharks came about us, one of which I succeeded in capturing. In the afternoon we joined the Porpoise and Vincennes, they having passed round the north & west ends of the island completing the survey. Two boats from each vessel* then attempted to land.[11] A number of the natives assembled to oppose us, threatening us with their spears and throwing stones. Every persuasion was tried, presents thrown to them which they eagerly seized, but still they resisted, when Captn Wilkes who was in one of the boats ordered a few charges of small shot to be fired when they fled and in a few minutes raised a large fire on the opposite side of the island. The boats could not reach the shore through the surf, but a few of us left our arms and swam or waded ashore over coral rocks on which we found a variety of shells and echini when the approach of evening caused our recall. These natives were about 5 feet 8 inches in height, well made and of a dark colour with a Malay cast of countenance. Their hair was bushy and tied in knots in the back of their heads, they were naked with the exception of a "Maro" round the hips

---

* excepting the Schooner
[11] See text p. 78 for a description of this event. Also Wilkes, *Narrative* 1: 312–315.

& passing between their legs. One or two had large tufts of hair fastened near the upper ends of their lances. They were evidently quite unacquainted with the effect of fire arms. They wore no ornaments that we saw, and were armed only with lances about 12 feet long, or with clubs. No women were seen. Lay^d to for the night to windward of the lands and in the morning

Friday 16th Took some additional angles and left the island without further examination. We do not know the number of its inhabitants, how they subsist or that they understood more than a few words of the language of Taheiti. Their geographic position is highly interesting; of their moral condition we know nothing nor did we learn whether the island would furnish wood, water or any refreshments for whalemen or other navigators. It was therefore with extreme regret I saw the Squadron leave the island without a single attempt to learn anything of its internal resourses. We learned nothing but that preceding voyagers have placed it nearly, if not quite in its proper position.

A long voyage at great cost to our government, with the time of many persons who might otherwise be usefully employed, I fear is likely to result in [unfinished].

A few hours sail brought us in sight of "Searles Island." It appears to be a low rim of land surrounding a lagoon like "Clermont Tonnere," and having the same picturesque clumps of trees. We commenced the same measurements for base by sound, and by night the squadron met again, two vessels having taken each side. The Vincennes & Porpoise on the N and Peacock & Schooner flying fish on the South.

Scient^c Corps as before all idle, as well as the boats, which could have easily made attempts to land, for there was every appearance of favourable places, at least so it appeared on our spy glass exploration. A few Terns, or tropic bird[s] and a few "Frigates" (Tachypetes) were seen. One of these latter came near enough to receive the contents of my old and tried friend "smash" when Captn Hudson immediately had the ship hove to to obtain it. Laid to during the night and found in the morning

Sat 17th That we had drifted during the night, a great distance to the n^d & westward. Signal was made from the Vincennes for us to hunt a boat which she had lost during the night (the Porpoise having run into her carrying away her starboard quarter boat and her own jib booms). The boat was found but so crushed as to be useless and so much time was lost in the search that Capt Wilkes made signal to bear away to the northward and abandon the landing on Searles Isl^d which was intended.

We of course know less of Searles Is^d than of Clermont Tonnere, because no attempt was made to land. Time cannot be plead in excuse for not doing so for a whole day was occupied in sailing along its shores & laying to measuring base lines for the survey, during which delay (had there been any disposition to afford the accomodation) the Scient^c Corps could have been

on shore without danger from natives as none were seen, or any signs of them. The surf was not high near the S W point, where there was a large group of cocoanut trees, and two clumps of trees having remarkably close foliage and about ¼ higher than the cocoa, and among them were large flocks of birds. The island is not so high out of water as Clermont Tonnere, not being more than 5 or 8 feet in any part. The lagoon had numeorus shoals and Islands in it, that latter of which were covered with bushes. Had a few slight showers of rain.

Sunday 18th The anniversary of our departure from the U.S. It is natural to form an estimate of the labors of the past year, which it grieves me to find have been unproductive, but as Patagonia, Terra del fuego, and the southern part of our cruise has afforded the only field not much could be expected. The stay in those places bearing but a small comparison with the time spent in well known places, Madeira, Rio de Janeiro, Valparaiso, Callao, etc. all being too well known to afford much expectation from an *Exploring Expedition*. The new grounds it grieves me are now being passed as quite unworthy of delay, it as I understand being necessary for us to be at Tahiti in the early part of next month. (Is Tahiti unknown or requiring a new survey?)

We had the usual religious service today. A slight rain in the morning but clear and pleasant weather the rest of the day. Saw a few Terns & Tropic birds.

Monday 19th Many Terns were screaming around us all night, giving a tolerably sure indication of the vicinity of land. The day was warm but made pleasant by a moderate breeze. Numbers of birds appeared in the afternoon and a little before sunset we discovered the land which appeared very low and not distant from us. Saw a few fish like "Skipjacks." Hove to for the night.

Tuesday 20th After regaining the land commensed measuring a base line by sound for the survey, which occupied us untill afternoon, when we obtained permission to land. Lt. Perry, Mr. Agate & I went in the Capt^ns gig. Lt. Emmons, Dr. Holmes, Mr. Dana, Mr. Hale in one of the whale boats. We found the landing very difficult on acct of the heavy surf which obliged us to anchor the boats off and swim on shore. Found great numbers of Frigates and other aquatic birds breeding on the trees which in some spots were covered with their nests, each containing one egg only. The Old birds were so tame that they suffered me climb the trees and take them by hand. We found a number of crabs, both terrestrial & marine, a number of shells and corallini, besides plants, etc., but it being past four oclock when we left the ship our stay was much abbreviated, being necessary to return on board by sundown. It was at the SW point of the island that we landed along the shores of which are clusters of Pandanus trees. They are not found in other parts as far as our observation extended. Here it was that Mr. Hale saw a small animal on a tree which he supposed to be a Squirrel (Crab?). I searched similar places with industry, but without meeting another. The getting off was not so difficult as the landing as it was easier to choose a starting point and a favorable sea to plunge through. The only disadvantage was the loads of shells, birds, eggs, and plants that each was anxious to retain, even at considerable risk of life. Gum elastic life preservers we found of great service in sustaining the weight, but impeded us greatly in swimming.

Wednesday 21st Two boats were again spared us to land but we did not succeed in getting off until noon. Succeeded in landing on the N E shore near at an old entrance to the lagoon which has been closed.

The quantities of birds found breeding in various situations was quite incredible and they were all so tame as to require us in many instances to push them off the nest in order to see their eggs. The most conspicuous was the Frigate (Tachypetes aquilus) with nests constructed of a few sticks only, covered many of the trees by their numbers. The hoarse croaking and screaming as we disturbed them was incessant. The old birds inflated their blood red pouches to the size of a child's head, looking like a blood stained bladder dangling to their necks as they flew. The next most singular were the gannets which laid their eggs on the ground without any nest under a shady bush on the shores of the lagoon bordering a sandy beach. They had each one egg (rarely two) which they guarded with great care refusing in all cases to leave them, even when pushed off. Sooty Terns were in countless numbers on the ground among low bushes; it requiring great great care to prevent both the young and old from being crushed under our feet. Young nearly ready to fly. In all there appeared to be about 7 species: 4 Terns, 2 Salas and the Frigates, besides 2 species of sandpipers and Tropic birds. When young are beautifully spotted with black, the old ones being of a fine rosy salmon col[r] which is fugitive.

The Island is not more than 8 feet above the surface of the sea and much cut up by the lagoons; about 9 miles long and 3 broad covered with clusters of trees and bushes. Some of the trees were 18 inches in diameter and 50 feet high. No Palms, but on the south side abundance of Pandanus trees filled with fruit. No fresh water that we could find. Two beautiful & large species of land crabs were obtained, besides numerous small ones. Abundance of beautiful fish & shells, corals, etc. A number of fine Turtle were caught and served out to the ships companies, affording us a great treat. Our embarkation towards night was not so easy as the landing, the *tide* had fallen, and the surf was rising, obliging us all to swim. I abandoned a part of my birds rather than endanger the boats crew in getting them off, but retained all that were new or particularly interesting. One of the peculiarities of this isl[d] is the absence of *"house flies"* which abounded at the two others we have left (Clermont Tonnere & Searles Is[d]) in the greatest numbers. We saw several species of Lepidoptera and spiders in great numbers, their webs

occasioning us some inconvenience. Our boat received some damage, but we all arrived safe on board before sunset, but very wet.

The squadron then steered a course for the Disappointment Islands. The weather was very warm with occasional showers of rains and pleasant breezes.

Friday 23d Finished the last of our preparations of birds, many having to go overboard, by reason of the warm weather, and the want of experienced taxidermists. At noon land was visible from the mast head, and by sunset we could see the natives on the beach. The land appeared thickly clothed with verdure and abounding in coconut trees, low, and with a lagoon in the centre as usual with coral isles. A heavy shower of rain & a squall. Stood off for the night. One of the crew of the Porpoise died this afternoon.

Sat[y] 24th On regaining our position to the southward of the Island again this morning 13 canoes with three natives each came off to us but could not be tempted on board. They were a thievish set and very dishonest in their attempts to trade. But very few curiosities were obtained from them, no fruit and nothing edible but a few roasted oysters without the shells which appeared to be the animal of the Tridachna gigas. These natives were well formed, of a dark brown colour, redder than Negroes, but blacker than N. Am[n] Indians, hair black and curly looking at a little distance like wool. They had but few ornaments and were not tatood. One wore a cap made of the feathers of the Frigate bird. All wore "marros" of wove Pandanus or palm leaf. They were vociferous and very anxious to obtain every thing they saw, frequently crying out "tapa" holding up some wove cloth, but always taking care to retain it after they obtained the article demanded for it. One or two had rather long thin beards, and all mustacios, which gave them a Moorish look. Their canoes were made of a number of pieces sewed together very neatly with a substance which looked like split cane. Two paddled with a curved paddle while the third baled the water out which was frequently requisite with a wooden scoop. The outrigers were made of light wood, placed on one side but as the canoes were shaped alike at both ends the outrigging was of course right or left, probably as the wind or sea set. Some clubs and knives were lashed to the outrigers, the knives being made of fish jaws, they would not part with them. Language, a dialect as far as we could find out, of the Tahaitian. A boat was sent in shore from the Vincennes but did not effect a landing. In making sail to obtain our position to measure a base to commence the survey the natives left us and returned on shore. Numbers hovered about the beach where a heavy surf rolled in but no more attempted to come off to us. The land is now but thickly covered with verdure, particularly at the west end, where the natives appear to reside, though no dwellings were visible from the ship. Sounded at a mile from the beach with 800 fathoms without bottom, temperat[e] at surface 80°, the depth 45°. The survey was continued until night without the inhabitants seeming to take much notice of us.

Sunday 25th After laying off & on all night we found ourselves this morning within a short distance of where we left last evening. Had our usual service & sermon, & after dinner Captn Hudson allowed three boats to make the attempt to land.* It was 4 oclock however before we set out when we met another boat from the Porpoise; had to sail several miles along the coast to the west before we could discover a place where it was practicable to land, a number of the natives following us on the beach, one carrying a green Pandanus branch which we supposed to be an emblem of peace. On landing our men however they fled with the exception of two old men who remained untill we obtained an interview when they were joined by four others. We made them some small presents, and went to their huts much against their inclination. We found but very little furniture, a few mats, nets and a stool carved from a solid piece of wood. The huts were but 6 or 7 feet high** consisting of a mere roof sloping two ways from a ridge pole to the ground, thatched with pandanus leaves, around were large piles of the husks & shells of Pandanus nuts, abounding with small rats, two of which as well as a bird (accentor) I shot without seeming to excite as much surprise as might have been expected, although they evidently did not know the use of fire arms.

They took us to their well of water, bringing us some first in cocoa nut shells, the water was perfectly fresh but had a strong marshy smell. The well was a mere hole 4 feet deep in the loose coral and loam. Collected a few shells and plants when we embarked, not having been more than an hour on shore, the natives apparently regretting our leaving them without visiting their village. Their arms were mere clubs, poles with porpoise jaws fastened to them, and wooden knives edged with sharks teeth, etc.

Monday 26th This morning made an Island about 10 miles to the west of the one visited yesterday, which took us all day to survey. We were not allowed to land. It was about 4 or 6 miles only in circumference, without a lagoon, was abundantly covered with trees, but no cocoanuts were seen. Many of the native huts were seen along the shore & the natives around them without much apparent alarm, although our firing of cannon might be expected to have that effect. The bright green foliage of wide spreading trees had a very inviting appearance the day being warm, but from some unfortunate whim of Captn Wilkes we all remained prisoners from our duty. A boat did land from the

Schooner but I believe without any of the Naturalists, showing however that landing was practicable, and the natives peaceable as the crew returned in safety.

We had several showers of rain early in the morning. These frequent showers no doubt being the main cause of the fertile and fresh appearance of these islands. At night quitted the Disappointment Islands standing SW with a pleasant breeze from the north & Eastward.

Tuesday 27th The day very warm 86° but with a pleasant breeze. Still Standing to the SW on about 5 knots per hour. A small Procellaria flew round the ship at dark, and a flock of Terns were seen which may be considered a good indication of the vicinity of land; a sight now becoming unpleasant to many of us from the few opportunities afforded to our landing. If we see no land, no accounts will be expected from us, but in surveying old discoveries we lay ourselves under obligation to the world at large to add something to the general fund of knowledge, but as those whose duty it has become to do so are at the mercy of a petty tyrant, no remedy remains but the mortifying one of reporting the *truth* to the world in *our* own defence. The people of the United States expect much from us after our long delays & vexations, to them we owe a long apology.

Wednesday 28th Still standing SW^d, nothing remarkable. Rather more luminous molusca than we have lately seen, no cetacea. All the men in excellent health & spirits, some amuse themselves in the evenings by rehearsing plays, others in dancing to the fiddle & drum. A few of us from the Ward room dined with Captn Hudson on his last Turkey.—No officer in the Squadron deserves more to have full coops than he, for none strives harder to make those around them happy. He plucks of no person under him. I hope he may receive his just reward.

Thursday 29th Reached the Island of "Raraka," circumnavigated and surveyed it with the squadron and boats. It like among all the coral islands is low, with a lagoon in the centre, and thickly clothed with trees. It is about 15 miles in circumference. The lee side afforded good landing. Several boats landed, found 2 native huts long since deserted, a quantity of coconut, and pearl shells (Aviscula) besides a few plants brought to Mr. Rich. The boats went from this ship (Peacock) one under Captn Hudson, the other Lt. Emmons. *No Naturalist were permitted to land.* The men collected a few shells differing from those on the other Isl^{ds} we have visited, but its other zoological productions are left for future and more fortunate Naturalists. The pausity of description and illustrations cannot with justice be charged to us. We are both willing and able to do our duty. It is our misfortune, not our fault, that both English and French are doing this kind of service in a much superior manner.

We have been close to this Island all day, could see it abounded in Scientific riches, & boats were swinging idly to their davits, men were looking as to a paradise,

---

* Capt. Wilkes wrote quite a severe censure on our return in which he expressed his opinion of the hostility of the natives, at the same time regretting that he had seen officers collecting specimens. The order was insulting to the Scientific Corps, but being addressed to Captn Hudson I have to regret not having a copy, as it is quite a literary curiosity as coming from the commander of a Scientific expedition, and wholy unworthy that branch of our government which allowed him to have the command.

** and 12 or 14 feet long.

but no, a survey is made, *nothing more* is requisite, and time flies.

WHAT WAS A SCIENTIFIC CORPS SENT FOR?

Friday 30th Made a large Island to the south of the one visited yesterday. It was immediately recognised as "Raraka" a doubt having been expressed whether it could have been an error in placing it on the charts, or what was more likely a discovery. Soon after commencing a survey an entrance to its most extensive Lagoon was discovered, and a few natives with the Tahaitian flag hoisted, an interview was had. They proved *friendly* and had a native Missionary among them. The Flying Fish was directed to land the Scientific Corps, with Lt. Perry. We stood in close to the land with the schooner, and entered the lagoon with our boats, a strong current setting out against us, the channel being about 200 yards wide. The Natives consisted of two or three families, about 40 souls, greater part being children. The Island is very narrow but the lagoon about 15 miles across, affording abundance of Pearl shells, etc. Cocoanut trees are abundant but are generally too young to produce much fruit. The lagoon abounds with a great variety of fish of exquisite beauty. Only one *land* bird was heard singing very sweetly (probably the same Accentor seen at Disappointment Isd). It was some time after night before we reached the ship. The sea was very heavy and our boat low, so that with the addition of a heavy fall of rain we were drenched to the skin. The night was squally and wet, the ship very uneasy.

Saty 31st The Scientific Corps put on board the schooner at 9 oclock, but did not succeed in getting on shore before noon. Found the natives too religious to fish or do any kind of labour to day, it being by a mistake of the Missionary who came by the Cape of Good Hope, considered the Christian Sabath. One crane (Ardea), 3 species of Tern 1 cerlew & 2 species of Pelidna, besides Sula furca and Frigates were the only birds seen here. Returned on board by the aid of the Schooner early in the afternoon, intending to survey another new Island seen about 10 miles to the N.W. In the evening several showers of rain. An English sailor was found among the Islanders, who says he was left here two months since by the Schooner Porpoise of Tahiti, to superintend the gathering of Pearl Shells. Solicited a passage to Tahiti which was granted and he was sent on board the Flying Fish.

*   *   *

The chief of Raraka is a man of middle stature, of less pleasing physiognomy than most of his subjects, is much tatood, and has lost his left hand by the bite of a Shark. He spent some time on board the Vincennes with Capt Wilkes, and when he returned on shore, shewed that he had partaken of his entertainment with delight.

Sunday, Septr 1st Last night past with some anxiety for the safety of the ship. We had stood over to an Island which we suppose a discovery: it lies to the NW of Raraka, 10 or 12 miles. The night was squally, dark, and rainy. At midnight the land was seen close under our lee; too close to tack ship when the Vincennes did, so that were were seperated for the night, but joined again in the morning. Sailed nearly around the Island which is about 45 miles in circumference. The lagoon very extensive, but the land very narrow, being a mere breakwater, not more than 1/4 of a mile wide at any part. In some places the sea breaks across, but we did not discover an entrance even for boats. Numerous birds in some spots appeared to be the only inhabitants. There was a few cocoa nut and Pandanus trees, but none others of any size.

Monday 2d Another squally and unpleasant night with rain and a heavy & uncomfortable sea. Landed for a couple of hours, killed some curlews, and Terns, and heard the warblings of the same species of Accentor obtained at Disappointment Isld. The landing was easy on the lee side (NW) on the coral reef which lies nearly level with the water; above which rises another dry ledge, not more than 4–5 feet higher, which is the most elevated of the land. Large bolders of Coral 6 or 8 feet high were seen in several places along the shore. They have evidently been thrown up by the action of the sea. The Island has been called Vincennes from our flag ship.

In the afternoon before a strong E wind we soon ran to the Island of Carlshoff, which is much better wooded than the Vincennes Isld, but night coming on we did not stand very close in before tacking ship to stand off & on for the night.

Tuesday 3d Stood along the south side of the Isld, the schooner coasting the north which appears well wooded and abounding in cocoanuts. The south side of its extensive lagoon is bounded by a reef of coral, level with the water, and being out of sight (10 miles) from the woodd part of the Isld. On the North is very dangerous for vessels at night. At the west end in a cluster of trees we discovered a white flag and several persons on the beach partly clothed in shirts, etc. We at first supposed they were persons who had been shipwrecked, but on a boat, landing from the Vincennes, they were found to be natives of Tahiti who were cutting wood and gathering pearl shells, etc. They consisted of four or five families, from whom we obtained a couple of jugs, some fish, shells and cocoa nuts. All the Scientific Corps and many of the officers landed at 2 oclock and remained untill sunset. Multitudes of black terns (Sterna stolida) were breeding on the trees around the native huts. Their huts were composed of a few sticks & leaves, of scanty proportions. One Heron, and two species of Dove were obtained. A few moths were seen, besides a variety of shells & corals. The Vincennes took a small quantity of water on board, and at dark we stood away to the northward.

Wednesday 4th A strong easterly wind has brought us rapidly to the northward enabling us to see the land of King Georges group this afternoon. The Schooner was supplied with additional provisions and despatches—we presume to Tahiti to the no small joy of her commander Mr. Pinkney.

Thursday 5th Until the middle of the afternoon we were beating again at a strong E wind to get to the windward of the Island in order to survey it with the wind, the Vincennes taking the North side and the Peacock the south. Night however overtook us before we met. The Island is of coral being a connected chain of small islets encircling a lagoon of about seven miles in diameter. The islets sustain numerous clusters of cocoa nut trees, besides considerable other vegetation. The natives on discovering in the morning made a large fire, which they repeated on our return in the evening, as we suppose to entice us to land, which however we could not spare the time for.

The only birds seen were black and White Terns (S Stolida & S. Pacifica).

Friday 6th Continued our examination of the Island this morning and on doubling the west end discovered an entrance to the lagoon; and saw another Island to the west of us. At ½ past 11 a.m. met the Vincennes, and obtained permission to land for two hours; which we effected without any difficulty, finding but little surf on the lee side of the reef. About 1½ miles from our landing place was a beautiful grove of Coconut trees abounding in fruit under which were a few huts, but no natives although a pile of several thousand cocoa nuts indicated a recent visit. These huts were better constructed than any we have seen, were beautifully thatched with palm leaves, had the sides constructed of mats neatly wrought, and were about 8 or 10 feet high, and eighteen or twenty feet long, the floors being also covered with mats. They were empty, with the exception of a few mats and baskets containing cocoa-nut shells used for carrying water.

Near these huts which were at the mouth of the lagoon was a coffin composed of a single piece of coral rock neatly hollowed out, with a double shelving lid of several pieces, fitted with *morter* and the joints whitewashed. The lid had been thrown off and broken, the coffin was filled with coral sand, but as a canoe containing 4 natives just then came in sight I was fearful of giving offense by a further examination, untill after the interview which *time* would not admit of.

The channel entering the lagoon was from 60 to 80 yards wide, and at least 15 or 20 fathoms deep, the water being of a deep blue like the ocean. The tide was setting *in* at the rate of about three miles per hour. The lagoon abounded with pretty islets thickly clothed with bushes. The natives* were stout athletic men

---

* They spoke the language of Tahiti (Otaheiti) so nearly that John Sack a New Zealander who was along seemed to understand them perfectly, remarking at the same time, "these folks, Otaheiti folks, New Zealand folks, all the same."

The chief claimed relationship with the chief of Raraka.

with but little beard, and good natured countenances, tastefully tatood principally on the right side and thigh but not on the face: had the lobes of the ear cut sufficiently large to admit a Segar. They brought a few baskets of shells to barter, and were persuaded to load their canoe with cocoanuts and proceed to the boats. Canoe about 12 feet long, 2 feet deep, the bottom dug out of a solid log and built upon by sewing planks to the sides, and had an outrigger. They did not like my gun, and continued holding my arm or the barrel of the gun, most of the time I was with them.

The highest part of the land we saw was about 10 feet above the sea, consisting entirely of broken fragments of coral, the highest part next the sea—the parts nearest the lagoon with a scanty but rich soil. The animal as well as vegetable productions, from so hasty a view, appeared quite the same as all the other Islands of the Archip^e. Two Doves, some snipes & terns were the only birds besides the musical accentor seen at this place, although from its extent more might be expected. Being distant and the day very warm, forty minutes had elapsed from the hoisting of the recall before I embarked, which I understand gave rise to some severe remarks by Capt Wilkes. A further delay however was occasioned by the desertion of one of the boats crew who could not be found.

An hour and a half brought us to another Isl^d to the west, the existence of which has been questioned. It bears the same general form with the others, having a lagoon and being low. Night overtook us before we had measured its extent. It has some clusters of very large trees with dense foliage of a dark green colour.

PEACOCK ISLA^d

Sat. 7th Passed round the west end of the Island in the morning and met the Vincennes, where permission was given to land for 3 hours. 3 boats left each ship, all effecting an easy landing, as we no longer regard a wetting as of any consequence. The productions are precisely the same as the other Islands visited, the lagoon, however, is shallower, our men wading across in several places to get to the cocoanut growing in very small groves on the lagoon shores. Traces of natives were seen who must have come here from some of the adjacent Islands as no traces of habitations were found. Small sharks abounded and attacked one or two of the officers while wading, but no harm was done on either side although it occasioned some diversion. Birds were not numerous, and consisted of the same species found before. Shells were not very abundant, but some interesting species were found: Tridachna jigas was the most plentiful, and a few specimens of Cypraea Mauriciana were also found, which we consider somewhat remarkable as the Isles of Franuad [?] Mauricias are quoted for its locality.

We embarked without accident at 3 p.m., if the loss of our boats rudder and anchor be excepted, the cable having become entangled in the coral. We usually anchor the boats just outside of the surf, and back them towards the shore, passing out a stern line to steady them, when by watching the waves a favourable opportunity is seized to run the boat in, jump out in the shallow water and pull the boat out until another opportunity. In this way we have succeeded in landing through quite a heavy surf without further injury than a good ducking, as the life preservers (India rubber) which are furnish[ed] to each of the boats crew are quite a safe guard to those who cannot swim. We all use them although they are inconvenient to swim with.

On leaving the Island we stood a SSWestʸ course under easy sail with the usual good breeze. The weather lately has been generally clear during the day but we have had frequent showers of rain during the night, the thermometer never indicating a lower temperature than 80°.

Sunday 8ᵗʰ By daylight this morning we were close in with Rurick Island, and alone, the Vincennes having stood on for Dean's Island. During the night we coasted along the east & north sides of the land. Natives occasionally showing themselves and apparently inviting us to land by waving parts of their dress, etc. Had the usual service and a sermon, and at two oclock 3 boats started for the shore. One only under Lt. Perry, with Dr. Holmes & I found a practical point. The others not seeing us concluded the surf was too heavy, and after some risk returned on board, but as we found a very narrow entrance to the lagoon we succeeded in landing dry near a cluster of cocoanut trees, where we found some old and very indifferent huts, but no natives. From the signs we concluded they had numbers of dogs, but in other respects were less civilised than those of the windward Islᵈˢ. The soil was better however and produced many plants seen for the first time by us. The birds were few and not remarkable. A few shells were collected and after remaining two hours we returned on board at the hoisting of the signal. The geological features were precisely similar to the others of the chain, no part of the land being more than 8 or 10 feet above the sea. The natives being seen only at a distance, we were not enabled to learn anything concerning them.

Mosquetos are troublesome among the trees & bushes, as well as *house flies*, the former appearing to take much delight in the discovery of skins thinner than that of the natives. They were about the size of those in the United States, and had black & white faciatia legs. They bite without any ceremony and

FIG. 64. Sketch from Peale's notebook.

leave a swelling which lasts several hours. Sharks are common in the surf, one of which I shot. It was of a very light colour with a black spot on the dorsal fin.

Monday 9ᵗʰ At daylight were in sight of Deans Island, and commenced a running survey of its Southern Side. It was a continuous reef with a tremendous surf breaking on it, connecting a string of well wooded but small Islands. The opposite side of its immence lagoon was not visible, excepting in one or two places. On the west end the Islets were clustered, and in the midst of a grove of cocoanut trees we saw a large house, though no other signs of Natives. The breese being strong we run the whole length of the land before sunset, and came in sight of Kruzenstern Island, where we bore up to the southward for Taheiti. No birds, but Boobies & Terns with one or two Frigates were seen, but abundance of Flying fish of several species.

Tuesday 10ᵗʰ At daylight found ourselves close to the Island of Maitea (Aurora) which present a strong contrast to those we have been recently visiting, from its altitude, and the cliffs on its eastern side rising about 200 feet perpendicularly above the sea, from a narrow belt of flat beach. It was all covered with a dense vegetation, and presented a rich and beautiful appearance. At 10 oclock two boats were manned, one under Lt. Emmons, the other under Lt. Perry. On our way to the shore we passed a canoe, with 4 natives & a cargo of fruit on their way off to the ship. The surf was very heavy, but we effected a safe landing near the foot of a high precipice and grove of cocoa trees: meeting about 100 natives on the beach who made every preparation to assist in carrying our boats on shore, but we preferred anchoring and tailing them in after our usual mode. The village we found on the beach appears to be a mere temporary residence, the main village being about 3 miles off across the hills. All the women have their hands covered with tattooing; the men having the lower parts of their backs radiated in rather a pleasing manner [fig. 64]. I did not observe any tatooed on the face. Their disposition was amiable and mild, quite honest, but aquainted with all the little arts of trade etc. The summits of the crags and terrace land was much broken up with picturesque rocks (Coraline) which had precisely the appearance of melted metal which had been poured into water, if such an appearance can be imagined on a grand scale. It is excessively hard, and the loose pieces, in walking over them, clink like hard baked porcelain. The appearance of the grass, and tropical vegetation along a path which I followed shooting Pigeons was more picturesque than any similar spot I have visited. Everything united which would form beautiful landscapes, but as my pursuits were ornithological, and time precious, I could not indulge my propensities. Here was the first place we encountered the magnificent Oceanic Pigeon. They were in great numbers, very fat, and easily shot; but as variety was desirable more than numbers, I obtained but 6, quite load enough with other matters, for an excessively hot day, and a toilsome path, after the confinement to ship board where walking propensities are inconvenient.

Met several species of Lepidopterous insects, amongst which that known to old entomologists by the name of Papilio Bolivia was the most common. The Taheitian parrokeet Psittacus Taitanus, of Gm. Lorius Vini of Lesson were plentiful in small scattered flocks. At 4 oclock on the Signal from the Ship to embark, discovered that one man from each boat had deserted, which detained us some time unprofitably, and finally they were left. Several of the Natives wanted to embark with us for the Island of Tahaiti, but not knowing Captⁿ Hudsons sentiments we did not take them off.

Thursday 12ᵗʰ Yesterday morning we were in sight of Einico and Tahiti, but the wind being ahead, and today being calm we could not succeed in getting into the harbour untill near night. A pilot came off to us in the middle of the afternoon and we anchored near point Venus just before sunset, near the Vincennes & Porpoise, they having arrived two days since.

Friday 13ᵗʰ Having received instructions from Capt Wilkes last evening to be prepared for a journey to the interior, Lt. Emmons, Mr. Dana & I, with two seamen repaired on board the Vincennes for further additions to the party, etc. [See map at end of this diary, fig. 68, p. 160, for the route of the journey.] At 9 oclock met four guides, and the interpreter* who had previously been engaged for us, at the Revᵈ Mr. Wilsons (Missionary) on point Venus, from whence we set out, our party being increased to 16 persons. The course pursued was nearly east along the coast for about 7 miles passing the village of Ahon, etc. to the mouth of the River Popinok. Here we left the coast and ascended the River about 5 miles, fording it a number of times although it was very deep and rapid, at the second ford obliging us to swim. The day was clear and very warm, so that some of the party suffered from the effects of the sun. On the faces of the hills we passed through large groves of Casuarina which much resembles some of the northern pines, emitting the same mournful sounds during gusts of wind. The "bottoms" in many places were covered with large patches of Bamboo, which is used by the Natives for a variety of purposes, but particularly for carrying water to their houses, where it takes the place of Jars or buckets, a piece 8 or 10 feet long & 4 inches diameter being kept with one end on a forked support affording a very convenient reservoir [fig. 65], cocoa nut shells taking the places of glasses, cups etc. used in other places. We found no inhabitants on the ruin, and took possession of an old encampment. A pig and some taro purchased on the road furnished us a hearty supper, the guides cooking it in the Tahiti mode which I think one of the best which can be adopted by travelers in the woods particularly. After a good fire

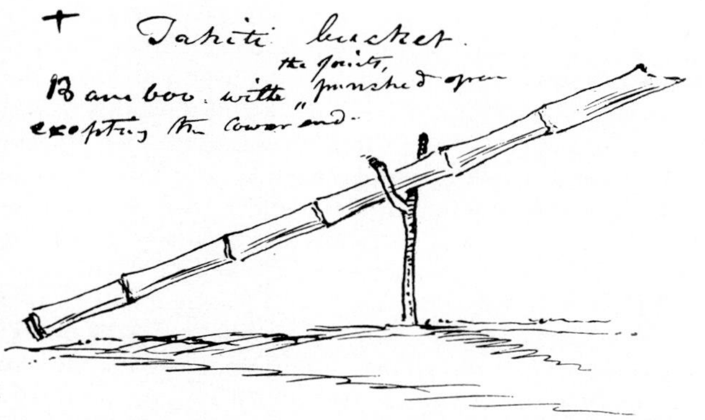

FIG. 65. Sketch from Peale's notebook, "Tahiti bucket. Bamboo with the joints punched open excepting the lower end."

is made (large in proportion to the meal) it is coverᵈ with pebbles, rather larger than hens eggs when such can be had. As soon as they are well heated or red, the fire is raked away, and the Pig, Fowl, or Taro, are placed on the Stones and covered with green leaves, over which earth is thrown so as to entirely confine the steam. In about one hour the meal is cooked (between a steam and bake) and is served out on large leaves spread on the ground; no kitchen utensils whatever being used. Cocoanut milk affords the usual beverage at such times. We found it both refreshing and wholesome, although taken in inordinate quantities.

Our shelter was made of palm leaves under a large "Vi"* tree on the banks of the river, and had it not been for mosquitos we would have spent a pleasant night. On the following morning our pig was baked and the march commenced by sunrise. By 10 oclock the river had been crossed five or six times. As it was very rapid and about waist deep with a bottom composed of large bolders of rock several of us fell, but with no other injury than a complete ducking, which I regretted much less for myself than my gun and ammunition, much of the gun powder being spoiled. Our road part of the time was through large patches of Bamboos and Sugar cane, the ground in many places being covered with the roots of wild ginger. A few birds were seen and killed, but the variety of species was limited to 5 or 6 including two species of Swallow, Tropic birds which appeared to have their nests high up in the mountain precipices (they were smaller than the phoenicurus, with white tails, longer than the body) and small Herons. About 10 oclock we arrived at the place where the last battle was fought between the Christian and heathen Natives, where our party divided: Lt. Emmons, Dr. Guillon, and I with two guides Sutton and the interpreter (Louis Saches) continuing on the main river intending to cross the mountains at its source to the Lake Wahereah, while the rest took a western branch in order to attain the high-

_____

* Lewis Saches

_____

* 14 feet in circumference 2 feet from the ground; we saw but one or two trees, larger on the Islᵈ.

est mountain peak. Our party halted at noon at the first natives hut we have seen on the river, but finding it deserted we were obliged to make our dinners on a few cocoa nuts and Fryers or wild plantains. (Musa rubra). It was a poor one, consequently we did not wait long for it but continued our wading march untill near sunset when we arrived at the solitary residence of a Native family in the mountains, situated in a most romantic gorge on a point of mountain, a range of Bamboos forming an aqueduct to the front of the hut where a delightfully cool stream poured forth on a rude pavement. There had been some rain. We were very wet and cold, but a building used as the family church was given to us, a large fire was kindled at our desire in front, and a baked pig on taro terminated the day. It was raining next morning on the commencement of our march at daylight, and continued to rain with little or no intermission until night. We hired an additional guide to conduct us across the mountain which divides the waters of the Island. The course was S Easterly, up the bed of a torrent, most of the time so hemmed in by enormous rocks that our road was from necessity in the bed of the stream which through the interstices with great velosity, rendering our foothold very slippery and dangerous. On leaving the stream to ascend the mountain we found the path very steep & narrow, requiring great precautions, not only to clamber up, but to prevent starting the numerous loose rocks to the great danger to those in the rear. Fayees of enormous size, and tree

ferns, some 40 feet high, give particular interest to the scene, and the various parasitic plants from the abundance of moisture covered most of the trees, even to their topmost branches. The moisture is almost perpetual from the fact of clouds almost always resting here, the slope being in such a direction as to condense the trade winds when they attain this elevation (550* fathoms by sympharon*) upwards of 3000 feet. On attaining the summit we had a most magnificent view on each side, the lake being to the South of us about 1000 feet below the mountain making a frightfully rapid descent towards it. The ridge was so narrow as barely to afford a pathway and the rain descending so fast on us who were already drenched and shivering made us glad to descend in the *Crater* to a more genial temperature. Sought a spot safe from the flood which was descending over the mountains side to the NW of the lake and constructed a hut of Fayee or wild plantain leaves. To kindle a fire we found no easy matter, the wood of the vicinity being at the best of times almost incombustible, and soaked as we found it quite so. To dry our clothes therefore was impossible, and being without a second suit, we had to make the best of a comfortless night, and commenced our survey of the lake as soon as light in the morning. It was of an irregular figure about ½ mile long and ⅛th wide, 90 feet deep, and without any outlet that we could discover. Our survey detained us untill after 3 p.m. In the meantime the other portion of the party having failed in their attempt to ascend the highest point had turned back and overtook us. The east and west sides of the lake being bounded by perpendicular mountains rendered it necessary for us to construct rafts to cross. Wild plantain stalks were the only materials we found which would float, and they but heavily, consequently we had to make a number of passages causing much delay. The natives swam across. Still continuing to rain, we suffered much from wet and cold. Our southern descent was more rapid than the ascent from the north. The mountains steeper and more covered with dense vegetation, the Course was almost all the time *in* the bed of a mountain torrent which was now considerably swollen and rapid. Canes covered the banks in dense masses, affording excellent harbour for the numerous wild hogs, Taro, Appe, and other roots abounding on which they feed. At night built a plaintain leaf hut but having nothing to eat and great difficulty in getting any fire to burn, we were constrained to go supperless and dripping to a cold bed on the muddy bank, during a heavy thunderstorm, but had to have a ditch dug round us in the night to carry off the water which collected beneath us in the cavities made in the soft soil by our bodies. As there was no breakfast to cook, our camp had no comforts to detain us and the sun had it shone would have found us well on our way down the valley still wading the

FIG. 66. Drawing. Caption reads, "Hamai (Autograph)/
    Tahiti / TRP. 1839."

* 550
  6
  3300 feet

stream, and to our great joy we reached the coast about 10 oclock where a pig was killed at the house of one of our guides, a fire made in the yard to dry our clothes, the women washed our shirts while our trousers dried on us. Our guns were put in a state to burn powder, or nearly so:—and in the afternoon the Journey was continued for seven miles to "Poplar" where we quartered in the Governor's house. The family were absent, but a young native arrived who informed us that the old chief wife had seen us on the road, & sent him to attend on us in her name and offer us all the civilities of her mansion. A fire was made in the yard to complete the drying of our clothes & instruments. A good supper was served on the floor (ground) which had been covered with leaves in the Native style, but there was a great addition in honor of us strangers: plates & bowls, some tea, arrow root and Slap Jacks were sent to us by one of the neighbours, which goes for to show the hospitality of the islanders.

* * *

Vincennes & Brig leave
Schooner repaired.
Left Papeete Thursday October 10th at sunrise; passed the W of Limas, warm weather, etc.
Friday the 11th passed, Oakino, Ulitei, Balabolo, and ————Islands SW.
Saturday the 12th Lowered Hood Isd Birds etc. in heat.
Sunday the 13th Rain —

* * *

Wednesday 18th An early march of 5 miles brought us to the House of Tatoo, who governs the adjoining district. We passed a Morai (ancient) on the sea shore at a place where there is no reef. It stands on a point of land, is built of coral blocks, is about 40 feet high, 20 feet wide on the top with a base of rather more than 50 feet. It is a parallelgm 140 feet long and had formerly about 10 steps of 4 feet each, like the pyramids of Mexico, but these have now almost disappeared, and I should have felt doubtful whether they ever existed had not the Hybiscus trees with which the sides were covered, preserved the form with their roots, even where the stones had been removed: obliterate the angles on the adjoining sketch* and you will have its present aspect. The drawing [fig. 67] is what might have been but there is now no means of knowing whether it had not some wooden structure on its top. The natives who pointed it out to us could give no account of its age or uses.

At Poplar we visited the remains of several morais, one or two being in an excellent state of preservation. They were in a fertile valley, filled with bread fruit trees, and consisted of oblong square enclosures, with

FIG. 67.

walls very neatly built of *lava*. The pieces were all gaged of uniform size and nearly round. (The natives called them Turtle heads from the shape) of these there was five rows, then a single row of square ones, the corners being strengthened by large square blocks. These walls are about 4 feet high. The enclosures about 30 × 60 feet, one end wall about 10 feet thick, the others about 2 feet. In some the thick end was north, in others it was west. No vistige remains of any wooden portion of the structures.

A native who was engaged at a pit of Bread fruit* within one of the enclosures told us that they were used by his forefathers whenever they captured any of their enemies, a large fin being made where the wall was thickest, in which the bodies were consumed, the ashes being afterwards buried in another enclosure. Some of our party being harased by sore feet and the fatigues of our journey endeavoured to get horses but were unable, but in making the enquiry it became known to one of the missionaries (Mr. Asman) who was about to go to Papeeti within seven miles of point Venus, he immediately sent an invitation to as many of us as wished to proceed with him in a whale boat which he had manned by four natives. Lt. Emmons, Dr. Guillou and I accepted the invitation and after breakfasting with Mr. Smith, who has a sugar plantation we started, leaving the rest of the party to follow by land.

Our passage was made with two exceptions between the reef and Island, at one place only there was no reef, and the sea broke heavily on the Island. Passed through one or two good harbours for ships, but generally speaking they have no good entrance like those on the north side of the Isd, or are much encumbered with coral banks. The shore was thickly peopled, very fertile, and picturesque. At 4 oclock arrived at the village of Papeete, where we remained to Supper when a boat arriving from the Vincennes, we took passage in her and arrived on board our ship again at Matavai (point Venus) at midnight. The rest of the party arrived on the day following, much exausted by the fatigues of the Journey.

---

* Morai restored. Great Morai of Temorre. Mr. Wilson's Missionary voyage of the Ship Duff. It is there figured at page 204 and was nearly perfect when the Wilsons visited it (18th July 1797).

---

* Bread fruit wile not usually kept for any length of time, but by burying it in pits, in which it has been well marked and covered with leaves and stones, it then ferments and forms a substance which tastes much like "*Bee bread*." In this state it will keep for several years and is used for sea stores by the natives visiting the low archipelago when fishing for pearls, etc.

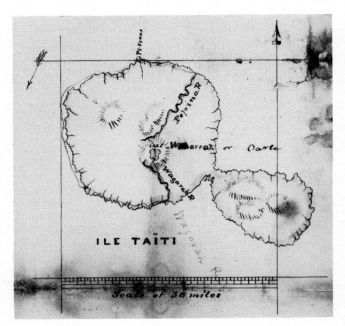

FIG. 68. Map from Peale's notebook.

The Vincennes left point Venus for Papeete bay where she was joined by the Peacock and Schooner, the Brigs having sailed for Deans Island some days before. On the 25ᵗʰ the Vincennes left the Island leaving the Peacock to await some repairs which were found requisite for the Schooner. She had to be hove down to repair her kelson which was loose, and to shorten her mainmast, found to be badly sprung in the bitts. These opperations detained us untill

Thursday Octʳ 10ᵗʰ when we left the harbour of Papeete at sunrise followed by the Schooner, leaving two whale ships (Carroll & Jefferson) and the British Brig of War Sparrow hawk, she having arrived from the Sandwitch Islᵈˢ the evening previous.

The general aspect of the Island of Tahiti on approaching it is much like that of the Island of Madeira with the exception of its being much more verdant and clothed with vegetation to the summits of its loftiest mountains. It is volcanic and of course partakes of the usual peaked and serrated forms common to Islands of that formation. In many places the fronts of its mighty precipices are flanked with columnar basalt.

The tops of the mountains and vallies are alike covered with a luxurient vegetation, only a small portion of the hills on the NW portion of the Island being without trees.

NOTES

No. 3

T. R. Peale

TAHITI   1839   SEPTʳ

24ᵗʰ The Brig Porpoise left the harbour of Matavai (Point Venus) a few days since (to visit again Deans Island for a further examination?). The Vincennes also removed to the harbour of Papeete, about seven miles west of point Venus and today the Peacock also sailed with the Schooner for the same place, where I understand we are to await sundry repairs on the Schooner, her mainmast being sprung and her false keel loose, etc., Papeete affording the greater facilities for heaving her down. Several of the officers prefered a pedestrian journey and I among them. About noon it fell calm, of course we arrived long before the ship.

25ᵗʰ The Vincennes sailed, leaving us to wait for the schooner, when repairs detained us untill

Thursday, Oct. 10ᵗʰ When we sailed at sunrise, shaping our course west NW past the Island Eimao, which by night was left out of sight astern.

Yesterday the British Brig of War Sparrow Hawk arrived from the Sandwitch Islands. 22 days leaving the U.S. store ship Relief there expecting to sail in about 2 weeks. We also left in port the Whale ships Charles Carroll & Thomas Jefferson of Nantucket, both bound home, the former in charge of Capt. Chase, the latter Capt. Swain, by each of them we sent letters. Several of our men deserted at Papeete but all were returned by the Natives who claimed their reward of $10 each.

On *Friday 11ᵗʰ* passed close by the Islands of Oahine, Ulitea, Bolabola, etc. We had a pleasant breeze and clear weather, but uncomfortably warm. All the deserters were flogged and returned to duty.

Sat. 12ᵗʰ In sight of Lord Hoods Islᵈ, and had a number of Tropic birds and gannets around us, particularly after dark when they were so numerous and noisy, that I think we must have been near some low Island not inhabited or on the charts. The wind ahead and but little of it.

Sunday 13ᵗʰ Heavy rain but a cooler atmosphere; the customary divine service, and on

Monday 14ᵗʰ The wind commenced blowing from E S E in quite a gale, but being favourable to our course we were not much incomoded by its violence at first, but the sea continued to rise untill it became so heavy as sometimes to role the gangways on the spar deck under water. Of course our ports on the gun deck had to be kept closed as tight as we could get them, but still all our rooms were made very wet and uncomfortable, and the motions of the ship was too violent to draw or even write.

But few birds were seen, one was a Booby (Sula furca?), the others Tropic birds (Phaeton phoenicurus). Had to keep under reduced sail to enable the Schooner to keep up with us.

Friday 18ᵗʰ The same *strong trades* and heavy sea. Left the schooner during the night. At 10 oclock got sight of the Island of Tootooillah and entered the harbour of Pag-paggo* this afternoon where was found the Vincennes. Some of the native chiefs came on

---

* Pago-pago
Pronᵈ pango pang-o

board, and a few of us spent a short time on shore where I found several interesting birds and the Colored Vampire (Pteropus ruficollis). Contrary to my expectations they were abroad flying in daylight, and one that I wounded uttered loud screams when captured. The Natives are most of them converted by some missionaries to Christianity and are strictly observant of the laws made for them; the women being forbidden to wear flowers in their hair, now go without that fanciful mode of dress for which they have always been admired and what is still more remarkable have ceased to have intercourse with the sailors. Cypraea Mauritiana is very common here, but we have not seen a single specimen of c. tigris which is so abundant at Tahiti. The harbour is very secure and surrounded by high mountains, which are covered with a dense and luxuriant verdure. Cocoa nuts and tree ferns give the principal character to the beautiful scenery.

Sat. 19th This morning landed on the south side of the bay with instructions to return at 12 oclock, at which time the ship was to leave the harbour for the Island of ————.

In the luxurient vallies we found a variety of Bulimii, cara[?] colla, & other terrestrial & fluoriated shells, besides many birds, and the red neck^d Pteropus. The sun was excessively hot but we found abundant refreshment in the nuts along shore where we procured an abundance of cocoanut milk, but could not induce any of the Natives to trade their shells, or curiosities with us, it being the Missionary sabath. On a trial of some of our officers to induce them to break some of the missionary laws, they were told that the missionaries could not see them, on which they pointed to the heavens and replied there missionary. "He see" —it was conclusive.

An attempt was made to beat out of the harbour but the passage was too narrow to succeed with a light wind and we anchored again.

Several of my best birds spoiled before I could prepare them, my drawings and notes requiring too much of my time to allow of my accomplishing all in such warm weather. An assistant has been furnished me by Capt. Wilkes for this purpose, and he has been rated on the ships books with extra pay for the service, but on my application for him to be excused from ship duty today to skin my birds, the First Lt. Mr. Walker refused, and Capt Hudson being out of the ship no redress was left, consequently I have to submit both to the loss of specimens which are numerous, and to the necessity of stuffing skins myself at the sacrafice of more important labours.

Sunday 20th At noon left the harbour with the Schooner Flying fish in advance of us, for the Island of Upolu (Opoloo) and had a very difficult time beating out against a heavy sea, but by 9 oclock in the evening had a good offing and laid too a part of the night, the wind being fair and our destination but about 40 miles.

Monday 21st Reached the east end of Upolu early. A canoe with a number of Natives and two White men came off to us, the Whites were retained as pilots, and a survey with the ship and two boats was commenced and carried on as far as the harbour of "Apie" on the N side of the Island. We beat between the coral reefs and anchored opposite the mission house just before night. A number of canoes came off and a brisk trade for shells & refreshments was commenced and carried on again in the morning untill it was found to interfere so much with the ship's duties that "all hands" were mustered and the barter from the ship forbidden, and the Purser with an interpreter went on shore to make the necessary purchases, no easy matter as the Natives have learned to extort by every means in their power—without having any regular currency a knife or hatchet being sometimes charged for a single shell. Pigs cocoanuts & Tarro being the only articles with a standard vallue, an axe for a pig— 8 yards of calico for 16 Tarros, etc. Found a great variety of birds, and the greatest abundance of Pigeons (Columba oceanicas) three or four dozen being killed by two or three persons in a few hours. Large Bats (Pteropus ruficollis) were quite abundant, they appear to be quite a diurnal species in their habits. The Island although high is not so mountainous as Tutuillo (Tootooilloh). The Natives number about 20,000 souls of which a considerable portion are converted to Christianity. They are a fine, athletic race but not so mild in appearance or disposition as the Tahitians. They wear their hair short and bushy, not shaved on the crown like the Tahitians, but like them are almost destitute of ornaments, excepting tatooing on the legs and thigh, but not on the face or hands exepting now and then a single individual. Very few shirts or other articles of European clothing are seen. Many cases of curved Spine, and blindness of one eye are seen (Catarract?) and some are disfigured by ulcers but by no means the numbers which are met at Tutuilloh. Spent the evening with the missionary (Mr. Mills) and his lady and with other information he informed us that the "Heathen" natives practiced circumcision (a pretty strong proof of Asiatic origin) and that their language, or many words of it was quite different when speaking of a chief from what it was when addressing a plebian. There is no king but a republic of chiefs, each governing a small district, which is one reason why Christianity flourishes only in spots. About 100 whale ships visit the group annualy, though all do not come to anchor. About 6000 children attend the schools on the Isl^d but there is but 6 missionary teachers in the group, (Navigators) Samoa being the native name for it.

29th Rec^d instructions from Captn Wilkes to procure guides etc. and proceed on an excursion to such parts of the Island as were deemed most interesting, and to return by Sunday, 3^d prox°. Accordingly after procuring the services of Wm Cowley, a seaman who has resided some time on the Island as interpreter, and a native to carry my pack and act as guide, besides one of the ships boys (Hughes) I set out through the village Apie, in the bay of which the Peacock then lay to the heathen town of Vaiouse, about 3 miles west. It is the residence of Cowly, & went there to allow him to prepare for the journey across the Island. From thence we set off south through a beautiful valley of great fertility, abounding in heavy timber and wild Pigeons (Colª Oceanica) many of which I shot without leaving my path. After proceeding about 3 miles we came to another "heathen" town called Susingha. Here it was concluded to spend the night and cross the mountains in the morning. The chiefs house at which we stopᵈ was small but very neatly built, the roof in the usual form—that of an oval dish cover, elevated 4 or 5 feet from the ground, and the sides neatly closed with split and wove bamboo with small windows about 10 inches square. The floor was of small loose pebbles. Each house in this village was elevated about a foot above the general level on a square stone platform about 50 feet angle. My host like my guide was a priest of the "gimblet" religion, and a sick native having been brought from the coast to a house opposite, he was called on to pray for him. This gave me an opportunity of learning some matters connected with their faith which otherwise I should not have understood: The priest is supposed to hold converse with the Deity, and by this means learns the fates of his fellows. On this occasion the prayer was to all intents and purposes Christian. The priest stood on the stone platform fronting the house, with his face west. He opened a book which had previously been carefully enveloped in tapa, and calling on *Jehovah* he returned thanks for the many blessings which had been confered on his poeple and asked a continuance of the same, invoking the aid of *Jesus,* and ended by asking the divine will concerning the sick man, asking mercy for himself. I could not see distinctly what the book was, but believe it was a *blank* note book.

These people in cases of sickness *confess* their misdeeds to one another, have a number of fast days, which are rigidly kept, and on the whole I believe their faith to be a kind of mongrel Christianity although they are much opposed to the present race of Missionaries. The story of the origin of religious faith is simply this. One of the natives of a neighbouring island Savai, was taken away by a whale ship not many years since. He was "gone a long time" and on his return possessed to hold converse with God, to raise the dead, and work miracles, etc. He soon gained many followers and founded the sect called by the whites "Gimblet" from his cognomen while on board the English Whale Ship.—the sailors of which had dubbed him *Joe Gimblet.* The sect continue to thrive but he has been obliged to quit this island and now resides in Savai, because he could not restore to life the son of a powerful chief* who had been murdered. The story as related to us in the presence of the chief is this— After the death of the young man "Joe" who said he

_____
* named *Lelomiana*

was not dead was called on to restore him. A house was built over the body and *Joe* used to take food there and said the body eat it and would soon recover. No person but Joe and the chief were suffered to enter the precincts. The dead did not rise and ultimately the chief's patience was quite exausted, and Joe had to clear out to avoid the vengeance arising from their disappointed hopes. The body was buried, but the chief still keeps the head in a box under the peak of his roof beneath which the story was related to us. Old Lelomiana is now neither heathen or Christian. He has been a great warrior and now expects soon to join his son in another world.

To resume my journey on the *30ᵗʰ* crossed the mountains to the south side of the island, comeing out at the village of Lotofungas about 4 p.m., having passed several beautiful Banyan trees of enormous dimentions; one which I measured, as supported on its thousands of roots, was 85 feet in diameter, and about 100 feet before arriving at its enormous horizontal branches. I also ascended to the extinct crater of a Volcano at about 2000 feet elevation. It contained a lake of water over ¼th of a mile in diameter, nearly circular, in the form of a bowl, the rim quite sharp and clothed with a most luxurient vegetation consisting of arborescent ferns, palms and bamboo, etc. All the rocks being hid with soil or moss. Eels are found in the lake but no other kinds of fish.

The houses on the south side of the island are more numerous, better built, and neater in appearance than those on the north side. The climate is more moist and rains more frequent, consequently the vegetation is richer and more varied. I spent one night on the coast and the next at the Town of Vimangha, 3 miles interior on the road to the north side. On resuming my route next day across the mountains visited a water fall which I estimated at about 900 feet perpendicular. The water makes but a single leap, and is lost in spray before reaching the bottom. Numerous Tropic birds & Petrels breed in the precipice, and large as they are in hovering below the cliff many are lost to the eye in the vast space below. It rained all the time crossing the mountains both in going and returning, rendering us very uncomfortable, the path muddy and slippy so that I was glad to return on board the ship again on the evening of

Satʸ 2ᵈ of November. Found that during our absence an unsuccessful attempt had been made to take a chief at the Island Savai who has been guilty of the murder of many Americans. We had previously taken a native who had murdered in cold blood an American sailor who was living on shore for the sake of his knife, shirt, etc. He was put in irons on board and a notice sent to the Chiefs to have him tried and executed by them, but after proveing his guilt they declined the execution, giving him entirely over to us to do with him as we chose, & it was concluded the punishment would be sufficient if we removed him from the island. He was therefore kept in irons under a sentry.

Having heard through Mr. Cunningham that there was a remarkable cave on the opposite side of the Island inhabited by Swallows which never saw the light of day, I was directed by Capt Wilkes to make another journey across the island to ascertain the fact and obtain specimens.

A party was made up, consisting of Mr. Rich, Dr. Fox, Mr. Blunt & myself with Cowley as interpreter, Sutter and three natives.

Tuesday 5th We set off and proceeded on the village of Alua by 3 oclock, and as it was too late to cross the mountains without camping on the way with every prospect of a wet night we concluded it most prudent to wait until morning and reach the settlements on the south side before night. We acted prudently for it rained heavily all night and in the morning notwithstanding it still rained heavily we crossed and were sadly drenched finding the road very wet and muddy. Attempted to measure the water fall visited on my last jaunt, but our line was too short. By using rattans which grew abundantly close by we might have succeed but by too great a loss of time, and we gave it up, after lowering 36 fathoms of them over the cliff. Several Stones of different sizes were thrown over, which consumed 6½ seconds in falling, the sound 2/3ds of a second in returning, by which I estimated the height by the falling stone 784 feet, and by the return of sound 754 feet. I regreted exceedingly that the line sent was not sufficiently long, as it appeared to all of us that the height must have been much more. The highest range of mountains by simpler was about 2000 feet. At 3 p.m. we arrived at Vaguamgha and here Mr. Rich (who had been most overcome by the fatigues of the journey) concluded to stay; for although it rained almost incessantly the thermometer in the valleys was at 82°. The rest of us proceeded to the coast, and about 8 miles east to the village of Sieumu where we spent the night. On the following morning we crossed several rapid mountain streams and a bed of lava about 4 miles wide which in many places appeared as though it had been cooled suddenly on the surface, and the liquid portions below had flown out leaving extensive [?] caverns bearing evident appearances of their formation. At Sanga we called on the missionary Mr. Bachman who received us with great hospitality, and conducted us through a heavy rain to the cave, which was the object of our tour. It was about 3 miles from his house and about 1½ miles from the sea.

This cave was formerly dedicated to the God "Moso" by the natives whom supposed him to reside in it. We found a wall about 3 feet thick across the entrance but could not ascertain whether it was a land mark or intended to confine the entrance which was about 4 feet high and 6 broad, enlarging to quite a spacious chamber inside, with a regularly formed tunnel, from out of which the molten lava had flown in a S E direction 908 feet, where we found it filled to the roof with water. Another branch ran about 500 feet in a N E direction, but was much more encumbered by fallen portions of the roofs, etc. The average height of the S E tunnel is 8 feet with an almost even floor of 15 feet: the roof and floor much covered with Stalagmite of a light yellowish Colour, but not calcareous. On ledges of the rock forming the roof in various places we found the nests of *swallows* whose bat-like voice struck us on entering. It bore a strong resemblance to the rattling of small hard pebbles. These swallows, contrary to what had been represented to us by Mr. Cunningham, were the common species of the island and were constantly passing in and out of the Cavern, having merely selected it as a place to breed (in the dark). Their nests were made of moss *glued* together, and but one egg—a very large one in proportion to the size of the bird—was found in each, or a single young bird. Some ready to leave the nests, others just hatched, etc. Eggs white.

We returned to Mr. Cunninghams to dine in our drenched and dirty clothes, having none left dry to change, after which we went to the next village and lodged with the Chief, returning next morning to the residence of the Chief Lelomiana, visiting several other caverns on the way, which we were enabled to do with the more facility by carrying a Lantern with us. We spent the night and were well feasted by John Maitland, a Brazilien adopted by the Chief. Maitland and another White man accompanied us next day across the Mountains on our return to Apie bay. We came out at the town of Vaimouse, and arrived at the ships again in the afternoon of *Saty 9th*—finding all the Squadron, expecting to sail immediately for Sydney.

Sunday 10th One of the missionaries, Mr.* gave us a very able sermon on board the Vincennes. The Porpoise & Schooner returned from Tootooilla, and in the afternoon the whole left the island with a fair breeze.

The natives of "Samoa" differ in many respects from those of Tahiti. They are not so mild in disposition, are more covetous. Tatoo the thighs only like breeches, wear a belt of long leaves (Titi's) in place or more frequently than tapa. It is the ordinary dress of both sexes. Their hair is usually cut short, and frequently smeared with lime to make it stand up stiffly and turn it brown, which is greatly admired. They circumsize, and have a singular and disgusting practice of rupturing the Hymen of their young girls in public previous to marriage. It is done by a chief, friend, or the intended huband, by introducing the two forefingers into the vagina and tearing the Hymen asunder, when done smearing the faces of the bystanders by whom the compliment is estimated in proportion to the daub.

The mode of thatching is neater than that of Tahiti but the materials are not so durable. There they use pandanus leaves, here the leaves of sugar cane for which purpose alone cane is planted.

---

* Mr. Williams, this was probably the last sermon he preached. He was killed by the natives of Eromanga shortly after. He was the author of a very good book, a treatise on Missionary enterprise in the Pacific.

Wild hogs and Dogs are found in the mountains, which have become so from the tame stock in times of war, but we saw no poultry wild. The only mammalia indigenous to the group are rats & flying foxes (Pteropus ruficollis), the latter are very abundant and destructive to all kinds of fruits, never allowing any to ripen on the trees. They do not seem to have any carnivorous propensities.

*   *   *

The canoes of these islands are beautifully built of numerous pieces, neatly sewed together with sinnot made of cocoa nut husk.

*   *   *

Sunday 10th The Brig & Schooner arrived this morning from Tootooillah, one of the missionaries preached a sermon to us on board the Vincennes, and at noon the squadron left the harbour with a fine leading breese.

Tuesday 12th Off Wallaces island, which appears rather to be a small group of 8 or 9 islands one of which is low and flat, the others mountainous and apparently fertile. They all appeared to us to be joined by a coral reef, or shoal water, it being of a light blue. We saw many houses from the ship and a canoe with 3 or 4 natives in it went on board the Vincennes, when a signal was made, and our prisoner from Upolu sent on board after a charge to the natives not to allow him to escape to his native isle, he was sent with them on shore much to his joy, and we continued our course.

Wednesday 13th At 7 a.m. we were close to Horns Island. It is high and mountainous, apparently very fertile, the mountains being clothed in bright green vegetation, and the shores lined with cocoanuts; but we were not close enough to distinguish any natives, and a fine breeze soon carried us out of sight again, not only of the Island but of the Brig & Schooner which were not able to keep up with us.

Thursday 14th from our Change of *Longitude* it became requisite to Change our *time,* and consequently a general order was received today to drop *Thursday 14th* and call it

Friday 15th When all hands were mustered and Captⁿ Wilkes order rec'd to change the day in all journals, orders, reports, etc.

Monday 18th At day break discovered what appeared like land to the west of us, which we ran for and around it at 8 a.m. It is laid down on the charts as Mathews *rocks.* It is an island with very abrupt shores and rises about 1300 feet above the sea. The south side and top is covered with grass, and some bushes in the ravines which offered resting places for multitudes of Birds which here rear their young undisturbed by the approach of man. Amongst them I could distinguish Phaeton Phoenicura, Tachypetes aquila, Sula bassanus, S furca, Sterna fulignosa, etc. After a short delay to determine the position of the Island during which time one of the Vincennes boats landed, we resumed our course.

Tuesday 19th Still before the wind with all sail set and making from 7 to 10 knots on our course. A Sniper (Pelidnes) flew round the ship. It probably came from the island of New Caledonia, which lies at no very great distance north of us, but not in sight. The quantities of Molusca in the water increase as we get south.

Sunday 24th Still going before the wind at the rate of 8 or 9 knots. Had the usual service in the morning, but towards night the wind increased to a gale; broke the mizzen topsail yard in two and had but just replaced it by another when the gale came on in great violence with a heavy sea. The air was kept in a blaze of lightning, quantities of which discharged through the ship to the sea. Several of the officers received shocks and the conductors, and yards were tipt with luminous points (the men called them "compass hands" probably a corruption of corpus santos!!). The gale commenced from the NW but shifted to SW directly ahead for us and it became quite cold, 65° and continued unabated untill the afternoon of the day following when it began to lull, but the sea still remained very heavy and kept the ship, and our gun deck rooms very wet this day. Lat   Longᵉ   .
Saw the first Albatross met in comeing south.

VII

Australia
And New Zealand

Tuesday 26th Gale died away and we again were enabled to make sail. The wind was ahead; passed Lord Howes Islands to the north of us; the first we discovered was Balls pyramid (properly named pyramid). It rises directly from the sea and appears to have no level land on it. The next island rises more gradualy but is still very steep on all sides and very high—2000? feet.

We entered the harbour of port Jackson during the night and lay snugly at anchor when the good people of Sydney looked abroad in the morning. Much to their surprise they Saw a Yankee Squadron and their streets alive with the officers half wild at being once more in a civilised community who spoke their own language. The immense numbers of Locusts (Cicada) which filled the trees near the landing was truly astonishing. Their din was heard long before I left the ship, but when walking the street near the government domain it was deaffening. This however seems to last like the cicada's song at home, only from 9 in the morning untill 3 in the afternoon with a few exceptions. Next in numbers is the police; we were seldom out of sight of a Constable. Then the "Chain gangs" looked like the coffee carrying slaves of "Rio," but without their merriment. The well filled European stores brought forth pleasing recollections, but on the whole the appe^ce of the Town was not prepossesing. We were however greeted with the utmost hospitality, every attention was paid us by the authorities and citizens. We were elected honorary members of the Australian club, who gave us a splendid entertainment under the patronage of his Excl^y Sir George Gipps, the Governor. This was followed by a constant round of entertainments, both public and private, which lasted while we remained.

In the meantime the ships were undergoing all the necessary repairs and preparation for the voyage towards the S Pole, where it was expected there would not be much for the Naturalists to employ themselves with besides the necessity of economy on the score of provisions and rooms. Therefore we received orders on application to Captn Wilkes to remain in Australia on the sailing of the Squadron which we were to rejoin at the Bay of Islands, New Zealand on the 1st of March. According as parties were formed to visit various parts of the Colonies, I accepted the pressing invitation of Lachlan Macallister to visit his estates in the district of Argyle. Dr. Pickering & Mr. Dana ascended the Hunter River, Messrs Rich, Drayton and Agate went to Illawarra, Mr. Hale to Wellington Valley, and Mr. Couthouy whose health was seriously impaired remained at Parramatta.*

The squadron sailed from Sydney on the 26th of Decr 1839, and on the following day I started for the interior in the steam boat to Paramatta, where I took the stage and reached Liverpool the same evening, putting up at the "Wheelwright's arms," from whence on the following morning I made excursions to the neighbourhood, visiting the *dam* erected at the public expense to divide the fresh from the salt water of Cooks? river which enters in to Botany bay. It is at the head of *tide water* and is indispensable to the existence of the population, being the only water attainable, the soil being based on Sandstone rocks and consequently ordinary wells are useless. I was hospitably received by Dr. Hill at the public hospital of which he is Superintendent. He insisted on my removal to his house where I remained untill the 30 of Decr when my friend Lachlan Macallister Esqr. arrived from Sydney in his gig, and we started on our Journey by the way of Camden, the seat of James Macarthur,

* Eventually the Phis^ns of Sydney recommended his not going to N. Zealand, and he took passage in a colonial vessel to Tahiti, intending to go from there to the Sandwich Is^lds where he expected to join the Squadron.

Esqr., where we dined and spent the afternoon. This most magnificent mansion and garden is on the river Stepear and is attached to a farm of about 30,000 acres of land on which the first successful experiments to breed sheep were made. (They are now the staple product of the colony). In the garden I found figs, peaches, plums, pears, etc. in the greatest profusion and of the finest quality, besides Mulberrys and grapes. Some apples and oranges grow in the open air, but the product of the latter is poor. Around the house Magnolias and other trees from N. America flourished by the side of Acacia pandulu, etc., the natives of Australian mountains. Arrived at Cliffton, the seat of my friend Macallister at dark.

On the day following day I took my gun and followed the meandering course of the Nepen, struck with the productiveness of the soil although everywhere deficient in moisture and the singular voices of the Birds, particularly the quaint and varied jargon of the "laughing jackass"* a common species, as also the native Magpye, "Wallabys" a species of Kangaroo are common here, besides "Oppossums."

January 1st Started again on our Journey to Argyle, overtaking Mr. Wallace Arthur, with his servent in another gig, after we had proceeded but a few miles. He was well provided for collecting seeds which were fortunately now ripening in great variety, and we were very successful in obtaining them. On the 2d day we arrived at the Wallindilly river, and although it rained heavily stopped to hunt the Ornithorhyncus which abounded and although several were wounded I did not succeed in killing one until the following morning when I was obliged to swim for a fine male which I killed, besides five Ducks, which Caused some delay, but we succeeded in getting to "Strathara" at night. This is the seat of my friend Macallister. It consists of about 16000 acres in one tract of the most fertile land I have seen in Australia. It is geologically speaking "trass," the decomposing black rocks forming a rich chocolate cold mould which retains the moisture much better than the gray sandstone of most other parts of the Colony. The timber is closer and heavier than in the sandstone districts but is much of the same Character, mostly Eucalyptus of two or three different species. The *grass* is thinly spread over the ground and of course the Cattle and Sheep require a great range. One sheep to an acre is considered the utmost and even at this number in dry seasons they suffer severely. There are no running streams of water except in rainy seasons but by a happy and unusual circumstance the soil washes into deep pits, and form "water holes;" a most happy circumstance for the colonists, as from these alone are the cattle supplied. Argyle is the only place where I saw *Springs* and there they are small compared with other regions.

The crops of wheat are this season unusually good, but it is the first for three years. There was bitter complaints wherever I went for the want of Laborers, as the system of Assignment is being gradually abandoned by the british Government. The convicts are now to be sent to Norfolk Island, where emigrants are not allowed. Something wrong in the whole system—saw 900 women confined in the prisons called "factories" at Parramatta; in common with them were 400 young children!!—for the benefit of their education??

January 15th Returned to Sydney, receiving on the road the same liberal attention from the Messrs Macarthurs, McAllister, Dr. Hill, Thompson, Etc. to Mr. James Macarthurs I was indebted for a fine case of plants put up in the best order for transportation and a package of seeds which I sent to W. Norris Esqr. Amongst the plants was 6 Monton Bay Pines, and 6 Norfolk Isld do. These trees flourish well in the colony, and are amongst the most beautiful trees in existance. They will not however stand severe frosts.

In Sydney passed a pleasant round of dissipation at the hospitable tables of Mr. Denistro, Alexr Macleary Esq., Mrs. Scott, Dr. Nicholson, etc., etc., and boarded at the Australian Club house until the morning of

February 6th when we embarked on board the Colonl *Brig Victoria* for the Bay of Islands, N. Zealand. We sailed during a gale of wind, and having shiped a sea in the cabins windows which besides sundry other mischief filled the only chronometer with sea water, and obliged the Captn (Moore) to put back again to exchange it for another; are shored in Port Jackson again on the night of the 7th when we had a beautiful exhibition of Aurora australis. The corruscations were of a pale straw coloured light in the Southrn Sky, some reaching almost to the Zenith. It lasted from early in the evening untill 10 oclock.

Febry 8th Sailed again. We find the little Brig very uncomfortable and crowded having upwards of 20 cabin passengers besides a number in the steerage.

Nothing remarkable occured untill the 16th when we had another exhibition of Aurora Australs, much like that of the 7th. We passed a large shoal of Spm Whales, and a Noddy remained on board the Brig for several days, and was very tame, suffering us even to handle it. We encountered a heavy gale of wind from the east which obliged us to lay too for two days. Made the "North Cape" New Zealand on the 22d, and on the 24th entered the Bay of Islands, and anchored at "Korrorurika" where we immediately landed to look for lodgings, but found the "town" crowded to excess, and had to return on board at night for a bed.

Feb. 25th The U. C. Consul (Mr. Clendon) called upon us and we went in his boat up the Bay to the residence of *Mr. Tibbey* where we were all accomodated in the same house, viz. Mr. Rich, Brackenridge, Dr. Pickering, Drayton, Agate, Dana and myself, Mr. Hale not having come with us in the victoria, having been detained by heavy rains which rendered the roads impassable in Wellington Valley. To the Consul we were indebted for little or no hospitality, which is not remarkable as he is *not* an Amrn but an Englishmn,

---
* Ducelo gigantica

master *of a vessel, married to a* former serv^t maid of Lady Sir Francis Forbes.

Made many short excursions around the *Bay* and neighbourhood, and was much surprised after all the reports we have heard of N. Zealand, to find that the soil was very poor, the country hilly and in fact but a very small portion of it fit for cultivation.

The hills are very steep and nearly destitute of trees, but covered with ferns* which are so entangled that traveling amongst them to any distance is almost impossible. The timber is mostly in the ravines; in which I obtained all my birds, amounting to about 30 species, none of them can be considered numerous.

Mr. Clendons farm on *Man of War* or *Manoná* Bay was the only one we saw where there was more than 100 acres together of sufficiently level land for cultivation. All communication is in boats, the only passable *paths* being on the ridges. Fish abound and are very excellent. Peaches are raised by the natives, but they never suffer them to get ripe. The same with grapes. We did not see any other fruits. Irish potatoes are raised in abundance, and considering the rude modes of cultivation are good. They form the principal subsistance of the "Mowries," (Natives). Sweet potatoes ("Cumera's") *koomera* are cultivated in considerable quantities, are of a peculiar variety, but are not good compared with those of Tahiti. The natives raise hogs but they seldom eat the pork, it being to valuable for common use, as they usually sell a middle sized hog to the settlers for 15 dollars, sometimes in money, but generally in goods.

We were very much annoyed by the Mosquetos, sand flies & fleas. They were trifling however to the annoyance of the meat flies, which were so numerous and hungry as to deposit their young in our blankets & stockings, and on our food while we were eating, etc.

March 10th The Schooner Flying fish arrived from the Antarctic reg^ns having parted with the squadron in a gale off Magnarii Island. The Crew suffered severely from the cold and wet but suffered no loss of life. Capt Pinckney was slightly frost bitten and a few of the men scorbutic. They were wet almost the whole time. They of course could give us no acc^t of the rest of our friends. Mr. Hale arrived in the ship Achiles on the 2^d.

Monday 16th Received a letter from Capt Hudson

---

* And in some situations Leptospermum Scoparium or "Tea plant" of Cook & others.

announcing his arrival at Sydney on the 21 ult. with the Peacock in a damaged state in consequence of having been jammed in the ice, besides other damage she had lost her rudder, cutwater, bulwarks, etc. and was saved almost miraculously.

It was a general rejoicing amongst us to hear that they were returned in any condition.

Thursday 26th The Brig Porpoise arrived all in good health, having seen the Antarctic Continent, (bringing us a quantity of geological specimens) and fallen in with the French Exped^n under d'Urville, who declined intercourse with our exped^n.[12] He made sail when the Porpoise was near enough to speak with him—so near that the faces of the officers could be distinguished without a glass—the respective flags & pennants of both vessels were hoisted. The Porpoise had been seperated from the Vincennes in a gale. Dr. Holmes and sundry officers landed on the Auckland Islands, and found great numbers of birds which were so tame as to suffer themselves to be taken by hand, they even alighted on their heads. When walking over the hills he collected and brought me the skins of five species which I think are new.

Tuesday 31st The Vincennes arrived all in good health and high spirits having been favored with good weather, discovered and sailed upwards of 1500 miles along the *Antarctic Continent*.[13] She put in to Sydney for water, and brought the unpleasant intelligence that the Peacock was to go direct to Tongataboo, and those who belonged to her were to embark in the Vincennes. All our specimens were now packed, and sent on board the Ship Lydia, bound to Salem, Mass^tts, likewise those of the officers collected south and on Sat^y April 4th we went on board, and occupied ourselves in preparing letters home, etc.

---

[12] Henderson, Daniel, in *The hidden coasts*, 119–125, discusses this event and says that it was a case of misunderstanding on both sides. He cites a statement of d'Urville written after the Frenchman had read Wilkes' published statement. d'Urville, upon seeing the American ship, apparently hoisted his flag and maneuvered his sails with intention of speaking to the American vessel, but the officers of the *Porpoise* interpreted this as an intention to remain aloof.

[13] See text p. 82. Most modern experts agree that though Wilkes' measurements may have been incorrect as to where land began, he was correct in proclaiming the existence of a continent. Wilkes was the first to explore the coastline for a sufficient length to prove its continental character, though not the first to discover Antarctic land, as Palmer had done this twenty years earlier.

VIII

The South Pacific—
Tonga And Fiji Islands

Monday 6th Sailed from the Bay of Islands with a fair wind and smooth sea. Variable weather and calms. Off Sunday Island which was high land on the 13th and were in sight of it for two days. Sooty Terns**, Gannets, White Terns***, etc. constantly around us, besides a few Tropic birds (P. phoenicurus).

15th Passed the ship Tobacco plant Capt Swain an Amrn Whaler who sent a boat on board to buy newspapers from home about the same time with ourselves.

Sunday 19th Easter, calm & light air, with showers of rain on all sides, about 5 p.m. a water spout commenced a little to the W. of us within ¼ of a mile. It was about 30 feet diameter, the spray was raised from the sea with a rotary motion 12 or 15 feet—no commotion in the clouds above—lasted 12 or 15 minutes and vanished. Just the same opperation as the whirl-winds on shore, as seen when raising leaves, etc.

Tuesday 21st Left the Brig & Schooner last night, as they went in search of land reported as seen to the eastward of us yesterday. "Albions" have been ard us for several days past, one or two of them have been taken, & a shark. Have seen but one species of Delphinus which was 12–15 feet long, blunt nose and a White spot behind the dorsal fin. It looked [like] one we saw off Cape Horn last year?

Wednesday 21st Made the Island of Eooa this morning and stood in between it and the Id of Tongataboo, but a heavy Storm with torrents of rain, thunder & lightning prevented our making a harbour, and we had to stand off again.

Friday 24th Sailed along Eooa, and entered the harbour of "Tonga" late in the afternoon; in passing between the reefs struck on a rock about midchannel, but

passed over it without damage and anchored off the Missionary Station, two of whom visited us in the evening.

Saty 25th Landed to pay a visit of ceremony to "King Josiah" and "King George" and found we arrived just in time to prevent the ravages of a civil war, between the Christn and heathen Natives of this Island. King George with upwards of a thousand warriors having arrived from his own dominions (Vaovao) to assist in the extermination of the *heathen*. In our interview they expressed a great desire for peace, when Capt Wilkes offered intercession for that purpose.

A messenger was sent off to offer our mediation, to which they will give us their reply on Monday next. Our offer was to guarantee safe escort to the opposing Kings, with a suite of 10 each, to hold an interview on a neutral island.

This is the first time we have seen a numerous assembly of armed warriors amongst the Islands. They were gaily ornamented, all wore mats of tapas, and were painted with Turmuric, charcoal and vermillion in various devices. Each armed with heavy carved clubs, spears, and muskets. An attack was made on the Christian party last night, which they say resulted in the loss of eight Killed. There are two families of White Missionaries residing here. Mr. Tucker & wife, Mr. & Mrs._____14 and three children, one only 2 weeks old. They are Wesleyans, sent by the London W. Society. They inform us that they have 6 ministers of their society at the Fegees.

Dr. Pickering and myself recd orders today from Captn Wilkes assigning us the additional duties of Conchologists to the Expedn

Friday May 1st All our interceeding has been unsuccessful in arranging a peace between the Christn and heathen natives, and yesterday hostilities were recom-

---

* Sterna fuliginosa [No single asterisk in above text.]
** S. stolida?
*** S alba? Pacifica.

---

14 Rabone. Wilkes, *Narrative* **3**: 7.

menced by the Christⁿ party under *King George* who started for "Beah" with 1400 men. We saw much smoke in the direction of the contending parties, but have not learned the result. The Brig Porpoise arrived just as were getting under way, and as the Pilot was missing we anchored again abreast of the town. The weather has been excessivley warm with variable winds and calms. Although we have been anchored nearly a mile from the shore for two nights sleep has been quite impossible from the immence swarms of mosquitos which filled every part of the ship, even the tops were filled by the officers and men in vain endeavouring to obtain a place to *sleep*. Our excursions have been extended to several miles in various directions. Botanically they have been successful, but the Birds with a few exceptions are the same as those of the *Samoa* group. Large Bats (Pteropus ruficollis) are also equally abundant and are seen hanging from the trees in all directions.

The natives we have found uniformly intelligent and honest, and are a fine formed and handsome race of people. I think superior although much like the Samoans. They cut the hair short as a mark of Christianity, and lime it like the Samoans. Many carry fans to brush off the numerous flies. The Chiefs useing a *brush*.

Satʸ 2ᵈ Again under way after some little arrangements with King "Josiah"* about the Pilots having been kept on shore. Just as we were making sail the *Peacock* hove in sight and after having joined us the whole squadron anchorᵈ on the reef about 5 miles from the Island north of the Town.

Sunday 3ᵈ Calm. Messʳˢ Rich, Dana, Agate and myself ordered to join our ship. Mr. Hale retained temporarily on board the Vincennes. All glad to join our friends and shipmates—1st Lt. Walker exepted, he refused me his hand—the remains of his old grudge for reporting sundry inconveniences he has placed me at in taking my assistant for ships duty, refusing my stores on board, etc. A busy day getting our rooms to rights, etc. At night a canoe with two women came on board who immediately threw away their paddles and begged to be taken to the Feegees. They said their houses had been burned by the "*Christians*" who would kill them if we did not save them, etc. New paddles were made and they were sent from the ship, but they went to the Brigs and there supplicated again, and when sent away, they went to the Schooner, threw the new paddles into the sea, sunk the canoe and swam on board. They were sent to the flag ship and from thence landed on a small Island and left.

This war has been provoked by the *Wesleyan Missionaries*. They have represented to "King George" their ally, that the people of Beah and other towns of the interior would not let them preach in their towns.

That they resented with blood shed the destruction of their sacred places and yam crops. The ultimatum of the allies is Christianity and a Missionary amongst you or—Extermination—the result ought to be obvious, when we know that the Missionʳʸ party is the strongest & best armed. They muster about 2000 men, many muskets, but a small supply of ammunition. The Beah people are now besieged in their forts which are very strong, mount 6 ships guns (remains of the Port au Prince) see Mariners account—who has given a singularly correct description of these people.

Monday 4ᵗʰ Sailed from Tongataboo with a pleasant breeze and clear weather.

Wednesday 6ᵗʰ At sunset got sight of Turtle Isᵈ one of the Feegees and on the day following saw a number of Islands, some of them quite high land, but there appears to be great discrepencies relative to names on the Charts. The weather thickened with rain and high winds rendering it somewhat dangerous running. The Brig was detached to survey some of the lands passed. No birds excepting a few Phaetons seen, & they appear all of one species.*

Friday 8ᵗʰ After spending yesterday and last night with light and variable winds, we arrived this afternoon in the harbour of Lepouga** and landed for a short time in the town and were struck with the marked difference in the natives who are "*Papuans;*" much darker colored than the friendly Islⁿʳˢ. They are naked with the exeption of a *small* marro; the women wearing a fringe about 9 inches wide arᵈ the loins. The hair is carefully cultivated and frizziled up looking like an enormous wig, like the Natives of N. Guinea. They were quite friendly and danced for us.

Houses are more peacked, higher ridge pole and are thatched or enclosed with small canes to the ground, having very small doors.

Satʸ 9ᵗʰ A large party including Captˢ Wilkes & Hudson started for the highest point of the Island. It was clear and very hot. Capt Hudson and 2ⁿᵈ midship Eld gave out the rest after four hours toil reached the summit from whence there was a magnificent view of the Isᵈ and and surrounding reefs, with the ocean studded with large & elevated Islands. Our path was about 5 miles long over a wooded wild, the elevation about 2000 feet (1 inch of mercury) distance from ship 10″ by sound. Saw several villages in the interior whose inhabitants challenged our native guides, the coast & interior natives not being on the most amicable terms. The challange was by a loud yell in unison, something like the N. Amⁿ war whoop. Some of the party did not get back untill after night, being detained untill sunset taking bearings, etc. of the diffᵗ Islands in view.

---

* "Josiah" is King of Tongataboo, "George" of Vavao and the Hapai Islands & only comes now as an ally against the *heathens*. He has been joined within a day or two by a large party of Figis.

---

* Phaeton aethereus?

             w   v

** Island of Oveloo. Lefonga town
                 Leruca

The *pottery* of this Island is exceedingly like that of antient Peru, and nearly if not quite as well made. It is the only Island we have yet visited where *any* is made. Here it is not only well made and baked, but glazed. We saw some jars capable of holding about 30 gallons.

Canoes. have the outrigging wider than usual, and are *not paddled* but sculled at the inner edge of the outrigger by an oar held nearly perpendicular, the persons using it always standing.

Archery. The bows of oveloo average about 6 feet, arrows 3–5 ft. cane with a cocoa nut point 1 foot long, sometimes having another point of "Rays Sting." In preparing to shoot the manner of holding the arrow and *nocking* is precisely according to the British manual, but the fore finger of the left is kept over the arrow while shooting. The arrow is drawn to the *breast* by the *thumb & knuckle of the fore finger,* shooting better than could be expected from the mode of *drawing.* Bows good, arrows too full of knots.

Monday 11th The schooner arrived having run on a reef on the 7th, lost her false keel but does not appear otherwise damaged.

Wednesday 13th The Feejee King Taonoa having arrived from Vao, the capital last evening was invited on board the Vincennes to day where he was accompanied by his suite of about 40 natives of Tongataboo, who from their manly bearing and noble stature made a most striking contrast to the Feegees. We however measured one of the finest looking Feegees and found his stature 6 feet 6 inches, and beautifully formed.

The King was under 6 feet, lightly formed and rather feeble. He is apparently about 60 years of age, wears a beard reaching to his breast and is very dark cold, had but little to say. A copy of the Samoa laws was offered for his adoption, and as appeared; the old man promises all that could be wished from the protection of traders and persons and property wrecked within his territory.

Some shotted guns were fired, but the King became alarmed and begged that we should desist. The marines fired a few vollies, refreshments were given and presents of shawls, hatchets, tobacco, kettles, etc. being made, the King & suite departed for the shore, receiving in addition to the above presents one of Halls patent rifles with brasses etc. . . .

These people are lavish in expressions of surprize *whew -eu* being uttered at every new spectacle, and *"kanaka"* (good) at every new manouvre of the marines, etc.* Men had little or no tatooing. The women have only the *pubis* and corners of the mouth, and sometimes an imitation belt. Their enormous heads of hair are covered on state occasions with white tapa (bark cloth) of fine texture, which closely resemble large turbans.

Both men and women have nearly all lost both of their little fingers in mourning for relatives (a practice only just ceasing by influence of the Missionaries in the Friendly Islds).

*Thursday 14th**
Started for an excursion to the mountain ridge, with a clear morning and very hot sun, tempe 91° but before reaching the summit of the first range of Mountains we were envelloped in clouds and soon after torrents of rain. We were drenched of course, but were successl in finding many plants and two new birds, one a Pigeon resembling the Oceanica but without the coral knob on the bill and having a note like the barking of a dog. Sutton lost his pistol in decending as it was impossible to prevent falling owing to the slippery mud in the precipitous path. Numerous mountain natives met going and returning. They have gone to trade yams, taro, clubs and curiosities with the ships. I bought on our return a wooden pillow, dish, etc. from them, for a knife, string of beads, tobacco, etc.

Friday 15th Had an unceremonious visit from King Taonoa and retinue. He remained on board untill afternoon and the ship under way to leave the harbour. He beged for everything that pleased him, as well as his Tonga attendants, some of whom to my surprise did not speak the Feegee language although several knew a few words of English. Dr. Pickering & Mr. Hale came on board our ship to visit several of the Islands with us and rejoin the Vincennes at Sandal Wood bay. Stood off and on during the night, and entered Turzon bay harbour a little afternoon, but to late to visit the shore which distant. A boat was sent up the *River* to the Town of Rava to invite the King on board. He declined coming but his brother *Tokonato* (alias *Phillips*) came in the boat. He speaks good English and is partial to foreigners besides having great influence amongst his people. One of the Missionaries (Wesleyan) came on board with a crew of Tonga men. Their success is but poor. A musket under his seat in the canoe did not bespeak much confidence in the natives.

Sunday 17th Our Launch and the Vincennes 1st cutter staid with us last night. They are surveying under the direction of Lt. Emmons. They were not well received at Vao the capital town, the natives would not sell them provisions. Having refreshed and replenished their provisions they left us again today.

Lt. Budd was directed to take charge of two of the Peacocks boats, and Survey the River Rava; to return in 4 days. I was directed to accompy him. Toconoto, the Kings brother and heir presumptive accompanied us. He speaks pretty good English. He took his seat with Mr. Budd & I and Passd Midm Davis took charge of the other boat. 5 men in each, well armed.

Left the ship at ½ past one, and soon crossed the

---

* No women were present with the King, and only two Tonga women in the large double canoe which brot off his suite, the King himself and a few favourites being honored with the Comns gig.

---

* Mr. Rich, Dr. Pickering and I accompd by Sutton and one Native. Passed Midn Dehaven went a short distance but turned back.

bar at the entrance of the river where we saw many natives drawing seines. About 4 foot water only on the bar, inside about 2 fathoms. Soon after entering the river it commenced raining heavily and obliged us to stop at the fishing town of Butia, and take refuge in the "Booray" ("Spirit house" of the Whites), properly speaking a kind of town hall, built at the public expence in which all strangers are lodged, and provisions sent to them. Here all the councils are held, Judgments passed by the chiefs, etc., and a store of arms are kept, each male being taxed a spear, which are more prized the older they get, as being placed on racks over a constant fire they become glaced with smoke and dirt—and as the natives say being kept in a consecrated place wounds from them are certainly fatal, while the same kind of a wound from a new spear—or one kept by its owner will heal. Wherever the natives saw Phillips they immediately dropped on their hams untill he passed, and when he spoke to them they clapped the palms of their hands, and in his presence they did not walk upright. In this village we saw the shells of quantities of Cypraeas and Lingula which were eaten by the inhabitants. The former we eat subsequently up the river and found that they made excellent soup. In this village (Butia) they make quantities of earthen ware of different shapes and some of large size capable of holding a barrel of water. The earth is dug on the banks of the river, is a yellow clay modelled by hand without a wheel and baked in a fire, open to the air and glaze as some say with the *sap of the mangrove?* The pots are very light, of fanciful shapes, but fragile.

When the showers had somewhat abated we started in our boats, but were soon overtaken by another storm and drenched to the skin. Arrived at the town of Rava at dark, and were quartered for the night in Phillips house, one of the largest in the place. It had a very steep roof about 50 feet high and was covered with a thick thatch to the ground. Inside was in one hall, divided by screens of ornamented "tapa." The beams were all joined by colored cinnet[15] neatly plaited in different patterns, and the floor covered with mats. The furniture consisted of a hand organ, several arm chairs, a closet, *table and benches.* Our supper table was covered with a cloth plates, dishes, knives and forks by his *White Stewart,* he has also a carpenter. The former left here sick under his charge by the Brig Currency Lass by Sydney. The night was not a comfortable one in consequence of the noise made by the numerous natives assembled to drink Cava, Phillips bowl for making which is at least 3 feet in diameter.

With genuine savage hospitality, a wooly headed wench was offered to each of the party for the night—

all our arms were put in order and kept at hand and a guard kept at the boats.

Monday 18th Started at eight up the river, the banks are diluvial and from 6 to 8 feet high, covered with reeds and rank vegetation. Large proportions of the level grounds are cultivated with yams, Tarro, Bananas, Bread fruit, etc. Phillip brought his stewart to cook for us, and a messenger passed the town of Mugumato of 1000 natives on the left side of the and nearly opposite Corninbidi of 1100. Those numbers were given by Phillip, but subsequently I found that from his warlike propensities only *men* were computed. Passed close to the town of "Nasslye" where the marks of savage war were still visible in the dead trees etc. and burned houses; the town having been destroyed but a few months since, and all but 70 put to death. This part of the river is called *Wy-laboo.* At noon stopped at the town of *Now-Souri* governed by Phillip's brother, who after sending a quantity of cooked yams and tarro for our mens dinner embarked in his canoe with 3 men to accompany us up the River. Shores lined with Shaddock trees loaded with fruit of enormous size (red inside). Now-Souri is on the right hand side of the river, and opposite is the town of "Davooi-lavoo" of 250 men. Here is the first high ground on the river. The town is built on the hill, and rocks appear in the river. All the shores of the river below this are diluvial Islands which our guide Phillip says were formed by the frequent floods from the mountains *since he has had whiskers!!* He is not more than 35 years of age now. They are from to 8 feet elevation, and are frequently covered during the freshets to the depth of several feet. Most of the native houses have a solid basement of about 4 feet, surround with piles to prevent washing away on these occasions. Rained again as usual so heavily as to wet everything & fill the bottom of the boat. Passed the towns of "Natacala" "Cassavoo" each of about 500 men and stop[d] for the night at "Coronganga" of about the same pop[tn] having shot some Ducks and a very beautiful parrot by the way.

We were lodged in a Booray, taking care to dry our arms and keep them handy, and centries at the boats. We passed today a small stockade on a hill. It was built with Bamboo by the boys who practice upon one another with bows & arrows of cane without the usual hard wood points but a cushion of "tapa." Current of the river 1½ miles p.h. Our sleep in Coranganga was sound, but not from the comforts of the "Booray," but our fatigues. Every one of us were wet to the skin & our extra clothes "soaked." The mosquitos bit villanously and the *rats* made determined attacks on our bundle, etc.

Tuesday 19th At 7 oclock were on our way up the River taking with us the pig & yams cooked by the natives for our breakfast, which we did justice to a few miles above by mooring the boats to the shore. As we find it much more pleasant to eat our meals in the boats than on shore surround by a crowd of curious

---

[15] Sinnet (cinnet) is described by the *Oxford English Dictionary* as a nautical term of obscure origin and is defined as "A kind of flat braided cordage formed by pleating together several strands of rope-yarn, coarse hemp, grass, or other fibrous material." The Smithsonian Institution has a coil of sinnet brought back by the Wilkes Expedition.

natives. At the town of "Nytashiri" we saw another of Phillip's brothers, but he would not stop to speak with him having quarreled about the disposition of 200 hogs belonging to Phillip. We passed on but the brothers manned a canoe and followed for several miles, sent us loads of cooked yams from the next town "Toobootooboo" of some 700 men. Here the brother stopped. He appears to be in great dread of our guides anger. Very fine sugar canes were sent off to us; they were of the red striped variety. At 1 oclock passed the point at which Captn Bethune returned, and the village of Viti. Flood marks of drift reeds, etc. were here seen at least 25 feet above the river and high over the diluvial banks. The hills were very irregular in figure —rocks, sandstone, in this strata dip^n about 10° E.

We continued on untill we had reached the first range of Mountains and could see the pt where the river forked, and about 5 miles above Capt Bethunes's pt. & town of "Viti." The Mountains were about 1000 feet elevation and at the point we turned back from shore was a remarkable water fall of several 100 feet leap. Rained heavily all the afternoon and night. Reached "Coronganga" at dark, and again spent the night there, but the pig provided for supper was *raw* and we did our best upon 3 ducks which I had killed as plenty of yam & tarro remained from the days presents.

Wednesday 20th This is the last day allowed us and we returned as rapidly as possible down the river which had risen 3 feet during the night. Rained all the morning and a part of the afternoon. Made presents of axes, cloth & beads to the Chiefs who accompanied us and reached Rava in the after^n. Phillip force^d Messrs Budd, Davis & I each a spear, parasol, and a piece of Tapa, armlets, etc. to each of the boat crew, 2 fathoms of tapa.

We met Capt Hudson and a number of the officers in the town and learned that the King had visited the ship during our absence when every attention was shown him, shotted guns fired, rockets blue lights, and the marines were paraded, clean shirts & *white pantaloons* (hard work to raise them).

Phillip & his brother of "Now-Souri" returned on board with us in Turon bay.

Thursday 21st The King, Queen, and two brothers came on board to receive presents and it appeared that *Vindobi* another brother was expected by Capt. Hudson.[16] He has been guilty of several murders of whites, and it was designed to arrest him, but he was too cunning. In the afternoon while we were at dinner and surrounded by canoes, the crew were beat to quarters, [?] and all the royal party informed they were prisoners untill Vindobi was forthcomeing. It created

great consternation at first untill assured of kind treatment, and as the King suggested that the alarm spread by the canoes leaving the ship would cause the destruction of all the whites on Shore, they were all detained and the natives about 70 in Number brought on board and kept for the night. In the meantime two of the Kings brothers were suffered to depart in a large double canoe (Galinango & _____) in order to bring the other brother prisoner to us—the orders were dead or alive.

A canoe with 3 or 4 men tried to escape, but one musket shot brought them back.

Every attention was shown to the royal family, books, pictures, instruments and every curiosity was exhibited, and Jim Crow by the ship tailor performed for their diversion.

Friday 22 The large double canoe returned and *Vindobi* was delivered to us by his brothers. There appeared to be great distress in consequence and many tears were shed before and at the leave taking. They have been assured that his life will be spared, but that he must be taken to Am^a as a prisoner. He was placed in double irons in their presence. They all soon afterwards left us and we have once more a quiet ship.

* * *

Examination of Prisoner Vindobi
Her majesties Brig Charles Doggett, Capt. Bachelor Salem 7 years since the massacre.　　Sat May 22/40
　　　　　　　　　　　　　　　　　　　　　Rava

Prisoner says the vessel came to *where we anchored* and "Galmingo" sent pris^r to take the vessel over to "Cantab." and Galmingo had arranged with the Chief of Cantab to have her taken when she arrived. Chief of Cantab named Hevali. Prisoner took her over. Prisoner was to have her taken in behalf of Galmingo, was promised nothing but what he could take. gal^o cared little whether he was killed or not. Galin^o wanted to have pris^{nr} out of the way. 10 of the crew killed. Massacre commenced in the Biche-Le-Mar House.[17] Prisoner was in the boat. Pris says the plot was made up to come down and kill the crew at night. Heevali chief of_____ was at the head of the murdering party. All were killed on shore but the chief mate and a boy who were killed in the boat.

When pris went on shore all the natives were waiting in ambush. Quest^n Did you kill the men with a spear or club. The Cantabs threw spears and prisoner had to dodge to escape them.

---

[16] Peale's rather confused notes and comments on the story of the arrest of the Fiji chief, Vendovi, begin here. See text pp. 83–84. Hudson waited until Peale's party returned before inviting all the royal family, which included Phillip and his brother, on board. Hudson had hoped Vendovi might have come with Phillip and the others.

[17] "Biche le mar" was a kind of "sea-slug," more accurately the echinoderm, *Holothuria edulis,* written "beche-de-mer." It was prepared and cured for sale to the Chinese, who used it as an ingredient in rich soups. A large building was required for the curing process. The ships engaged in this trade usually built these temporary structures. Often as many as fifty or sixty natives were employed during the collecting and curing processes. A comparatively few ships engaged in this trade and for them it was highly profitable. For a full discussion of the processes involved see Wilkes, *Narrative* **3:** 218–222.

Nambewalla, Leweti and Roro were the 3 towns concerned in the mass[e].

Natives cut large vines to pass under the cable during the night to haul the vessel on shore. Vessel got off too soon. Chief whose design it was, now dead. Pris[nr] did not eat any of the mass[d] excepting a Negro. The rest were returned on board. The Capt. had them sewed up in canvass and sunk, but they afterwards drifted ashore and were roasted, eaten by the natives.

Four towns on the Island of Cantab. Head town Vambay. They had nothing to do with the mass[e]. Chiefs name "TeVambay." TeValey is chief. Chief of Roro is Te Qui Te Valey was the chief engaged in the slaughter, he was the agent of the Rava chiefs.

The mate of whaler, the Ship Nimrod of Sydney, came ashore to buy provision. Pris[nr] seized the mate and detained him untill he who wrote to the boat crew an order to give all his whales teeth, etc. (50 teeth 4 axes, small chest of pipes & a quantity—a bale—of cloth, a large quantity of fish hooks, iron pot) as a ransom for his liberty. This was at the Island of Cantab two years since. When he obtained the property he gave the mate a "head" of tortoise shell and sent him off.

* * *

Sat 23[d] A few canoes came along side to trade provisions & wood, but the ship got under way and at breakfast time was standing for the Island of Cantab with a fair wind, but it soon died away. Saw five or 6 large canoes standing in for the Island of Rava.

* * *

Ten cal[r] months constitute a Feegee year. They count from the planting of their yams—to the "harvest home."

* * *

Tuesday 26th Once more at anchor this evening on the west side of Rava being bound to Barr about 60 miles NE. We did not reach Kantab* owing to some mistakes of our Pilot which led us out of the proper course untill the wind changed and became foul for us, and this being the day appointed to be at Barr to pick up our surveying boats, it has become necessary to abandon our exped[n] against the refractory chiefs of Kantab. We have surveyed several small Islands near our track, but having no opportunity to land at any; very few birds or fish have been seen, a few Sooty Terns (St. fuliginosa) and a Tropic bird comprises the whole. Indeed these Islands are so thickly inhab[d] that few of the sea birds find an undisturbed place to breed.

Wednesday 27th Our anchorage last night was at the Harbour of Navula, where there is an entrance to the inside of the most extensive reef we have seen. We were under way betimes this morning and have sailed

about 40 miles the north shore of the Island of Livu in perfectly smooth water; the main shore is mountainous and volcanic, the mountains covered with trees near their Summits, but their sides with grass and scattered clusters of trees. Forrests in the vallies. All inhabited. The towns most visible being on the summits of some of the highest hills near the shore. Grounded just before sunset but soon got off again with the help of a Kedge. Some of the smaller islands to the north of us today were very picturesque, abounding in fanciful peakes, interspersed with forrests of palms and other trees, and grassy plaines. Anchored at sundown. Saw many lights along shore in the evening which appeared as though the natives were fishing—an office our pilots inform us belonging entirely to the women. The 8 oclock gun followed by a blue light and 3 rockets assigned to our launch & cutter which we suppose to be within sight of us, put all to flight, an answering rocket was seen to the north.

Thursday 28th Our experience of yesterday convinced us of the necessity of not sailing until the sun was at a sufficient altitude to show the reefs which were covered, and we availed ourselves of half an hour on a dry reef collecting shells, etc. Launch and cutter joined us about 10 a.m. and we took them in tow and beat with a fresh wind towards Barr. But about 4 p.m. we were going so rapidly that the launch was unfortunately run under and immediately sunk in 15 fathoms water. The two men who were in her saved, and the ship anchored in order to try and raise the launch again. 8 oclock gun, blue lights and rockets fired again for the benefit of the Vincennes boats, and astonishment of Natives. Lt. Emmons, Chapl[n] Elliott and P[d] Mid[n] Blunt have been 14 days living in the boats, while surveying the reefs, etc. Very little intercourse with the Natives, consequently they were nearly out of provisions and just joined us in time to prevent their suffering.

Friday 29th All boats out dragging for the sunk launch, but being unsuccessful, two boats were left in charge of Lt. Emmons to continue the search and the ship got underway and worked a few miles up the shore to a "Biche le mar" house used by the Am[n] ship Leonidas recently. We expected to find her here. A number of canoes passed us this morning as they came

FIG. 69. Drawing. Caption reads: "Feejee (Viti) Canoe TRP."

---

* Kan, ta, vu

out of Barr river, paying no attention to our signals to come on board, a musket was fired, but they took no notice of it. A great gun was fired with grape and they made all sail to get out of our reach. A few others were seen kindling fires on the hills. No boats were permitted to land.

Satʸ 30ᵗʰ The boats returned last night without finding the launch. She had a howitzer, shot, chain & anchor in her. They sailed her full. Several boats landed at the "Biche le mar" house before breakfast and as we were directed to return at 8, killed only one bird, collected a few Lepidoptera & shells and saw just enough of the country to ascertain that its features and productions are quite different from the vicinity of Rava. Hills covered with fragments of black volcanic rocks and grass interspersed with clumps of trees. Beat all day up the coast in front of high & picturesque mountains, and anchored again at night opposite to the town of Tabooa, situated on a flat, apparently a river in an extensive recess of the mountains admidst groves of cocoanuts. We have seen a number of canoes today, but they all shunned us, only one passing within hail. Fires were kindled on the mountains as we passed.

Sunday 31ˢᵗ Chaplain Elliott gave us a sermon, accompanied by the ritual service. Afterwards we got underweigh and were all day beating about 8 miles in a very narrow channel between the reefs and about 2 miles from the shore which is here very mountainous, and in most parts destitute of forrest, but covered with grass and volcanic rocks. After anchoring in the evening a canoe with 6 natives came near us but would not venture alongside.

Monday, June 1ˢᵗ The channel was so narrow and the wind still being from the NE & ahead, we had to anchor about 3 miles from the town of Rag-Rag. Landed on an Island opposite the ship. Had an interview with the Natives and one of the boats visited the town, but none of the natives. An unfortunate accident happened to one of the men when weighing anchor. His hand was caught by the cable and so crushed that it became necessary to amputate 3 of his fingers.

Tuesday 2ᵈ Wind still ahead, but we continued to beat through a channel less than ¼th of a mile in width. At 1 p.m. anchored, and a number of us landed on an Island, opposite the ship. We found a few natives fishing, and numerous traces of a former extensive population, and the remains of *forts* consisting of Stone walls 4 feet thick and about the same height surrounded by a dry ditch. They are always on the crests of hills. On our return on board the pilots informed us that this place was attacked by the people of *Vao* some time since and all the adults slaughtered, and many children were taken to Vao & Rava where they suffered a similar fate by the hands of *Juvenile Warriors* in order to practice them in the arts of war with the club, spear, etc.

Wednesday, 3ᵈ Anchor up soon after reveille but after beating through a very narrow channel had to

wait untill the sun attained greater altitude in order to see the reefs, and even then we run upon a corral knob. Had to back off and anchor, as the day was then too far spent to reach Sandal Wood Bay before night and there is no anchorage, before we get there—the reefs too dangerous to lay too. "An evil wind which blows no good." We the Scientifics had a profitable ramble on shore all the afternoon, finding much that is interesting on the shores, but no birds & not many plants. I shot a fine specimen of Pteropus ("Flying fox"). We were not anoyed by the company of any natives, having our own way, once more.

Thursday 4ᵗʰ The wind was adverse & we lay at anchor all day. Permission was not granted to land untill after dinner, ½ past 3, consequently we could not go far from the ship. Collected Shells on the reef and fished with little success.

Friday 5ᵗʰ Under way shortly after daybreak and stood over to the Island of Viti Nenua. It rained heavily. Anchored in Sandalwood bay in the afternoon and found an anchored keg containing dispatches from Captⁿ Wilkes who has been here in the Schooner. A boat also arrived from Ovelooa under the charge of Lt. Underwood to get a rudder pintle for H M Ship Sulphur run on shore at Rava just after we left there. Capt Belcher in the Sulphur, with the Schooner Grayhound, has been surveying the N W coast of Amᵃ, and is now on his return home, but unfortunately ran on a reef near Rava a few days since & lost his rudder.

Sat 6ᵗʰ Could not succeed in getting a boat to land us untill noon. In the meantime several canoes came off with some chiefs, and one with sandalwood to trade. Capt. Hudson left the ship to seek the Ship Leonidas, said to be in a harbour a few miles west of us. Our excursion was a long and tiresome one. The face of the country is hilly, trap rocks, and very rich soil, few trees except on the mountains & along the streams, but all the hills covered with a rank groth of grass, and sprinkled with pandanus. We landed on the wrong side of the river to visit the native town, and did not see any of its inhabitants excepting those who visited the ship, most of whom were suffered to remain on board, and they were greatly astonished at our usual display of fireworks at 8 oclock. (First the drum and fife, followed by a great gun, then a blue light followed by 3 rockets.)

Monday 8ᵗʰ Sunday passed as usual. Chaplain Elliott officiating in place of Captⁿ Hudson. Landed at the town which is situated a short distance up a small river. It is fortified by a stockade and ditch, and has a number of very narrow and low gateways, with a kind of watch box over each. About quarter of a mile up the valley is another town similarly fortified. They are both surrounded by tarro patches, which are trenched and the earth thrown up between them forming a kind of causeway on which the paths wind about, the Tarro beds being a little below the surface of the water, abounding in Melansia of several different species. On the drier grounds are groves of Cocoanuts, bananas, etc. In wandering through one of the cocoanut groves near the edge of a Mangrove Swamp we came to a consecrated piece of ground on which there was mounds of stone, and a wooden Idol, surrounded by others of rude stones set up endwise, and dressed with Turbans & hair pins such as are worn by the natives. They had been painted, but exposure to the weather had washed it off. Sundry offerings of spears, arrows, cocoa nuts & trinkets lay arround, and the place appeared to be much venerated. A large party of natives who were following us deserted our company the moment they saw our direction was towards the consecrated grove, exepting two, a man and boy from the upper village, who were anxious for us to partake of the cocoanuts, amongst the offerings, and offered to sell the *Idol* which I bought for a paper of vermillion, but neither of them by any means could be tempted to touch a single article, although expressing a desire that I should carry off whatever I wanted. This however we would not do without knowing more of their superstitious regard for them, fearing it would occasion

trouble from those who turned back. A beautiful species of Parrokeet was found here. Birds generally are scarce and the variety of species small. The hills generally are destitute of timber, but covered with a rich groth of rank grass, with here and there a pandanus.

Tuesday 9th Landed again, and had a long excursion to the mountains taking a few natives as guides. Obtained a few plants not found near the coast and returned much fatigued at sunset, when I went to the consecrated grove and took the Idol with me to the boat. The purser has been most of the day trading provisions with a few curiosities from the Natives—fish hooks, hitherto not much vallued are here in great demand, Vermillion and beads also. They bury their dead in the houses in which they have lived; and the reasons assigned was, the apprehension they might be disinterred and eaten if not under the immediate guard of the family.

They bury the superannuated *alive* when too old to work as at the other Islands, but we have not heard of its being done except by request of the person buried.

FIG. 70. Oil painting on cardboard. Pen and ink sketch of same scene is labeled, "Taunoa, Tahiti / John's House, Fenna [?], tree in foreground, young orange."

One man said he heard his Mother whom he had buried under the floor of the house, breathing for two days afterwards.

Lt. Emmons with the first & second cutters started to survey some of the smaller Islands but the second cutter under P^d Mis^n Blunt returned last evening, having landed on one of the Islands to cut a *"sprit"* when the man fell from the tree and broke his leg. Another was put in the place of the wounded man and the boat started off again this morning. The King of Venna Levu came on board today with Captn Hudson, who has been down the coast. He made peace with his brother, the Chief of the town opposite to which we lay. They have been at war for a long time. They have more firearms than most of the natives we have seen in this group, nearly every chief carries his musket, and one had a very pretty small brass cannon; the carriage being inlaid with bone.

Wednesday 10 At 3 p.m. left the Bay and anchored a few miles to the NW, picking up our boats by the way, they being *all* out surveying.

Thursday 11th Under way at daylight, but about nine oclock ran on a rock with great force and were obliged to kedge off—no damage. Anchored again at 5 p.m. opposite a high point of rocks on which there was a town. A boat landed and obtained a few Cocoa nuts, but as yet we have not been able to obtain a single hog.

Friday 12th Arrived in the harbour of [Naloa Bay] and found the Ship Leonidas at anchor, with part of her crew on shore drying "Biche le mar." She is from Salem Mass^ts and under the comm^d of Capt. Eglesford; saluted us with 9 guns. At 2 p.m. landed and shot a few birds, and wandered through the most barren district we have yet visited. It was thinly covered with Pandanus and Casuarina, the rocks basaltic.

Sat. 13th Made rather an unprofitable excursion a few miles into the country under the guidance of a chief of one of the towns at the mouth of the river. I saw but few birds, & Mr. Rich & Dr. Pickering were equally unsuccessful amongst the plants. The soil is rather barren except in the delta of the Streams. No woods, but abundance of springs. Saw a quarry of basaltic columns, which the natives dig out and plant in various situations as a kind of Idol (as the interpreter explained to us "Devils"). They are generally left without ornament and about 3 feet above ground. A native was killed today at a village near us. He belonged to another village at war with them. The occurrence appeared to create little or no excitement. We were shown five pits in which as many had been recently cooked. They were laid upon their sides and the spears & clubs captured at the same time were formed into a kind of fence over the pots and the baskets in which the meat was carried were hung on them as trophys. A stone Idol dressed with *tapa* alongside. All our questions in relation to the feast were answered without hesitation. Saw several natives with gunshot wounds received in battle.

We have suffered much inconvenience from the arrogance of the 1st Lt. Mr. Walker who entertains great contempt for the operations of the Scientific Corps. Today when leaving the ship he ordered my assist^t Sutter out of the boat when we were leaving the ship, under the pretext that I had not asked his permission to take him with me. Sutter was sent on board by Capt Wilkes to assist me, and I had *presumed* a report to the officer of the deck sufficient. The circumstance was reported to Capt Hudson on my return and occasioned some little excitement, but as I deem the duty on which I have been sent by the government my first obligation, the wounded dignity of a subaltern shall not change my course while I can retain the support of higher authority.

[Peale's Journal ✳ 4 has not been located, and may have been lost. In the interval between June, 1840, and January, 1841, the squadron completed their survey of the Fiji group, and arrived in the Sandwich, or Hawaiian Islands, in September, 1840. Here the naturalists made many short expeditions. Early in December, 1840, the *Peacock* and the *Flying Fish* were ordered to leave Hawaii and to return to the Samoan Islands to re-examine some of the surveys made by the *Flying Fish* which Wilkes felt to be inadequate. From there they were to visit the little-known groups of the Ellice and Kings Mill Islands. (See text pp. 85–87.) When the new Journal begins they are endeavoring to reach "Clark's" Island in the Phoenix Islands group, enroute to Samoa.]

IX

South Pacific Revisited

T R PEALE

U S SHIP PEACOCK*18

SEA   1841   JANUARY

Friday 1st Still endeavoring to beat up to *Clarks Island* or shoal, in order to get some magnetic observations, it being near the magnetic equator, but for the last ten days, although we have had a fresh trade wind, it has a head for *us* and a strong current was always setting us to the westward, so that we sometimes could not make an eastward course of one mile per day. *Day* celebrated with church service in the morning, and a sermon written by some presbiterian in *winter* and not intended to be preached on the equator. A little better dinner than usual, and something to the health of absent friends.

Tuesday 5th Passed over four or five positions, where Islands are laid down which we supposed to be "*Clarks,*" only one remained, which was so far to windward that it was concluded to abandon the search, and proceed down the magnetic equator to the west. When we put about the ship went off gallantly before the wind, the current also being strong in our favour.

Sat 9th This morning made Enderbys Island in Lat 3° 6' S: Long: 170° 49' W. It is a low Coral Island not more than 10 feet elevation, about 5 miles long and ½ mile wide, without water or trees. After a running survey ar^d the Island we landed in 3 boats in the afternoon. Found great numbers of Birds breeding consisting of Frigates,* [No asterisked note given but supplementary comments added on opposite page.] gannets, boobies, Terns, etc. Obtained the eggs of each & one new species of Petrel. Returned on board before dark, when we stood off south. This is the first Coral Isl^d where soundings have been obtained ½ a mile from the shore, 200 fathoms, coral & sand. Whilst on shore today I found a Booby (Sula fusca?) which had lost its entire wing. The wound was perfectly healed, the bird fat and in good plumage, being fed as I sup-

---

18 Marked No. 5 on the outside.

pose *by others*, although an adult bird. Their food (fish) being caught by plunging from the air like Terns of course would prevent the cripple from helping itself.

*   *   *

Tachypetes. Here building on the ground a very slight nest, etc. Young with lt. brown heads.
Gannets. On the ground. One young very rarely 2. They are at first covered with a very white down the feathers than come out ashy, but *not spotted.*
2 species of Booby. on bushes nest very slight of Sticks only. Eggs greenish like the gannets, & covered with the same lining encrust^n.
Sterna Pacifica. No nest, 1 Egg. On a stone or drift logs or the ground. Egg greenish wh^te spotted with Chocolate.
St. Stolida? on the ground, 1 egg
St. fuliginosa
Procellarie 2 species
Golden plovers
Turnstones
Red tail Tropic birds.

*   *   *

Monday 11th Made Burney's Island and sailed around it. A narrow sand bar 4–5 feet above water ¼ of mile wide, and less than one mile long, affording nothing but a few scanty tussocks of grass.

Sunday 17th Made *Hulls*? or Sydney Island and i§ being to windward it took us all day to beat up to it, and consequently nothing was done untill

Monday 18th Two boats, one under Lt. Emmons, the other sail^g Master Baldwin left the ship with the Scient^c Corps, and landed on the S W end of the Isl^d while the ship and schooner made a running survey. The Island is of coral formation with an extensive Lagoon, the usual Botanic productions of the coral Islands, and great quantities of Birds, consisting of Tachypetes, 3 species of Sula, 2 Phaetons, Sternas fuliginosus, alba, cenisens[?], a curlu charadrius pluvi-

177

alis, etc. but not a single land bird was seen by us, but great numbers of rats. A small party of Turtle fishers have lately occupied a small cocoa nut grove, and were apparently very successful in Turtleing. We remained on shore untill the ship came round at 5 in the afternoon, the sea having risen we found more difficulty in getting off than we did in landing, and the day being the hottest we have experienced we all suffered with sun burns from the reflection from the white coral sand.

Nothing remarkable occurred excepting two or three heavy showers of rain, more warm weather, and some variation of wind. We searched for sundry islets which do not exist and on

Monday 25th At sunrise made the Duke of Yorks Island. Low coral formation with an extensive lagoon, without entrance. It affords abundance of cocoa nuts, and is in most places covered with trees. Three canoes* containing 30 natives came off to barter bringing models of canoes, fishing nets, lines, and mats, but no provisions. They did not come on board, and immediately pulled for the shore when we commenced firing for base. Three boats landed with the Corps, found the natives timid, but good natured. All the women and children fled in the canoes to the lagoon, and did not return excepting two or three very handsome boys. There was about 20 houses in the village, thatched with Pandanus, open at the sides, and the floor of earth raised 12–18 inches above the general level and covered with mats. Wharves six or eight feet high were built out into the lagoon, and near them very neat canoe houses. Canoes of several pieces sewed together, made light & neat. We saw no poultry or hogs, but several tame birds, being a plover, a Noddy and a Pigion (Col^a Oceanica). I saw no land birds, but abundance of Terns and other oceanic species. The woods swarmed with rats, which came out many at a time when the Natives commenced op^g cocoa nuts for us. There is no water but that which collects in hollows made in the cocoa trees, which we have always found sweet and good. I wish we could say as much for that in the ship.

These are the first natives we have seen who do not value tobacco, and seemed to know nothing about smoking.

They are a well formed, handsome & mild people. At 1 oclock we embarked and stood for the Duke of Clarence Is^d.

Thursday 28th The two days past we have been becalmed in sight of the Duke of Clarence Island, and today were enabled to get pretty close in. It is a low string of coral Islets surrounding an extensive lagoon. We saw no natives but one or two poles set up on the shore with nets flying on them. Made a partial survey, but did not get close enough to land, and an unusual wind springing up which enabled us to stand east, it

———————
* double

was too great a favour to let pass, and we accordingly took leave without landing.

Friday 29th Heavy rain, squalls & calms. Lt. Emmons having the morning watch reported that he heard breakers. It fell calm and very dark. We lay untill day light in a state of uncertainty, untill the dawn discovered to us an extensive Coral Island & lagoon. 18 canoes each with five natives were seen fishing with a long trolling rod in the stern of each canoe. They would not approach us untill two boats were lowered and went off with some presents when they were with some difficulty persuaded to come alongside. They had no arms and were a well formed, good looking set of people, rather lighter col^d than the Kanakas.

Three boats landed, through the surf, and most of the natives followed us, but we found we were about 3 miles from their village. After exploring the western portion of the Island we embarked to visit the village, but Mr. Walker concluded from the stormy appearance of the weather that it was best first to return on board.—During the night it rained in *"torrents"* (no rain gage on board!!!!) two or three days water collected.

Sat^y 30th Made a survey of the Island, and early in the afternoon Capt Hudson & the Scient^c Corps land^d at the town. All the women and child^n had disappeared, but about 200 men with the chiefs met us on the shore fronting the Town which covers the whole *islet*, they were very much alarmed until we set down upon the mats, placed on the shore. A tremendous Jabbering was kept up by *all* the Natives for at least half an hour. Mats & belts were given to all of us and everything done which they imagined would keep us in good humor and prevent our entering their town, but we soon got tired of sitting in the hot sun, and perambulated the Island. It is nearly circular, closely covered with cocoanut trees under the delightful shade of which their houses are built of an oblong oval form, slightly raised and on the sea side protected by a *dry* stone wall about 10 feet high. The thatch reaches to within 4 feet of the ground and the sides are left open for the free circulation of air. In the centre of the Islet is a well about 10 foot deep, and 8 in diameter, circular and neatly walled, the whole enclosed by a fence, showing that great vallue is placed on their small supply. They have great numbers of canoes protected by good houses, nearly 100 canoes were seen laying off in the lagoon, which contained the most of the women and children. A few of the former only were found concealed in the town. They were described as being quite beautiful and the girls quite full grown before they began to wear any clothes *all* of which consists in a mat peticoat which stick out widely at the sides. The town was beautifully clean, without fowls or any kind of domestic animals, exepting a few tame pigeons which we saw in and about the spirit house. A god about 12 feet high was enclosed in mats so that it was quite hidden from us, but there were many stools for it and *other* gods carved from solid pieces of wood. They were 4 leged, concave on top, oblong square 3 by 6 feet & 3 ft high. These were with many relics inside of the temple around the *centre* post which was 20 feet high, and at least 5 feet in diameter, perfectly smooth and round. The house was 50 or 60 feet long and 30 wide. In front was a cleared and paved space of twice the above dimentions over which the common people did not pass. In the centre of it was one of the *seats* for the gods, on which was a very large cassis and some other shells all held Sacred. Great numbers of rats roamed here undisturbed.

Fish hooks and everything made of iron or steel was in the greatest demand and but little vallue placed on cloth. They proved quite expert thieves in a small way, but their constant terror prevented any bold theft. They were very light col^d compared with the Sandwich Is^{ds}, well formed and regular featured with fine and slightly curled hair. The boys were really beautiful, a few being allowed to approach towards the last of our visit.

From many signs and a few words they led us to believe that they supposed we came from the sun. They were in great dread when we struck fire and smoked, remaining uneasy untill the segars were burnt out, or thrown away.

Whenever pleased with a present they would sing quite a lively and musical air, differing much in not being so monotonous as the airs sung by most other islanders.

Tatooing not general, but somewhat peculiar in the figures. The most general one is a square body with the *cross of St. George* [fig. 71]. These they have in a line across the breast, surmounted with fishes and Crescents, etc.

They were very desirous that we should leave their town, constantly telling us it was late. The sun was getting low & accordingly at 4 p.m. Capt Hudson gave the word & we embarked followed to the shore by a great part of the older men, who seemed greatly delighted at our departure. At night it again rained. The ship was put before the wind and we stood on our course South from the Island. The Scientific Corps addressed a petition to Capt Hudson to remain and give the *Discovery* a better examination, with time to make drawings, portraits of the inhabitants, etc. But he refused the request upon the ground that the ship was getting short of water.

Monday Feb. 1ˢᵗ This afternoon land was again seen, which although far out of place we suppose to be the island of "handsome poeple" disc^d by Quyros in 1606, and not since visited. Calms, squalls & heavy rain all night.

Tuesday 2^d Cloudy & squally nearly all day, so as to make the survey of the Island unsatisfactory, and we were obliged by the weather to stand off during the night, but with the intention of returning to complete the survey and land the Scientific Corps.

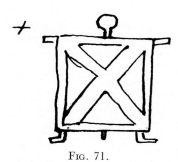

Fig. 71.

Wednesday 3^d By some bad management in the officer of the deck* either designedly or otherwise, notwithstanding the weather was squally, with showers and thick weather, with a heavy sea: three boats with the Scientific Corps were started for the Island when the ship was about 5 miles off, & having a current against us it took us two hours hard pulling to get in near the reef, which we coasted for some distance without finding a safe place to land. Lt. Emmons, Mr. Rich & I were in one boat, Mr. Baldwin & Mr. Dana in another. Mr. Davis, Mr. Agate and Mr. Hale in the other. Mr. Baldwin was the only one who attempted to land and in doing so his boat parted from her anchor and was dashed with great violence high on the reef, but fortunately going end over and alighting on a smooth place she received no material injury and our boat being manned by Kanakas, they swam to the assistance of the stranded crew while we lay at anchor outside. By diving they recovered the anchor and cable of Mr. Baldwin's boat which enabled him on the rise of the tide, to pull out by the aid of a line from Mr. Davis's boat outside the breakers.

Our Kanakas obtained a few excellent Cocoa nuts, but saw no traces of inhabitants. The island is nearly circular, the lagoon filled up and overgrown with weeds & bushes, but the outer rim of the Island covered with large trees. Scarcely any morning birds were seen, which is very singular and unaccountable unless they have been driven away by the great number of enormous land crabs, which we know to devour the eggs and young. These crabs are larger here than any we have seen elsewhere, and the birds are fewer than they are even where inhabited by men. Alternate showers, a hot sun, and heavy sea with a long pull before we could again reach the ship made it an extremely uncomfortable day for us, and the getting on board after we had reached the ship we found both difficult and dangerous from the heavy Sea. The whole *landing* was illy advised, and I regret having a suspicion that there was a little *malice* at the bottom of it.

Sat^y 6th Yesterday we found ourselves half way between the Is^{ds} of Savai and Upolu, the wind failing us we lay there for the night and this morning fitting out

---

* *Lt. W. Walker*

boats to survey. This afternoon two under the charge of Lt. Perry left us and a fresh sea breeze setting in we entered the harbour of Apie before four oclock. The Missionary Brig—Camden was lying at anchor having been in about 3 weeks from Sydney. No canoes or natives came off, it being their sunday, but sundry inquiries were made for their old friend, the "good shot," a cognomen I find they have given me.

*   *   *

Manutang⎫
mamitagi ⎬ The young of Ptiln[s] purpuratus?

g — by the adopt of orthography of the Samoans is pronounced ng as in Pango-pango—spell[d] "Pago Pago" a harbour at Tootooillah Is[d].

*   *   *

Monday 8th Yesterday and today it continued to rain heavily with some thunder, etc., notwithstanding which Mr. Rich, Mr. Agate & myself accomp[d] by Dr. Guillou started on an excursion across the Is[d] about noon. The delay of engaging an interpreter and four native carriers delayed us some time but we finally after much wading of swollen creeks and a thorough drenching from the incessant rain, we reached the village of Susinga about 8 miles from the ship. William Cowby the interpreter, and my carrier Papau are the same who accompanied me on my former excursions in 1839. It was too wet to shoot birds & I was obliged to be content in collecting land shells which are abundant particularly a large species of Succinea, and one or two species of Cyclostoma. The susinga was stop[d] in the "public house" and found thru my old friend the chief priest of the "Gimblets" who reads (pretends to) his religious services from an old book, much thumbed, which he readily exchanged with Mr. Agate for a better one. It proved to be the *Rambler*. It has for several years answered the full purposes in his estimation of a *Bible*. The whole village, men, women and children collected around to satisfy their curiosity, which was not in the least abated by their seeing the necessity of our changing to an entire suit of dry clothes. We had lines stretched in the house on which an attempt was made to dry the wet ones and fires made to dry our caps, handkerchiefs, etc. A "Siva" or dance was got up for our amusement while our pig and Taro underwent the process of a native oven, and after supper a "Siapo" or mosquito bar of tapa was hung over our mats and we tried to rest, but unfortunately we had no other than Native pillows—thick pieces of Bamboo raised on legs—and they proved little better than neck breakers to us for the want of early practice.

Tuesday 9th Had the remains of our pig recooked, it being nearly raw last night, and about 8 oclock we started across the mountains. It rained in torrents so that nothing could be kept dry and we could see little or nothing off the path, on which we had to look for foothold rather than plants, Shells, or anything. It

was the same road I passed in 1839 so that I did not regret it so much although it was raining then but not so hard as now. Reached the south coast at Lotofanga about 5 in the afternoon, but having taken the precaution to send two of our men forward they had purchased a pig and cooked it that we might dine before dark having neglected to bring candles with us, we were now in a Christ[n] village and of course had to return to rest without witnessing another "Siva."

Wedn[y] 10th Lt. Perry & Mid[n] Blair in two boats joined us. They had left the ship previous to our entering Apie, but from incessant rains have suffered much and done little surveying. Not liking our quarters on acc[t] of the extortions practiced by the chiefs, we all removed a few miles further west to the village of Satona, where we spent the day and night. A few strangers being in the *Town hall,* we took up our quarters with the Chief, but went to a dance at the town hall at night. Rained all day & night.

Thursday 11th Started in the first clear weather we have yet experienced, but it was of short duration. It soon commenced raining and we had our wet march as usual for about 17 miles to the village of Farisolá, where our reception was not of the most hospitable character. We had some trouble to purchase provisions, and there was much reluctance in spreading us a mosquito curtain, etc. and in the morning

Friday 12th we found they had stolen Mr. Rich's spectacles, a knife, etc. Mr. Rich began to load his pistol, and sent after the Chief, but the alarm was taken, all the men disappeared, the spectacles were returned by the women, and we departed leaving them to find the knife as their only reward for our lodging, etc., paying exorbitantly for the few fowls we purchased. Our course now was north across the Island again in a heavy continued rain. We had a long tiresome journey of 17–18 miles and lodged at the village of Tufulali, where we purchased a hog and received excellent entertainment and found them very hospitably disposed towards us.

Sat[y] 13th Continued our route in the rain as usual to Waiusco, the residence of our interpreter Mr. Cowly. Here we embarked in 3 canoes and arrived at the ship in time for a late dinner. All harrassed by a most uncomfortably Journey by which we gained little or nothing by reason of the continued heavy rains. My legs broke out in numerous and troublesome boils which confined me to the ship the remainder of our stay in Apie, in which time we had the only clear weather.

Tuesday 23d Left the harbour of Apie with the ship, the Schooner being absent surveying the E end of the Island, our destination being Saluafata to punish them for the murder of an American Seaman. The town is about 8 miles east of Apie. The chief refused to give up or punish the murderer when the Brig Porpoise was here last year on her way from the Feegees to the Sandwich Isl[ds].

Wednesday 24th Becalmed nearly all day and could

not succeed in reaching Saluafata bay untill late in the afternoon, but a few Natives were visible in the Town and no canoes appeared.

Thursday 25th A canoe from the east end of the Is⁴ boarded us. It contained two whites and several natives who had been detained by the Saluafateans last night for fear of their pilot⁸ the ship in. The Schooner Flying fish came in during the night. After breakfast all the boats were maned, and a few broadsides of round & grape shot were fired from the ship into the town.* The boats then landed the men in three divisions and fired the Town which was soon destroyed.¹⁹ They then went to "Salalesi" and "Fonsi" two other towns under the government of the Chief of Saluafata, they having promised to assist him in case of our attacking his Town, the whole were soon reduced to ashes without a shot being fired, all having fled on the first appearance of the boats near shore. The whole being accomplished without accident we weighed anchor and left the Bay at dark. A carpenter, an American shiped from an adjoining Town, his life having been threatened by the Natives. It blew a gale while we crossed the reef going out of the harbour and for a short time the ship was in some danger. It was excessively warm all day. In the sun the therm* rose to *150°* in the shade it was 95°, water 87°.

---

* on which about 70 men who had remained untill then fled to the woods.

¹⁹ This is another example of police action taken by the squadron for the protection of whaling and other commercial vessels. Hudson interviewed the chief of the village of Salufata on the twenty-first, demanding that the murderer, Tagi, be given up. "It was distinctly stated to Sangapolutale [the chief], that the murderer must be either punished or given up, in conformity to the regulations adopted in their fono, composed of all the principal chiefs in the island, and that if neither of these stipulations were complied with, Captain Hudson would be compelled to employ the force under him in burning the towns that concealed and protected the murderer, and set their own laws and us at defiance.

"Three days were given him from the time of the interview, ot comply with the demand. He promised to do what he could, but he was fearful of the result, as his people wanted to fight, and had been promised aid from many quarters.

"On the third day, his messengers arrived at Apia, and brought word that the chiefs and people were determined that the murderer should not be given up or punished; that they defied the Papalangis [white men] and their power; and that, if Captain Hudson chose to come and take him, they would give him a fight...Captain Hudson now saw the necessity of taking some steps that would check this criminal and audacious spirit, and prove to the natives that we had the power to punish these aggressions on our citizens....The missionaries also saw the necessity of doing something to insure the safety of those who may hereafter have communication with the natives, by renewing in their minds the fear of our power....[The attack and burning described.] This act was performed with great reluctance, and not until the most perfect conviction of its being absolutely necessary to secure the safety of the crews of such of our whaling fleet as touch at this island, as well as to restore the respect due to our flag and those who sail under it, and to correct the erroneous opinion, that our forbearance was the result of fear of their prowess and numbers." Wilkes, *Narrative* 5: 25–32.

Friday 26th Sent a boat into Apie for Tubo a chief to pilot us into a harbour at the Is⁴ of Savai. He came off in the boat late at night. The natives at Apie express satisfaction with our operations yesterday at Saluafata. They report one man dangerously wound⁴ in the arm by one of our grape shot. Their intention it now appears was to wait partly in concealment untill our boats landed when in the confusion of disembark² they were to rush upon their crews and slaughter them; but unfortunately for them, they found no concealment which could protect them from our shot, and their hearts failled when they saw our men cooly and without noise advance and set fire to the houses as though no defence was expected.

Sat⁹ 27th Still lying too off Upolu. One boat under Lt. Emmons and the Schooner dispatched on secret service last night. Two more under Lt. Walker today.

Sunday 28th Still in the same position waiting for our boats. Weather clear and warm during the day & frequent showers at night. Lt. Walker & Dehaven returned after dark, but without the Chief Mariatoa, who we now learn they went to bring off as a hostage. The natives were suspicious of the object and armed to the amount of about 70 with muskets, and Mariatoa disapeared during the night. I think it not to be regreted as any act of treachery on our part will lead to the destruction of confidence which is of the greatest importance.

Monday March 1st Squally & much rain. Still laying off and on Upolu.

Friday 5th Since Monday the weather has been Stormy with much rain and westerly winds. Yesterday it cleared and the winds being more favourable we ran into the achorage at the town of Matautu in the Island of Savai. A few natives came off and brought a present of Tortoise shell bonnet from one of the Missionarys to Capt² Hudson. Preparations were commenced to survey the *road stead*, harbor it cannot be called. The shores are densely lined with Cocoa nut trees, and the mount²² being 4 or 5000 feet high the Island presents a very picturesque appearance.

The Schooner passed here the day before yesterday, having probably missed the anchorage.

Sat⁹ 6th Parties landed to water ship, trade for provisions. It being the Sabbath of the Christian portion of the inhabitants (about half) they of course brought no provisions or anything else to sell, but the Tutiauris (heathen) sold us yams, tarro, hogs, fowls, spears, clubs, etc. The landing is bad, a heavy surf constantly breaking over the reef. Several boats were badly stove. Here as at other Islands of the group we find the natives errant beggars, and coveting everything they see, but remarkable as it seems, seldom stealing. All the houses are provided with their favorite Pigeons (Col² Oceanica) and we constantly met the indolent chiefs on the paths, each with his bird perched on a stick, and fastened by one leg with a long string to the extremity of which it was allowed to fly, being taught to return to the stick on a jerk of the string, this being the whole amusement of those overgrown children for whole days, the pets being their companions even in their carousing. It being a clear day—quite unusual at this season—I was very successful in collecting lepidoptera. The Schooner came in and anchored last evening. In the afternoon we weighed anchor and left the Island.

Sunday 7th Calm. Savai still in sight. The usual sermon, etc. and in the afternoon a breeze springing up, we were enabled to lay our course N W for the Kings Mills Islds and soon lost sight of the Samoas.

Saty 13th

Sunday 14th Having crossed the 179th degree of west Longitude a day has been dropped to balc the acct of time to agree with *space*.

We are now close in with Ellis's group of Islands, a coral group of low islets covered with cocoa palms, etc. The Peacock took the north side and the Flying fish the South and made a running survey. While firing to measure base previous to beginning which, two canoes came off but only one succeeded in reaching the ship. It contained five natives whose language bore a close resemblance to the Samoan. They were however tatooed in a very different manner from them. The figures on the arms and body being mostly triangles thus [fig. 72] being transverse on the body and longitudl on the arms. They were about the Stature and color of the Samoans but had more beard on the mental prominences. Two sharks teeth knives, and other curiosities were obtained from them in exchc for fish hooks & Iron.

Monday 15th Stood under easy sail for the night, and this morning were of Depeyster's Islands, but the weather set in squally with heavy and abundant rains, and westerly winds, which kept us all very uncomfortable untill

Thursday 18th When the wind again came round to the S E and we once more made the Depeyster Islands. A number of canoes came off to us and the natives

FIG. 72.

FIG. 73.

came on board without hesitation, being particularly desirous of obtaining plane irons, spikes, or any *Iron*. Their canoes were neatly made of small pieces of wood sewed together with cocoanut sinnet which unlike those of the Samoas exposed the sinnet on the outside.* Paddles [fig. 73] generally of two pieces, handle & blade spliced, spears armed with sharks teeth. Sea stock of water in cocoa nut shells neatly hung. Mats worn round the waist belted with a strong coarse hempen looking strap, some with cords. One woman came off. She was tatoo'd like the men but dressed difft having two wide fringes of bark, one like the Viti "Legu" worn round the waist, the other above the breasts. She did not paddle or assist in any labour. The men were well formed intelligt looking, much tatood on the arms & body, wear their hair in long filld roles and have few ornaments. They brought on board some *tarro* which is very remarkable on a coral Isld because thus far we have not seen one affording sufficient fresh water for its cultivation.

*   *   *

The natives were *all* affected with a species of Leprosy, it occasioned their skin to peel off in small flakes, like the effects of sunburns, but it did not appear to incommode them in the least.

An albino came on board, his eyes were *blue* and his beard red; had it not been for several dark spots on his back I should have suspected his being of European decent.

As it was many of the sailors insisted that he was an Irish man, and the test they proposed was to offer him a glass of whiskey.

*   *   *

A good ship entrance was discover'd to the Lagoon, with anchorage in 20 fathoms. A running survey was made by the schooners being sent round the south side while this ship took the N. Joined company at dark, stood our course, and by next morning all traces of the Islds were lost on the horizon.

Great numbers of Velella abound in this portion of the ocean, many hundreds being in sight at the same time. About 200 were taken in a hand net in less than 2 hours, amongst them was a few of ianthina which were feeding on them.

Sunday For two days it has been so nearly calm that yesterday we made but 10 miles. This morning it rained *heavily*—about 500 gals of water were collected in 2 hours by a gain sail about 15 feet square (it being the only rain guage on board.)

Sunday 28th The wind has been from the Northward & westward for this week, consequently *ahead* for us going to the Kings Mills Islds. The breezes however have been light and the weather clear and pleasant, so

---

* The out riggers of these canoes are made usually strong and the cross beams with a natl bend.

much so as to enable the crew to clean and air the ship, paint the iron work, guns, etc. We have seen several Islands, and on Wednesday 24 discovered one not on the charts. It lays in Long^e 176° 25′ 30″ East of Gr. Lat 6° 19′ 30″ S^th. It is a low Island covered with cocoa and other trees, apparently without a lagoon, and is inhabited. It is only 1¼ miles long and 9/10th of a mile wide. Made no attempt to land on it being sufficiently satisfied as the *Discoverers*!! We however made a running survey by which others can find it and give *us* some knowledge of its inhabitants & productions etc.

Sat^y 3^d April At sunrise were in sight of Drummonds Island. It was a low shore covered with cocoa & other trees, and almost lined with houses, some of which were very large. Fifty-five canoes were counted under sail towards us, a small portion of which only succeeded in coming alongside. The canoes were 12–15 feet long, 18 inches wide, and about 2 feet deep. The outriggers placed about 10 feet from the canoes, being lashed only in the middle. They were built of small pieces of wood [fig. 74], some of them exceeding two inches wide, and were sewed together with cinnet and some bark but very little considering the number of small pieces with which they are made. Sharp at both ends. Their paddles were very bad, some being only pieces of (pinna) shells, tortoise ribs or avicula, lashed to the end of a short pole. The sails however were very neatly made of mats, shoulders of mutton shaped, two beams, and a short mast mostly made of several pieces of wood lashed together. The men all wore mats protecting their stomach, but not covering their privates. This prepuce from long practice in pulling it was very long. They were neat tatood in curved wreaths, on the arms, body and thighs [fig. 75]. Many wore conical caps and some helmets made of the porcupine fish, and one had a cuirasse of thick matting curiously made with an elevated process to protect the neck from their sharks teeth, swords & spears. Several women were in the canoes. They wore no dress excepting a fringed belt of grass.

The articles brought to trade, were mats, poultry, yams, *molasses*, cocoa nuts, and tarro in return for which they were eager for tobacco only, a half onze being prefered to a knife. Many had frightful scars, although there was nothing in their appearance which indicated their being very *savage*. Colour about that of the Sandwich Islanders.

A shoal of Porpoises were around us this morning. They were about 6 feet long, black, dorsal fin long & curved, snout very blunt. They differed from any we have seen. They did not come in *striking distance*. No birds, but a great number of flying fish.

Monday 5th In laying off on Sat^y night we were swept by the current & wind to the S.W. and were not able to regain our position untill today. On nearing the Island the canoes came off to us as before, many

FIG. 74.

FIG. 75.

came on board, and some proved themselves adepts at thieving. The sides of the Ship became a perfect Babel while they remained, and a brisk trade was carried on for cocoa nuts, fish & curiosities. We crossed several shoals and finally anchored in—fathoms about 3 miles from the land; after sending boats to search for a better anchorage, or harbour. Several fish were bought which we have not before seen. The Natives refused almost everything in trade but tobacco which they sought with the greatest eagerness, some *eating* it immediately but generally it was stored with great care in small baskets or in the pockets made in their caps, and in case both had been traded away then it was placed in the folds of their belts. None covered their privates, whatever dress was worn.

Tuesday 6th Landed with three boats and all the Sc^e Corps. The tide being out we had to wade more than ½ a mile, its rise & fall being 6–8 feet. Found numbers of natives, both male and female fishing on the flats, some with long lines fringed with pandanus leaves used like a Seine, but only to drive the fish into their nets, small Seines & scoops. We were peaceably received and led to the public house, a large building 70–80 feet long by 40* thatched with pandanus leaves, the ridge pole & rafters being painted with black bands & points, the ridge ornamented with *ovula* Shells. Chests made of cane were arranged all round, about 20 ft apart, floor covered with cocoa leaf mats. The dwelling houses were parallelagrams also of about 14 by 20 feet, the eaves reaching to within 4½ feet of the ground at which height a floor was run across forming a garret in they slept. The lower part was clear of incumbrances and covered with coarse mats. But few were armed and they willing to sell anything for tobacco including arms, consisting ray spine pointed daggers, sharks teeth swords & spears, etc. Mr. Rich and I crossed the Island and found that the north side was not inhabited. It is less than half a mile wide consisting entirely of coral sand and very sterile, affording but little other vegetation than cocoa nuts & pandanus. Tarro & api are both cultivated in pits 6 or 8 feet deep, excavated at a great cost of labour, and the supply very small, and the plants less in size than usual in Polynesia. Water in wells about 15 feet deep, free from salt but of a rather vapid taste. The coral belt or reef on the north side at the point we visited was about 300 yards wide on which a heavy sea was breaking, beyond it no reefs or land was visible.

We did not see any musical instruments, but their singing was pleasant and their actions in dancing much like the Viti's. We had no further proofs of their being canibal, than some unequivocal signs as we had no interpreters.

It was stated that we should find here the widow and child of the Captain of an English Whale ship, which was here wrecked a few years since and all the crew murdered with the exception of the two above mentioned. We saw pieces of "wreck" used in making their canoes and the Natives showed us iron hooks & copper from a ship. Some appeared to know nothing about the woman, but others represented that she was dead, but stated they did not kill her, but from what we saw the food alone was quite sufficient, being only cocoa nuts, fish & pandanus nuts. The fibres in the latter appearing in their excrements in such quantity as to make them look like chopped old cow rope or the balls voided by owls, even the husks of young cocoa nuts are eaten. Two or three fowls only were seen, but no signs of hogs, and but a few dogs & one or two cats.

I did not see or hear a single land bird in the days ramble, but on the shores curlew, some golden plovers and turnstones, besides a few "Noddys" and White Terns. Many whales bones were scattered over the Island.

The men on shore go entirely naked wearing only a necklace. The women wear a fringe of leaves reaching to the middle of the thigh from the lower part of the waist. Girls to 10 naked, to 18 wearing a small fringe of leaves about 4 inches square fastened round the waist by a cord of human hair. All the females wear their hair long and hanging loose over their Shoulder. It has a very slight curl in some but is generally straight.

As we saw no timber on the Isl^d it sufficiently accounted for their not placing any value on tools.**

---

* by measurement it proved 45 by 116.

** This island although but 25–30 miles long and nowwhere 1 mile wide, we estimated to have a population of about 3000, which I think is entirely within bounds. Here we found the first true Tridachnea gigas. They were used by the natives as troughs for sundry purposes around their houses. Some were of enormous size.

Wednesday 7th Numbers of canoes visited the ship, and a brisk trade was carried on for cocoanuts & curiosities. In the afternoon Capt Hudson with four boats landed at the same place we landed at yesterday. Their reception was apparently as friendly, but it was soon obvious that there was some treachery, and previous to their return one of the men (John Anderson) had wandered and could not be found.[20] The natives were very impertinent, and some stones were thrown at P^d Mid^m Davis & a party of men who were sent in search of the missing man, but as no other proof was given of hostile intentions on the part of the Islanders, no violent measures were deemed necessary at present for his recovery, and the boats returned board.

Anderson was armed with a musket, pistol, and cutlass, and it is supposed by some of the party that had he got into difficulties the report of his arms would have given notice of it. My opinion is otherwise. I feel very certain that he has been decoyed into some of their houses at a distance from the boats, his arms secured, & he butchered to secure his property.

Thursday 8th All the boats out surveying, numbers of canoes came from the west end of the Island and a brisk trade was carried on for cocoa nuts & curiosities. The natives appeared to know nothing about our missing man but gave their neighbours of the east end of the Island a very bad character, none of whom visited us all day, but one canoe came from a neighbouring town and on enquiries being made for Anderson, they immediately left the ship, but we sent a boat in pursuit and soon brought them to. They represented that he was still alive on shore, & they promised to bring him off in the morning.

The Schooner has been round the Island with two of our boats since we anchored here, and returned today. They represent the natives as having acted very treacherously towards them, stoned the two boats but did no mischief. A shower in the morning but the rest of the day clear, with a S E wind. Numbers of human teeth and bones were procured today, made up into various ornaments. One bracelet that I purchased contained 473 teeth, which must have been taken from about 16 persons probably slain in war. Their thievish propensities are such that today I saw them stealing from each others canoes while trading alongside.

Friday 9th Receiving no intelligence of the missing man Anderson we are now fully satisfied that he was murdered by the Savages on the 7th, therefore chastisement was indispensable for the security of the numerous whalers who visit the vicinity of this group. Accordingly 7 boats with about 80 men were fitted out and started for the village Uteróa where the murder was committed. We started about daylight, but having four miles to pull, we did not arrive there untill after sunrise, and when the tide had began to fall.* We

---

* The schooner weighed anchor & removed further in shore in order if necessary to cover our retreat.

[20] See text p. 87 for a fuller discussion of this incident.

found about 500 natives armed and on the shore to receive us flanked by several hundred more behind the fences, and above & below the town. About 300 waded off towards the boats with the intention of forcably draging them ashore. A short parley was held and we demanded the lost man, but they treated the demand with contempt, brandishing their spears and swords to taunt us on. A rocket was directed into the midst of them, and it seemed to create a momentary alarm, but they soon rallied and advanced in the water to the attack. An effective shot was but a slight check, though a volley from all the boats startled them into confusion, and we were enabled to land by wading and form into three divisions: Marines in the center. I was in the left division with Lt Emmons and while the men were forming had occasion to single out two chiefs rallying their warriors to the attack. The shots were both long rifle range, the last being 217 paces and both fell dead in their tracks. This was too much for warriors who heard the sharp crack of a rifle for the first time. They were at first incredulous about the death of their leaders, but when once satisfied they would not suffer me to approach so near again retreating as we advanced. The town was soon reduced to ashes, with a number of canoes, and a great part of their property, as the probability of *our* being the visitors appears never to have entered their minds.

No projectiles were used by them not even stones. They seemed to depend entirely on their sharks teeth spears and swords. Many of them were clothed in cinnet armour,[21] and shirts and trowsers of the same, with fish skin helmets, but they disencumbered themselves of the armour on the retreat, probably from having seen balls fired through several on board ship in trial a day or two since. After the distruction of the town consisting of several hundreds houses, when the parties were rallying to embark, the Chief (unarmed) of the next town came to assure us of his friendship, and beg us to spare him exalting in the defeat of his neighbours whom he said were a bad people, and justly punished. Many of his people during the time of the interview were plundering all that we had spared and by the time we had waded off to our boats about ½ a mile, the ruins were crowded with these kind neighbours.

We regained the ship about 2 o'clock. Canoes in numbers had been off to her all the morning trading, and expressed delight in witnessing the flames, after they had been assured that it was only Utaróa which was destined to destruction. We estimated the killed today at about 20, as in the onset they carried off the dead & wounded, only 6 being left on the ground.*

---

[21] Armour made from sinnet and the skin of porcupine fish. One example is included among the Wilkes Expedition artifacts at the Smithsonian Institution.

* None of our men were hurt which we may consider fortunate considering the numbers of our Savage enemies. Not less

Immediately on regaining the ship we got under way followed by the schooner.

[A loose page inserted in this journal gives a supplementary account of this episode:

April 9th, Drummonds Island (Sergeant Forbes's acct) The Boats approached the shore in three Divitions, Lt. Walker Comg when within 100 yards from the shore the 1st Cutter grounded. Lt. Walker came alongside and held a conversation with Lt Emmons relative to the duty of Attack, etc. at the same time Lt. W. observed to Mr. Peale that the conduct of the natives was so grossly insolent and that no satisfaction could be obtained in respect of the Fate of Mr. Anderson that he would make another effort by means of Mr. Hale which if ineffectual he would make Signal and that Mr. Peale in his opinion would serve the cause of Humanity by using his Rifle on the Most prominent of the Leaders of the Hostile party who were at this time within a short distance of the Boat, in fact one had come close enough to the Bows of the 1st Cutter to touch it with his Spear, gesticulating with vehemence and Slapping his posterior, backed by a Rabble of Men and Boys who defied us in all possible ways, on Signal from Mr. Walker, Mr. Peale selected an object one of the most conspicuious and made a Dead Shot. A Rocket was discharged from the Boat amongst a multitude on the Shore which apparently consisted of at least 500. It went far to the centre, three men fell and was carried off when a general discharge from the Boats took Place in the 1st Cutter. Lt. Emmons made one Subject bow the Knee. From my observation there was at least 10 carried off severly wounded. 3 shot dead. We landed all the disposable force when they fled like chaff before the wind, leaving their Town and Council House unprotected, parties of them at times coming to show their Valour which in several cases resulted in wounds or Death for their temerity, amongst our oppenents was a number of Small Boys 8 or 10 years of age, after landing, with no foes to employ us we turned our attention to the Town and gave them such a House Warming that all the lots became vacant, the whole attack and Retreat was conducted with the deliberate coolness that reflects credit on the Officers and men engaged.]

Sat^y 10th Found ourselves close to Sydenham or Bishops Island which we surveyed. It is a coral Island without a lagoon like Drummonds, about thirty miles long, and not over a mile wide, and less thickly inhabited than Drummonds. Several canoes came towards us but at a time that was not deemed proper to stop for them and they could not succeed in reaching us. Their canoes were constructed of very small pieces, and were rig^d like those of the last described. A few Boobies and large "Schools" of blunt-nosed Porpoises were seen, and on one small Island we saw quite a large town where there was not a single tree, which is very remarkable here, where cocoa nuts contribute so largely to the subsist^ce and comfort of mankind.

I found it quite a task to pack & secure the curiosities collected at Drummond Island, the collection being far more numerous and bulky than we have made at any other place, in all constituting 18 small bales, amongst them about 40 lbs. of "wampum" Necklaces & belts, etc.

---

than 800 of whom were visible to us, at the same time that we saw them rallying from all points on the burning of their beacons, which were small houses built on piles over the water at telegraphic distances along the shores.

Sunday 11th Calm, two Islands in sight but the schooner being too far astern in the afternoon when a breeze sprung up, we had to abandon the survey which was commenced untill morning. It rained heavily before day break but the day was dry & pleasant, with a few scattered clouds. Saw a "shoal of Blackfish" a few Boobies, and several flock of Noddys.

Monday 12 Surveyed Hendervilles Isl^d. A few canoes came with a woman and two or three men in each came on board. The women were rather pretty and the men all young. The most desirable objects to them were tobacco and whales teeth. They quitted the ship when we commenced firing for base.

Tuesday 13th The weather unfavourable for taking angles in the morning at Halls Island, and afterwards the schooner from misunderstanding signals, was not available, consequently the survey was lost. A few canoes came off but the natives were afraid to venture on board and left us on hearing the report of fire arms discharged by the Armourers.

A number of fish seen (Scomber?) but no birds. Numbers of Vellela floating around the ship, many of them dead. Halls is a lagoon Island.

Wednesday 14th Returned to Halls Isl^d and finished a survey of it. Canoes around but too timid to venture on board.

Thursday 15 Surveyed Hopper & Harbottle Isl^ds. Two boats were lowered to survey Hoppers Is^d under the charge of Lt^s Emmons and DeHaven. They found a ship entrance to the lagoon with good anchorage in 4–6 fathoms. Lt De Haven landed and was civily rec^d by the natives who appeared without weapons.

Friday 16th Spent in surveying Woodle Island, in the afternoon a number of canoes came off, with both men & women who came on board without hesitation. Amongst them was a white man named John Kirby left here by an English whaler.[22] From his acct he was guilty of mutinous conduct, and deserted from the ship. Has been here about 18 months. He was desirous to be taken on board and Capt Hudson consented. The separation between him and wife was not remarkable for feeling, but he told her he intended returning. Kirby's acct of the Natives is that they *eat* their enemies killed in battle, carry the skulls of their fathers about with them & talk to them. (Those taken at Uteroa were much worn). They tap the cocoa tree tops for toddy, and boil it for molasses, etc. Fathers & Unkles synonimous, both allowed the privilege of cohabiting with "daughters in law," or wives of their sons. Polygamy allowed. At war with Drummonds and Sydenham Islands. In battle all males killed, females kept as concubines, infidelity in females punished with death—those comeing on board ship not having been married except to Whalers.

Sunday 18th After "church" occupied in a survey of Gilberts Island, found that Gilberts, Knox's, &

Islands were in reality joined, and but one Island in the form of a crescent with a lagoon open at one side. The land is all low, covered with Cocoas, Pandanus and a few other trees, and well inhab^d.

Monday 19th Surveying the open side of Gilberts Isl^d entered the crescent which is about 18 miles from point to point, 30 fathoms water gradualy shoaling to 3 about 4 miles from shore. No attempts were made to land, but one canoe load of Natives ventured on board, bringing nothing but cocoa nuts. They wore nothing but a mat in the form of a belt and were frightened away by our guns while measuring base by sound. Weather changeable & showery with "squalls" from these.

Friday 23d Surveyed Matthews & Charlottes Isl^d which were found to be connected by a reef, or in fact but one Island, with a very extensive lagoon.

Sat 24th It was determined to land early this morning, to take some dip and intensity (Magnet^c) observations, therefore the members of the Scient^c Corps have a small chance of relief from idleness, and the first L^t issued his orders to the boats, running thus, *2d cutter, Lt. Emmons will take 10 water bags, 2 buckets, 1 shovel & Messrs Hale & Peale.* One at Sandalwood bay was worse,—"bring off the yams, hogs & scientifics." Owing to the ships having drifted off during the night, we were not able to regain the land untill afternoon, when four boats land^d at one of the small Islands where we found a few families of Natives, who were very much alarmed but did not leave the Island. Their houses were built like those of the Drummonds Islanders (with a loft) and thatched with pandanus leaves, etc. Little other vegetation was seen than Pandanus & cocoa trees, and a few small plants found on most of the coral Isl^ds. A few shells which I was enabled to find differed from those of the other groups which we have visited. Pterocera are numerous, and quite distinct, but much resembling the variety figured by Sowerby. Planaxis, & nerita were abund^t on the rocks, but it was not easy to find full grown Specimens as the children have been constantly cracking and eating the largest. Found 2 species of Cardia, and abundant remains near the native houses of Tridachna gigas, and Hippopus, the latter being all "*bombé.*" I killed a new species of Pelidena, and found large flocks of curlew and Turnstones, the latter now in full plumage in dense flocks & very fat, evidently migrating, but in what direction I could not ascertain as they followed the course of the reef.*

The Schooner while we were on shore entered the lagoon and stretched several miles to the S along the reef towards another entrance but unfortunately gr^d and remained fast untill the next tide. The natives discovered her situation, and made signals to the small Islands around by fires, blowing conches, etc. and a few canoes approached her in the evening, but nothing

---

[22] Kirby was turned over to the British Consulate upon arrival in Hawaii. Wilkes, *Narrative* 5: 110.

* Did not see any insects on the Island, but seven leaves were observ^d which had been cut, probably by a species of *Lozotania.*

further occurred untill day light when about 25 canoes approached while the crew were engaged in wharping her off. A few shots however put them to flight and the schooner joined us outside in safety. The Peacock in the meantime laying too, drifted 20 miles in 8 hours of the night and also grounded on a shoal but without becoming fast, or receiving any damage, the sea being smoother to that in the morning.

Sunday 25th We had the usual church service & sermon, and thanks returned for our escape.

The natives told us while on the Isl^d that there was another Island to the northward called Merica stating to be one days sail in their canoes. Our course was accordingly shaped in search of it, but the wind and current both being against us, we did not reach it untill

Tuesday 27th When we found it to be Matthews Island of Duperry. It is a coral Is^d with the usual lagoon, without a sea entrance. Made a survey of it and from the ship could see nothing remarkable in its vegetation or appearance. Sev^l canoes came off towards evening only three of which succeeded in overtaking us. They could hardly be persuaded to come alongside. They brought nothing to trade, but were anxious to obtain iron hoops, placing no value on tobacco.

Thursday 29th Commenced an early Survey of Pitts Island which we reached yesterday. Its appearance was precisely the same as most of the lagoon coral Islands heretofore visited of which it is one of the largest being about 20 miles in length, and thickly inhabited. Many canoes tried to overtake us but going before a brisk wind, they could not keep up with us, although their canoes are the best built that we have seen amongst the Kings Mills.

On reaching the leward end of the Island in the afternoon 18 or 20 canoes came off towards the ship, containing from 5 to 10 persons each, and with them a white man clothed in mats. The ship was hove too, to take him on board, when he proved to be a Scotsman who was left here by an English whaler about 7 years since. His excitement was such as to render the poor fellow very incoherent at first, and occasioned some amusing scenes, as sometimes he would talk to us in the Native language and then to the natives in English, at other times repeating our sentences, as though he could not realize its being his native language striking his ear for the first time after years.

Seventy or eighty natives came on board. They were at first fearful but on being assured of our pacific intentions, they became quite at home, so much so that it was not easy matter to get them to leave the ship on the approach of night when we wished to make sail. There was no women with them, and the men were the handsomest we have seen, all stout and well formed, the chiefs being enormously fat. They wear their hair and beards long, mostashios & "imperials" neatly trimmed, teeth very regular and white, tatoo like long net trowsers reaching to the armpits, belts, capes, caps, neatly wove from very white prepared Pandanus leaves, hair pins like the Viti's.

Iron nails, spikes & hoops were the great object of the visit.

Gray—the new Robison Cruso who is kept on board, says that they have treated him kindly, and for the first few months carried him about on their shoulders, he being the first white man that many of them had ever seen. He says they have no wars, and few arms, that they seldom quarrel, and then always about the women, the chiefs having from 50 to 100 wives each, which of course leaves many of the poorer people without any, and they therefore commit transgressions which are always punished with death.

The Island abounds with fish, but no quadrupeds of any kind exepting rats.

Mr. Rich, Lt Perry and I landed on a small Island at the entrance to the lagoon. In the channel we found 4½ fathoms of water, the opening not exceeding 500 yards in width.

On the Islet there was a few fishing huts around, and under the eaves of which were arranged large shells of Tridachna gigas, to catch water. Rats were running in all directions. White Terns, and Noddys were breeding in a small cluster of trees, a few moths were flitting amongst the weeds, but nothing else remarkable was seen, and as the sun was setting when we landed, and the ship some miles off our stay was but for a few minutes.

Friday 30th Placed on a reduced allowance of provisions and water.

Wednesday May 5th This morning made the eastern-most of the Piscadores, of which the day was spent in a survey. It is a mere coral reef with two or three small islets but a few feet above the water on which numerous Pandanii & a few Cocoas grew. The form of the reef is that of a crescent, open to the westward. Many miles of the reef is on a level with the sea, not inhabited.

Since leaving the Kings Mills the weather has been pleasant, with a strong "trade wind" from the northw^d and eastward. Passed to windward of the Mulgrave Islands in the night but through—groups having—Arrowsmiths Island under our lee.

After finishing the survey of the east Piscador, we stood westward to the other, which having made before night, we beat off & on to windward in order to begin the survey in the morning. It was very squally with slight showers during the night, making necessary to call "all hands" to reef topsails.

Thursday 6th No land in sight, day cloudy, strong easterly winds and heavy sea, necessary to keep the ports closed. No birds but great numbers of Porpoises playing under our bows—their lateral lines of a whitish colour shape of snouts and dorsal fins bearing a close resemblance to the true Dolphins, none however were caught, as they moved with much too great velocity for any of our harpooners, as we have none of any skill. Made land towards night but before morning.

Friday 7th Nothing like land to be seen. Still a heavy

sea, but the wind moderate, with passing clouds. Made the land and in the afternoon a canoe was seen standing for us, we hove to for her about 7 miles from the Island, but soon discovered that she had put back, as I suppose from finding the sea too heavy & the ship too distant, as night was approaching. The schooner was sent in closer, but no canoes were to be then seen. We therefore obtained a further "offing" and stood before the wind to the westward and lee end of the Island, which we again reached in the afternoon of

Sat^y 8th But at a part which was not inhabited; at least we saw no signs of inhabitants, and as there was no cocoa trees, it was a pretty sure indication of their abscence.

Base was measured for a survey with the Schooner; soon after which Mr. Knox was called (by signal) on board and received orders and we then parted company, our ship steering N by W, thus abandoning the search for Captn Dowsett supposed to be detained by the natives, a portion of his boats crew having been murdered by the Natives of this Island some years since, when his vessel sailed without being able to confirm his death and the visit of a whaler in the vicinity since tending to create a belief that he was still amongst them, from the natives having informed the Captn of the whaler that a white man by the name of *Sam* was living with them on shore. Captn D's name was Samuel; his wife and child are now living in Honolulu, whence the interest taken to have us visit these Islands to recover him.

Sunday 9th Still holding our course N ½ west the nearest we can lay to a brisk trade wind towards Oahu, having abandoned our intended visit to the Island of Ascension from the lateness of the season and a want of provisions.

Sat. 15th We are now in Lat 26° 42' 4" N, Long^e 168 26' 300" E. The weather has been clear generally, but rather variable, and the temperature sensibly cooler, so that our half all^ce of water is found sufficient, by economy. (Therm^r 71°—10–12° cooler than whilst we were at the islands.) The water is much more abundantly filled with Mollusca and numbers of Janthina were seen today, and a very large Petrel, much like the Pr^a gigantea.* It had a white [?] and some light col^r about the base of the bill, which was pale yellow, General col^r of the bird sooty black; extent of wing about 4 feet or more. A few Noddy were also seen. Last evening we saw them in larger flocks, fishing.

Thursday 20th Nearly calm.

Lat. 28° 12' 16", North, Long^e 176 49 40 East. Great numbers of Janthina—fragilia? around us. A few Petrels (Shearwater) and the Short-tail Albatross, several

of which I shot but as they are exceedingly tenacious of live we succeeded in getting but two specimens in dif^t stages of plumage. The adults have the head, neck & belly white, wings and tail dusky black, back gray ?, bill lighter col^d than the young bird which I obtained. (See No. 590)

Friday 21st A large "shoal" of Sperm whales passed near us today and appeared greatly to enjoy the feast of Janthina, and Pentalisma which abound.

Sat^y 5th [June] Nothing remarkable has occurred of late. Th weather untill now has been quite cool, the therm^r indicating as low as 65 with a very humid atmosphere.

Today saw a ship standing across our track to the Northward. Finding she would not wait to speak us we fired a gun, which she answered by standing down to us and proved to be the whale ship Magnolia of New Bedford, 6 days from Oahu, and Commanded by Capt Barnard. He gave us about 400 gallons of water and some potatoes besides a few newspapers as late as the 11th Nov^r /40 by which we learned the election of Genl Harrison as President of the U.S.

Monday 14th Made the N W part of the Island of Oahu at a little past 8 a.m. and rounding the western end of the Island were for a short time becalmed under the lee of the mountains. Early this morning a large "shoal" of Blackfish (Delphinus___) kept us company while sailing 6 knots. They soon however dropped astern and left us.

Tuesday 15th Found ourselves this morning after beating all night nearly in the same position that we occupied at sunset last evening, about 12–15 miles directly to leeward of Honolulu. Purser Speinden and Lt. Perry were sent in a boat to notify the Consul of our arrival and wants; but in the afternoon he came on board with our letter bag and refreshments, etc. We continued to beat up and regained the Harbour of Honolulu, early in the morning of

Wed^y 16th when we found that the Vincennes and Porpoise had left here for the Columbia river on the 5th of April last, expecting to find us in the Columbia river waiting for them.

Capt Wilkes had succeeded in establishing his observatory on the summit of Mauna Loa, and was successful in all his observations.

The King Tameamea arrived from the Island of Maui, just as we dropt anchor, and was rec^d by his people with a salute of 21 guns, and military honors.

Found the foreign residents even more hospitable than on our former visit, never dined or supped on board while we remained. Made a visit to the top of Diamond hill, to visit its extinct crater which we found like a smooth meadow, & covered with dry grass, no boulders or stones. Succeeded by dint of hard labor in getting all our provisions and water on board and sailed again.

Monday 21st Much to the delight of the Kanakas of our crew who were in great dread of being discharged, as most were from the Vincennes, their appearance

---

* *Sunday 16th* I have now had a better view of the Bird which still continues to follow us, and find it agrees better with the description of the Short tailed Albatross. Diom^a brachyura Lesson traite d'Ornith^e p. 609. [R. P. Lesson, *Traité d' ornithologie, ou tableau méthodique des ordres, sous-ordres, familles, tribus, genres, sous-genres et races d'oiseaux,* Paris, 1831.]

while in port was a pattern of meekness for the rest of the crew. A fresh *"trade"* wind soon carried us clear of the Islands, with much less sickness amongst the crew & officers than might be expected from being restored to full allowance and total change of provisions.

Thursday July 1st Lat. 38° 47′ 18″ N, Longitude 157° 47 West. The weather has not been remarkable, until today when the thermometer fell to 57°, a degree of cold which to us *feels* severe. Few birds have been seen, and they have consisted entirely of the short tail Albatross (D. brachyura) and one or two species of Petrel. One of these is the white Ullica[?] Phalaidrona seen south of the equator. This afternoon passed over immence winrows of Pentalisma of the same species seen when going to the Sandwich Islands.

Sat 3d Passed immence quantities of the remains of Vellela, driven in "winrows" and covering the surface of the ocean. Most of them appear to have been eaten by the innumerable quantities of Pentalisma.—A small portion only of the Vellela appear to have escaped their voracity. Lat 41° 51′ North, Longe 156° 6 W Temperature of air 53, water 54.

Sea unusually calm, occasioned by the immence quantities of Vellela?

Sunday 4th Still passing innumerable Vellela, Thylavoi, etc. Temperature of the air 50, water 53°. Lat 43° 4 N, Long 155 W. Saw quite a large flock of what I at first supposed were "tringae" but they lighted in the water and swam with all the facility of Ducks, hence I suppose them to be *Phalarope*. At the same time there was large flocks of Guillemots* swimming in the sea. The species is as large as the *black Duck* (Surf D) and have a white breast, fly when roused very much like Ducks. Several short tail Albatross around. Air heavy, sun nearly obscured. A very large shoal of Porpoises came around us; they were of two species though keeping in the same shoal. The largest was a true Delphinus having a dorsal fin, and was about 5 feet long, of a dark lead color, with a bifurcate white line on the side. The other was a Delphinoturus having no dorsal fin; was quite black with a narrow white line along the belly; it was about 3 feet long, and looked very much like a seal. They both moved with great velocity and frequently leapt quite out of the water.

Tuesday 6th It has now been nearly two days calm. The vellela have disappeared. We crossed upwards of

---

* Uria—————

200 miles of sea, entirely covered by them. Today a large shoal of "Black fish" passed us. They were from 20 to 30 feet long entirely black, had a medium length of *dorsal fin*, tail much ancuated, and the hind parts of the body much attenuated and compressed. A few Petrels (Thalasidroma) and Albatross (D. brachyura) about us.

Late   44° 11′45″ N
Long 153 53′ 30 W

Therm.	morn	noon	night	water 54
	53	57	54	
Barom		30	40	

Atmosphere humid, weather hazy.

The cool weather gives full occupation to the players of the Fiddle, drum & triangle, and the heavy shoes and nothing to the comfort of smokers. When the forge ceases, then the shoes begin. I can't say they "trip it on the light fantastic toe" the crew dance the *Whole Horse.*

Saty 7th First obtained sight of land, and in the afternoon distinguished Cape Disappointment, the northern promontory of the Columbia river. The wind died away and a thick mist envelloped us, so that it was deemed prudent to stand off again.*

Sunday 18th Found that the schooner had drifted during the night far to the northward of us. Stood off, after getting Close in with the land, and Captn Hudson read us the usual church service, and a sermon—most of us were fearful we should loose the tide, but

---

Interrupted by the wreck of the ship; see notebook No. 6, p. 14 for continuation. TRP

[See text pp. 88–89 for a description of the shipwreck. After the wreck Peale was assigned as a member of an overland expedition under Lt. Emmons. Altogether the party consisted of thirty-nine persons and seventy-six animals. There were four officers and eight men plus five men from the Scientific Corps (Dana, Peale, Brackenridge, Rich, and Agate) from the squadron. In addition there were six trappers and a guide as well as three settlers, their wives and children. The journal (№6) begun immediately after the wreck was lost on September 22, 1841. The next journal, №7, begins on that date.]

---

* Saw a number of Cormorants, some large Sharks, and large shoals of very small fish.

X

Oregon And California

T R PEALE[23]

U S SHIP VINCENNES

Dec[r] 14, 1841

1841–1842
Sept. 22–Feb. 19

SEPTEMBER 1841

Wednesday 22[d] Crossed the Umpqua mountains, they are about 3000 feet elevation (from the plaines), very steep and covered with Spruce and Lamberts pine trees, with a thick undergroth of Arbutus, Dogwood (Cornus Nuttallii), etc.

The days Journey was a most arduous one although we gained but 16 or 18 miles. One or two horses fell down the steep side of the mountains with their packs but were recovered with some little delay. The bag containing my bed[g] and wardrobe was torn open by the brush and carelessness of the men in charge, and the case containing my drawing instruments was broken and all the instruments, my sketch book and Journal lost—with all my notes and drawings from the time of our landing in Oregon after the wreck of the Peacock; a loss the more serious by reason of my being destitute of the materials to continue my observations.

Encamped on the south side of the mountains before night, at which time only I became acquainted with my loss; the men restoring a *boot* picked up in the road.

Thursday 23[d] The party were delayed today, to allow me time to try and recover my Journal, etc. I returned over the mountains with two men (Wood & Black). I succeeded in finding my camera lucida only, and continued searching untill afternoon, when meeting some Indians in the path concluded it was useless to search further, and that my books and the remaining instruments and paint-box were irrecoverably lost. We searched the quivers and baskets of the Indians who were much alarmed; but their language being unintelligible to us, it was requisite. These Indians are known by the name of *"Rascals,"* and were the first of the tribe we saw. They have always been considered hostile to the Whites, and justly entitled,—though but little intercourse has ever taken place. They were armed with bows and arrows (with flint points) with which they kill Elks and Deer, etc. which abound in the mountains, but their principal food, to judge by the *signs* must be berries and roots. They appear to be scattered in small family parties over the country and have no houses, tents or permanent residence, their only shelter being made of grass thatched on hoops about four feet high, and only capable of holding 4–5 persons sitting—or prostrate.

The Umpqua mountains abound with Elk (C. Canadensis). I killed three, day before yesterday, our buck measuring five feet around his neck midway towards his head; the horns 4 feet 4 inches each. These are the only measures I recollect, having lost a detailed description with my notebook yesterday. The body of the animal was about the size of a horse. He was the leader of a herd of about a dozen, and this being the rutting season, I was led to the herd by his *neighing* which is not unlike that of a horse. It is called "whistle[g]" by the hunters, and can be heard about the ¼th of a mile. I shot the "old buck" first, and my shot passing his lungs he went but a few paces and laid down on the side of a mount[n] ravine. The rest remained and I killed two does, but unfortunately had to shoot several before they fell, as they stood close together, and merely changed places when I fired from the opposite slope of the valley about 140 Yds off.

Getting impatient at their remaining after I had shot as often as I wished, I imprudently ventured across to them, thinking they would run away when I appeared. All did so excepting the "old buck" shot first,—as I thought dead but as he could not see me untill I had climbed to within 12 or 15 paces of him, he then rose, looked up the steep side of the mountain, then at me, and his wound being severe, he seemed to conclude it was easier to use his enormous antlers than

---

[23] Marked ⚹ 7 on outside. After the overland trip from Oregon to California Peale was assigned to the flag ship, the *Vincennes.*

it was to use his legs in climbing—particularly, as about this time he must have discovered that I was the author of all the mischief amongst his does. Fortunately for me, there was some large pine trees behind which I found shelter when he plunged at me, there he stood keeping me at bay. A deliberately aimed rifle ball I thought would be sufficient to settle matters, but it seemed as though it had produced no effect, other than to make him rush on so quick as to get between me and the trees. I ran for "good life" down the mountain, and could hear him plungeing as I thought with desperation after me—the crashing did not cease for several seconds. I reached the bottom and stopped to get breath, and met Walker one of our fellow travel[s] attracted by the report of my rifle. We returned and found the animal *dead* having *rolled* down the mountain after me, the ball having gone through his heart. Meat too rank to eat, excepting the marrow bones and tongue.

The Umpqua mountains are the southern limit of the *"White tail"* Deer. (C leucurus) Here we kill[d] the last as predicted by the hunters who were familiar with the route. They were here replaced entirely by the *"Black-tail,"* which north of this we have seen only on rocky mountain ridges.

Friday Sept. 24th Started soon after sunrise, crossed rolling prairie land bordered by round[d] hills covered by Lamberts & long leafed pines, yews, spruce, cedar and Arbutus trees, with a thick undergroth. Saw frequent signs of Indians, but generally they were hid, or fled from us, a few were just seen in the dist[ce] and in crossing a mountain covered with thick bushed three were found secreted by the path side. They were betrayed by a miserable half starved dog who was mistaken for a wolf and shot at. Other Indians were heard calling from the hills to our left.

Saw numbers of Lewis's Partridge (Perdix Lewisii)* in flocks of from 30 to 40. They are exceedingly wild and the most vigorous of the genus. Besides them we saw today Goldenwing woodpeckers (red var.), Ravens, Crows, Stellers & Florida Jays, Californian Vultures, and a few Larks.

The country was mostly burned by the Indians. We traveled seven hours, and halted on *Youngs river* (creek) in a burned prairie, little or no food for the horses. Along the creek were numerous signs of Indians, old camps, etc. where we generally saw piles of Mussel (Unio & Anodon) shells which seemed to indicate that such formed a considerable portion of their food. Even snail shells (Helix Nuttallii) were found in piles where they had been roasted.

*Lepus (glacialis?) longicaundatus Gray.*** Many Hares were seen, both in the prairies & brush but generally in the latter. They rarely entered burrows (not their own) and in running carry their Ears erect, make 3 short and one long leap. Length (total) 2 ft. tail 5

inches, head 4 inches. Ear 5 9/10 inches long 2 inches wide, eye ¾ inches diam, light brown with darker radiations from the pupil. Foreleg to elbow 6½ inches; hind foot to heel (oscalius) 5 inches, to the knee 5½ inches = 10½. Circumference of the chest, 1 foot. ♂ still suckling her young.

Sat[y] 25th Being imprudently encamped on the banks of the creek the Indians last night approached within a few yards of our tents, under cover of the bushes. In their retreat a small, neatly wrought net bag was left. It contained cooked roots.

Started at 9 A.M. and continued our course over burned woods and small patches of prairie, abounding in black tail Deer, which we could not succeed in killing notwithstanding there was much firing at them. Indian tracks numerous though but few were seen. Reached and crossed "Rogues river" before night, pitching our tents on it South bank. Some Indians approached in canoes, but were not suffered to enter the camp. The river was at the camp about 90 yards Wide, and three feet deep with a gentle current, and an even, gravelly bottom.

Ignace (an Irraquois Ind) went out to hunt, and killed a buck; but while he was busy skinning it, he was attacked by about 20 Indians, with arrows, which he described as striking all round him. He remounted his horse, firing a shot from his rifle amongst them first, and then retreated at full speed to camp, arriv[g] just at dark.

The night passed without alarms, the woods here consist of Lamberts, and a long leaved pine besides two species of oak. On Lamberts pine we saw a few cones; one (old) measured 15¼ inches long, and 18 ¾ inches in circumference. (A very large species of gray squirrel feeds on them and like the ground squirrel seeks refuge in holes in the ground, leaving the trees when alarmed.) The gum or resin from the wider part of this tree where burned is sweet, and tastes like manna which it resembles; it is also a gentle purgative.

Sunday Sept. 26th Saddled and mounted at 8. Saw a few Indians behind trees near our path, who finding themselves discovered, came out professing friendship. We saw others and in one place about 50 were together on the bank of the stream up which our path led. The day was uncomfortably warm, although last night it was piercingly cold (47°). We frequently experience a difference of 40° between noon and night. Crossed the first granite rocks.

Several of the party have had recurrences of the ague, and today we had to halt & encamp when we had proceeded but twelve miles in consequence of Mr. Rich's being too ill to proceed.

Our camp was fixed on the scite of a former one on the banks of the river, where Mr. Young with a party of nine men were defeated a few years since by the Indians.[24] Many of their bones now lay bleaching

---

* plumifira Audubon.

** Loudons Magazine Vol. 1 New Series, p. 586, 1837. Brackman Journal A N S Vol. 8, p. 83.

---

[24] Drury, Clifford Merrill, in *Diary of Titian Ramsay Peale,* 39, makes the following note concerning this:

"H. H. Bancroft, *History of Oregon,* Vol. 1: 95–6 tells of a around our fires. The white people on that occasion suffered the Indians to come into the camp in great numbers (more than 100) who professed friendship, but who waited for an unguarded moment to attack the few whites and would have succeeded in killing all of them to obtain their property, had not a gigantic iron-framed fellow (Turner) laid about him with a tremendous firebrand, keeping back the naked assailants, untill his red wife brought out his rifle, when the Indians retreated with considerable loss. 2 whites were killed on the spot, & two died of their wounds after returning amongst the Umpquas.

(Some of our volunteers were of the above party.)

Some Indians appeared on the other side of the river and called to us, but did not attempt to approach. Another was hid nearer to us, and his Dog came searching for him, and was shot by a worthless vagabond of our party (Wood) before he could be prevented.

Monday 27th The night passed off quietly, although the yells of Indians close by us were constant untill midnight. After breakfast, we started at 8 oclock. Saw Indians on the opposite side of the river running apparently with the object of cutting off our passage across a rocky promentory covered with brush. The place was favourable to an ambuscade, and as there was no way to avoid it, we prepared for hostilities. All but a guard for the baggage, women and children who brought up the rear, dismounted to use our rifles with most effect, but on approaching a few savages only were seen retreating up a mountain on the opposite side of the river, and we passed without molestation.

Our course was nearly N E up Rogues river for about two hours, when we struck off southwesterly through a pass in the mountains and reached extensive plaines, where we saw three *mounted* Ind^ns who fled on our approach.

Today we saw the first antelopes (Antilocapra Americana) and succeeded in killing one from a herd of five. Hares were plenty, and we saw numerous places constructed for catching them, consisting of long hedges constructed of thorny brush, with openings left where snares were set (without springs.) The snares were made of a substance like hemp, neatly twisted.

Deer snares are set precisely in the same manner, but on a much more extensive scale, and the animals, being more cunning (I am informed by the hunters of our party) it becomes necessary to drive them in, which is accomplished by a whole tribe uniting to encircle a considerable district of country.

Encamped on the margins of a small stream, & the plaines being all burned, had but poor provender for

our horses. Some of them gave out during the march, but overtook us at the camp; atmosphere loaded with smoke.

Tuesday Sept. 28th Soon after starting this morning Messrs Rich and Colvocoresses were both taken sick, with fever, Mr. C. became delirious, and was unable to ride. Dr. Whittle and a small party of us remained with them as a guard, this being the most dangerous part of the country—where the natives are most numerous and avowedly hostile. It was necessary to deprive Mr. C of his arms, and to proceed in very short and easy stages untill we overtook Mr. Emmons at night.

The country was much the same as that already passed, excepting that we have a high mountain range on our left (estimated about 3000 ft). It was crowned with granite rocks, a few masses of which lay scattered about the prairies. Passed a sulphureous spring containing very small quantities of soda. Indian signs were numerous, though we saw but one, a squaw who was so busy setting fire to the prairie & mountain ravines that she seemed to disregard us. Her dress was a mantle of antelope or deer skin, and a cup shaped cap made of rushes. She had a large funnel shaped basket, which they *all** carry to collect roots and seeds in. The day was oppressively warm and we saw no game, which led us to suppose that Indians were numerous in the vicinity, and some anxiety was felt, as we expect to reach the "bloody pass" tomorrow. Several of our party have been engaged with the Savages there, and one of them (Tibbets) was dangerously wounded when attempting to cross with a small party who were defeated a few years since.

Collected a great variety of seeds; amongst which are two or three species of Aenothera, and a new sp^s of Nuttallia, having purple flowers. Saw but few birds, Sylvia siabi (Mexican variety) being the most common. They were in flock.

Wednesday Sept. 29th The sick were able to proceed again this morning, but Mr. Colvocoressis soon became worse as the sun gained power, which obliged us to make several halts before reaching the bloody pass. The rocks over which we climbed today were sandstone containing organic remains. One or two mount^ns on our left appeared as though cap^d with basalt^c columnar rocks, but they all proved to be of sandstone. Probably those we took for granite yesterday will prove to be of the same formation. Country everywhere overrun by fire.

Passed the dreaded "Bloody pass" without difficulty and without seeing an Indian, only a few of their tracks, and after surmounting a high mountain ridge, a view of Singular grandeur was spread before us. On our right the mnts were burning, and sent up immence masses of smoke. On our left was the snowy summits of Mount Chasty (Tchasty?)—extensive plaines were in

---

party of eight (*sic*) men who were attacked at the Rogue River in the summer of 1835. Bancroft writes: '... four of the number slain, the others with difficulty escaping.' In 1836 a different party under the leadership of Ewing Young was also attacked by the Rogue River Indians in September while driving a herd of cattle to Oregon. Calvin Tibbets, a member of the Exploring party of 1841, was with Young. Peale has confused the two incidents."

---

* Women of all ages, and of all the tribes in Oregon & California.

front of us. In decending we had to cross rugged sand-stone ridges covered with *red* cedar, and Buckthorn bushes. Soil barren and arid. No game, only a few wolves seen, and we had a hot and thirsty ride of about 20 miles to the Tchasty river, near to which on a small branch we halted for the night. Bread and tea only for supper. Although we saw no animals or birds, we found many curious plants and gathered their seeds. Several species of Oriogonun were conspicuous.

Thursday Septr 30th Remained stationary today in consequence of the illness of Messrs Rich and Colvo-ceressis, each having a recurrence of the ague with violent fevers following. Mr. Agate and I wandered a few miles up the river, no game, no timber, and an arid country. River about 80 yards wide, very rapid; shores lined with a strong groth of Rushes, something like salmon seen.

Washed clothes, cast balls and put up seeds.

Friday Octr 1st Started earlier than usual to cross the Tchasty, or Klamet river about two miles above our camp. It was about 3 feet deep, gravelly bottom. Had a hot dry and wearisome Journey of 20 miles over arid prairies, without finding water untill we reached a branch of of the Klamet, which we crossed and after-wards encamped on another about 10 yards wide, having a rapid current of clear water 3 feet deep. The prairie crossed today was surrounded by naked barren looking mountains of about 200 feet elevation. Our camp is surrounded by a great number of conic piles of bare porphyritic rocks varying from 50 to 100 feet in height—Saline encrustations along the ravines.

Saw a few herds of 12–18 Atelopes, but they were too wild to be approached.

Californian quails (Perdix Californianus) were very abundant. No shot to spare for such small game. They are found only along the streams.

Some Indians were encamped near us from whom we purchased a few salmon, for buttons. No timber near us larger than small brush of willow and a species of birch. One crane (Ardea herodias?) and one or two mallard were seen on the creek.

Sat^y Octr 2^d At ½ past 7 crossed the stream, and continued our route over dry plaines abounding with Antelopes in herds of 12 or 15 each, but too wild for our larder. Only a Black tail fawn could be obtained. The atmosphere was smoky and our views obscured. As we advanced the prairies became more arid and desert. Here and there were green patches near deep waterholes. One of the horses in attempting to drink was entirely submerged, and it became necessary to draw him out with cords. Saw a number of new plants, and a species of Bartonia with Pale sulph^r yellow flowers. Saw a few curlews, but no other birds, and after travelling 18 miles reached a small branch of the Klamet, just where it left the mountains, and en-camped, several of the party being sick. The thermom-eter indicated 90° in the shade, and at night 40°. Prairie wolves (Canis latraus) were numerous. Just after camping six Indians joined us. They were dressed

in deer skin with the hair on, belted round the waist with an ornamented hide belt, and "raw hide" mocka-sins. Hair long and without ornament, one or two had deer skin mantles; and one of the number was afflicted with leprosy. Their arms were bows and arrows, the latter having very neat points of volcanic glass. After shooting for us and receiving a few presents, they were dismissed before the night.

The summits of Mount Tchasty presented a beauti-ful view from our camp when its snow was illuminated by the pink rays of the setting sun, while the base re-mained invisible to us.

A herd of mountain sheep (Ovis Montana) was seen by one of our hunters, but none killed.

Sunday, Octr 3^d Crossed a spar of the Tchasty mts at about 2000 feet elevation, from which we had beau-tiful views of the snowy regions on our left and some beautiful granite peaks. Decending the opposite slope we reached the head waters of the *rio Sacramento* about noon, having crossed what may be called a nat-ural boundary of California.

Our days Journey was not more than 15 miles, all the way through open pine woods, recently burnt and in a few places still burning. A fine black tail buck was killed in excellent condition. Just changing to "blue." The horns were thinner and sharper than the white tail and I think more spread.

Monday 4th Ground white with frost, caught a spe-cies of *Arvicola* 6 ⅛th inches long; tail 1½ inch, lead col beneath; brown and black hair mixed on the back; ears nearly covered; eye small black; teats 4 ing (4 pect),—hind foot ¾th of inch long; teeth raw cienna col; tail cov^d with short glossy hair; feet d^o except the palms whiskers white & black.

Road hilly, and through pine timber, and like that of yesterday much burnt. Many of the trees are large, measureing about 22 ft in circ^e. None that we saw ex-ceeded 25 feet. Abundance of small grapes were found near the small streams. I killed two deer on the road. A great variety of plants were found differing from any we have seen, some of the annuals were beautiful. Rocks volcanic, trass. Stopp^d at a *Soda Spring* strongly impregnated with carbonic acid gas, Iron, and some of the varieties of soda. It was sparkling, and very re-freshing. Some of us drank plentifully of it without exper^g any bad effect. The horses knawed the harsh earth and rocks, and appeared very fond of the water. After traveling 15 miles we encamped at a point where the Sacramento was joined by a branch from the west. It came from high peak^d and broken mountains re-sembling those on Staten land; they are very steep and interspersed with strata of light colored rocks, which yesterday I reported as snow.

Tuesday Octr 5th Wood, a volunteer hunter was missing last night. After we had proceeded a few miles this morning, we found him waiting for us, having proceeded too far ahead to return to us last night. He had killed a doe & was not in want of provision. One horse was lost belonging to Tibbets. The road today was the worst yet passed. It was over a succession of mountain ridges, and ravines, over granite rocks, and through woods of pine and oak, and across numerous small streams emptying into the larger branch (Sacramento), the tortuous course of which we are following. We saw many fine springs, and in one of them a new species of Saracenia was found with leaves one or two feet long, besides a greater variety of singular plants than we have yet seen. It was a botanic harvest. I saw two species of marmots, and several birds not seen before. Sev¹ Californian Vultures, etc. and after hurrying on 22 miles we encamp⁽ᵈ⁾ in a rocky dell near the main stream, now increased to a respectable size.

Wednesday Oct. 6ᵗʰ Our road as yesterday, over rocks and mountains, deep ravines. The several of the sick left on the route. Passed several old Indian camps, at one there were several new graves, over which were bundles of provisions and near by on a stump a bundle of Salmon.

The stream is now about 30 yards wide, with a succession of rapids; the water 2 or 3 feet deep, and very transparent. I left the party to hunt alone, but falling in with a party of five Indians, who secreted themselves as soon as they saw me, and as it was near dark, I did not like their movement, and returned to the party, encamped on the river, without holding intercourse with them. One of our hunters saw several more on the river below our camp fishing for Salmon, which must have been numerous earlier in the season, as quantities of dead ones now lay along the rocky Shores. We saw the remains of fences and wiers for catching them.*

Cinclus

I was so anxious to see the disputed habits of this bird, that I lost this opportunity of securing the specimen.

Thursday 7ᵗʰ By requisition of Dr. Whittle we remained in camp today on account of the sick. The well ones occupied the time in gathering seeds, shoeing horses—and eating grapes,—but no game was killed.

Friday Octʳ 8ᵗʰ Started at the usual time, although Dr. Whittle protested against it, as the sick were thought unable to endure the fatigue. We crossed the river three times, to avoid two of the highest and worst mountains on the route. They are about 3000 feet high, and very rocky and uneven. The road we took was bad enough, along the shores of the river, over almost a continual mass of porphyritic rocks which were very angular and sharp; and in crossing the stream over round, smooth bolders, and rapid waters.

After traveling 13 miles we came to a pleasant valley with open oak groves, and abundance of grass for the horses. There we pitched our tents, and being destitute of meat, all the hunters started out. I killed three dear, but lost one of them. Meeting one of the horse guard I sent one carcase into camp for supper, and on my return reported the other to Mr. Eld with a request that men might be sent for the meat, but Mr. Emmons considered the report *informal* in not being made to *him,* and refus⁽ᵈ⁾ permission to the men to bring the meat. I therefore gave directions to the camp followers²⁵ (Wood & Mrs. Warfield) who consequently were better supplied than we were.

Satʸ Octʳ 9ᵗʰ Crossed the river several times to avoid mountain ridges, but still had to cross some, and a few very rocky ravines. In crossing the stream where it was very rapid, with a slippery bottom of large bolders a little Indian girl (Eliza) belonging to one of the camp followers, fell from her horse and would have drowned, being but 6 or 7 years of age, had not Dr. Whittle jumped off to her rescue. The current was too rapid even for him to gain a footing for some time, and other assistance became necessary. The advance portion of the party waited for upwards of an hour after crossing a mountain untill we learned the cause of the delay.

Many deer were seen, but only one was killed. Bear signs plenty.

Sunday Octʳ 10ᵗʰ Two and a half hours travelling over stony barren hills, brought us clear of the mountains, a wide plaine before us with open groves of oaks, and along the river cotton wood and willows. Sun very hot and the plains dry and dusty. In the ravines or dry beds of gravelly streams saw Bartonia's and a number of new plants, tobacco amongst them about 5 feet high with long white tubular flowers, the stems & leaves viscous and offensively odorous.

We halted early in the day on the banks of the river, and were visited by a number of Indians, who were entirely naked, wore long hair, and were unarmed until they found we wanted to trade for bows & arrows, which they make with great neatness, particularly the flint heads. They don't use quivers but carry a bundle of arrows in the left hand.

We purchased some cones of a new species of pine from them, the seeds of which are excellent eating, also both dried and fresh salmon. These Indians had no houses, but were living in mere brush camps, perhaps only for the Salmon Season.

Hares (Lepus glacialis?) are very plenty, sev¹ ran through our camp.

Eagles, crows & ravens abundant, though but few small birds were seen.

Monday Octʳ 11ᵗʰ Our route today was over undulating ground, with open groves of oak and buckthorn brush, and the poorest soil we have yet crossed, being

---

* While sitting on the bank of the river today near a pebly bar, I was agreeably surprised by the appearance of a Species of Cinclus. It was nearly black, and when sitting on the rocks was constantly "jutting" its tail, while its body was nearly horizontal. It clearly and distinctly walked on the bottom *under water,* where it was 6 or 8 inches deep, down the side of our rock, and up an another, out again without any apparent effort to rise or sink. The rocks were covered with moss, and there was many aquatic plants on the bottom.

²⁵ I.e., the party of hunters and settlers traveling with them. See text pp. 91–92 for Emmons' account of this day.

little more than coarse angular gravel; which has lamed most of our horses. Saw no game. Crossed one or two small streams in the morning; afterwards had no water untill night—when we again reached the Sacramento, now a still, deep and rapid stream, 140 yards wide. We travelled about 25 miles, and saw several yellow billed Magpies for the first time.

Tuesday Octr 12th Made but a short uninteresting march of 10 miles, forded the river opposite two islands with channels of 140–60—and 80 yards wide; the water reached above the girths, and was so rapid that it was as much as our horses could "stem" (broadside they would have been carried down.)

Game abounded, Elk, Antelopes, deer, and Bears: 6 Grizzly Bears and two deer were killed, and one black bear seen.

Wednesday 13th The wolves were so bold last night that they entered our camp and carried off a fresh bear skin from the side of a fire, and within a few feet of a tent. Numbers of Californian Vultures, Turkey buzzards, and Ravens were assembled this morning to enjoy the feast we have prepared for them.

Our Journey was dull and uninteresting, about south, over prairies (generally burnt) and through open groves of oak. We have seen no pine or spruce or any conifers since leaving the hills. We met with a few Indians gathering acorns. They were naked, excepting the women, who wear a fringe peticoat. Now and then we saw men with a wolf or deer skin, with the hair on, Slung their shoulders.

A number of Antelopes and a few deer were seen, but none killed, having abundance of meat left. One of the pack mules fell from a bank about 10 feet high, with the river destroying such portions of his pack as were valuable—Sugar, Tea and gunpowder, belonging to a camp follower (Wood). Birds more plenty, saw today—

Yellow bill^d Magpies	Sand hill Cranes (Grus Canadensis)
Mallard (Anas boschus)	Herrons—Ardea herodias
Sune D A Sponsa	Egrets —— —— egretta
Cormorants Carbo ——	Little E. —— —— Pealii?
	Rusty Grackles Quicala ferug^a

Ravens have been around every camp since we left the Columbia river. A pretty cluster Rose grows abundantly along the banks of the river. It is probably an ever blooming spe^s as we frequently clusters of fragrant flowers, & plenty of ripe seeds.

Thursday Octr 14th Our game this morning was 1 buck Elk, not fit to eat, and a Deer. The road was over a level prairie with oak groves and willow ravines; very dry and dusty now, but evidently covered with shallow ponds in winter. By refusing the information of the guides, much time and distance was lost, as we were obliged to return nearly to where we started from, after several hours travel.

The weather was cloudy and chilly being particularly unpleasant for the sick. Indian trails numerous, though none were seen, excepting two or three who came to our camp last evening.

Soil where kicked up by the horses abounding in bulbous roots. Passed several herds of Elk, Antelopes and Deer. Wolves & Bears numerous. The variety of plants not as great as usual, but birds more plenty, amongst others Curlew and blackbirds* in large flocks. Grapes just ripening and of passable quality found everywhere along streams.

Friday Octr 15th The warmth of the sun this morning was agreeable after a cool night. Our Journey was over a vast level plaine 25 miles. The atmosphere smoky, hills invisible on either side, and very few trees to be seen. This plain is evidently overflown in winter, the ground even now is covered in many places with goose dung and dead planorbis shells. Game 4 deer and one Antelope. Halted for the night on a small deep creek, near a beaver dam, numerous flocks of Summer ducks swam in the creek.

The "Butes" a range of insular mountains, were in sight from here. On them the numerous, bands of animals now covering the plains are said to collect in winter when *all* this immence extent of country is covered with water.

It was late when we halted and we remained dinnerless untill sometime after dark.

Yellow bill^d Magpies numerous in the small strips of timber along the creek. Curlews breed on the plaines.

Sat^y Octr 16th We crossed the base of the "Bute" after crossing prairie, which bore the marks of having been 10 or 15 feet under water in the winter, although now it is dry and offensively dusty. Mes^{srs} Agate & Colvecorcessis were both taken with a relapse of fever, and were unable to proceed. Water was searched for at an old camp of the Hudson B C near the Bute, but it proved unfit for use, being offensive and only to be obtained by wading in mud to the shallow pools. We had then to strike off east over a part of the hills, 6 miles further to another old camp, where the cattle and sheep were collected last spring. Here we found a few puddles of bad water filled with animalcules on the South side of the Butes. Game only one deer, Antelopes plenty but shy.

Sunday Octr 17th It blew a gale of wind from the north lasting all night, but with a higher temperature than usual. Crossed a perfectly level plaine of 15 miles to Feather river. There was but a few groves of Oaks near the Stream which is about 100 yards wide, deep, and flows with a gentle current of clear water.

We struck the river 8 miles above its juncture with the Sacramento, where some canoes were left last spring, but they were gone, and we continued down stream untill sunset & encamped on its banks. Saw many small herds of Antelopes & Elk, but the wind being fresh on our backs, they kept off. Only one Antelope was killed, and a Cow from a herd which were in excelent condition. No game will compare with *beef* excepting Buffalo meat.

---

* Icterus phaniceous

Monday 18th Several horses and mules were missing until near midday, a short ride brought us to the mouth of Feather river where we found it was fordable on the sandbar at the S Junction of the two rivers. After some little floundering in quicksands, we succeeded in crossing safely and encamped near the ford early in the day.

This appeared a favourable opportunity as the journey was drawing near a close, and not far to carry a specimen. I therefore determined on a hunt for a Black tail buck to get a drawing, skin, etc.

Dimen^ns Black tail Deer ♂

Total length including tail	6 ft.	1½	inches
Tail		10	"
Head to occiput	1 "	¾	"
" to horn		9	"
" to eye		7	"
Lachrymal sinus 1 inch long & ⅞th deep			
Ear 10 inches long 3 ¾" wide			
Height of animal in fore shoulder	3 ft.	2	"
rump at pelvis	3 "	3	"
From shoulder to anus	3 "	6	"
to angle of lower Jaw	1 "	1	"
Circumference of neck	1 "		
chest	3 "	8	"

Eye, brown, pupil very linear.

The horns of this specimen were not of the largest size or best characterized but are of fair proportions; one brow antler is deficient, which all we saw in the upper country had but of those killed in the lower country nearly all were without any brow antler. The horns are frequently like those of C. Virginianus, but as a common rule more slender.

They never carry the tail erect in running, which is so characteristic of the *"white tail"* that all the Indians use for its sign the same undulation of an erect hand or finger.

When seen from behind it shows only two white lines of buttock hairs. It springs up frequently to get sight of its pursuer, and altogether has more the appearance of an Antelope when running.

At the junction of Feather river, and the Sacramento we saw the remains of an Indian town, which a few years since contained several hundred natives, *all* of whom perrished in one season by a tertian fever. Their bones now are bleaching on the ground, strewed in all directions—in one of the skulls a bird has built its nest.

Tuesday Octr 19th We started at the usual hour and traveled over the same perfet level to the American river which was forded and here met Capt Sutter of "Nueva Helvetia" who came to meet us an conduct us to his house where we arrived about 2 oclock, and partook of some refreshment; then proceeded two miles further to the Sacramento and encamp^d, Capt Sutter accepting our invitation to sup with us.

The Mexican government have made a conditional grant of 30 square leagues of land to Capt Sutter, a Swiss gentleman, for the purpose of Settling this portion of California. He commenced about two years since, and is now building extensive corrals and houses of adobes, by Indian labor for which he pays in goods. He has now 1000 horses, 3000 cattle, and 800 sheep; all in a thriving condition; but this season for want of rain or the means of irrigation, *all* his crops have failed.

The house & Corral are nearly finished. We saw about 40 Indians at work, who appeared smiling and contented, but as a counterpart Capt Sutter has lately purchased a pack of artillery as a part of the *farm* stock, & about to remove it from Bodages, the Russian fur settlement which he has also purchased. A distillery also forms part of this establishment in which a kind of pisco is made by distil^ng from the wild grape.

Thursday Octr 21st Mr. Emmons, Dr. Whittle with the sick, and Mr. Dana, Started in Capt Sutters Launch to join the squadron in the bay. "Nueva Helvetia" is at the head of tide water. Mes^srs Eld, Rich, Brackenridge, and I with a few of the volunteers, and greater part of the horses, Started to San Francisco by land, about noon, the morning having been spent in dividing stores, taking leave of Capt. Sutter, etc. Romero, a Californian, was our guide. We traveled 15 miles over a level prairie when arriving at a pond of water, we encamped in a grove of oaks. On the route saw numbers of Antelopes (Calif^n "Berendes") and prairie wolves (Calif^e Collote). The Indians here do not burn the prairies as in Oregon and near the mountains.

Friday 22d Kept a *mounted* horse guard which is a decided improvement over our practice heretofore—men on foot can do little to prevent (cunning) Indians from stealing horses and riding off in the night. Crossed the Rio Cosmes soon after Starting. It is 20 ft. wide, clear water, and 10 days since was dry. No rain has fallen *here.*

Had a warm, dry ride over a level plain without water untill we reached the Rio de los Mogueles about noon. It is a rapid stream of about 50 yards in width. On the sand I saw the track of a grizzly bear exceeding in dimentions any hitherto met. At sunset we again reached some bad water, and "camped," having come 32 miles. Killed a *racoon* (Procyon lotor), a prairie wolf (Canis latraus) alias Collote, and several mallard, which were in all the small ponds around us in immense numbers.

Sat^y Octr 23d Started early, crossed the same kind of level prairie, to rio Joaquin, which is not usually fordable but the season being unusually dry, we succeeded in crossing without damage, though some few packs got wet. At about 11 a.m. reached a lagoon filled with geese & Ducks, once surrounded by Antelopes & sandhill cranes. Here our guide proposed that we should halt for the day, stating that we should find no more water or grass in a long days Journey; but it was concluded notwithstanding to push on: about the middle of the afternoon we arrived at a range of naked hills through the valies of which we threaded our way meeting a few springs of water, but no wood, once but little grass. Several strata of sandstone appeared in the hills abounding in organic remains, and the fragments of of an enormous species of oyster (fossil) were strewed about the surface of the ground. (Subsequently we learned that fossil fish were common here.) At night having crossed the hills & again reached the plain we were unable to find grass for the horses, and had to push on untill 9 p.m. when reaching a swamp abounding in geese, ducks, & Sandhill Cranes, we halted for the night, but it was too dark to find the water; consequently we had to go to bed, dinner & supperless. The *bed* however, was better than usual, being rushes, & we were tired enough after a 45 mile ride to enjoy it.

In the course of the day we saw several herds of Wild horses, Elk, and Antelopes.

Sunday, Octr 24th The innumerable geese & Sandhill Cranes we disturbed last night kept up a racket that would effectually have kept awake any other persons who might not have made such a Journey as we did yesterday. Killed a Bullock and with a few geese made a meal which would astonish people who eat more than once in 24 hours!! After it we set off on our course over naked hills or rather mountains. The road became plainer as we advanced, and the number of Indians increased. They were all clean and well dressed, most of them spoke Spanish, they told us they were returning from Mass at the Mission of San José. Each was loaded with beef, which is issued to them at the Mission in weekly rations. Once per annum they are allowed a recess to return to their native wilds to gather acorns, etc. now ripe, which accts for our meeting them away from the restraints of the Mission. Many had horses.

Arrived at the Mission of San José a little past noon. Our reception was rather inhospitable, notwithstanding we had letters of introduction; but fortunately we were lucky enough to meet an agent of the H B Company, Mr. Forbes, who invited us to his farm 6 miles further on our road, to which the party conducted by Mr. Forbes went while Mr. Eld & I having found a countryman of ours in the *Tailor* of the Mission (Ephraim Travel, formerly of Philadelphia) we staid to see the Church and Gardens—the former contains some good oil paintings, and the walls are rather neatly painted in distemper by a wandering Italian.

The gardens are extensive, and contain some good fruits, Peaches, Pears, Apples, Figs, Grapes, Olives.

40 bbls of wine were made this season, although a large portion of the grapes were improvidentially consumed by by the Indians.

Dormitorys in two or three paralel lines, forming a hollow square, with the Church in the centre, flanked by the officers & priests quarters.

1600 was the number of natives here in 1832, but now there is less than 600. It is the principal Mission of California & the priest is Vicar General.

Passed a rancho, on our way to Mr. Forbes's around which were walls built of Bullocks skulls. Plaines in all directions covered with carcases in different stages of decomposition, the hides and tallow only being preserved. As we traveled in the dark last night, the continued rattleing and breaking of bones under our horses feet had a most singular and unpoetic effect; any but Californian horses would have been frightened by it.

Monday Octr 25th Slept in a bed last night, under roof, for the first time since leaving fort Vancouver in August. Mr. Forbes accompanied us a short distance on our road this morning untill we came in sight of the Mission of Sta Clara. We then sent on the men and horses to a place some 10–15 miles beyond called San Francisquito, where there was a little grass, our horses having had little or nothing to eat these two days.

The rest of us visited the Mission, and were hospitably rec^d by the padre dressed in the gray Capote & cord of St. Francis. He conducted us over the church and burial grounds, etc.

On expressing a wish to see the gardens we were conducted to the superintendent who was probably judging by our appearance (we were dressed in deer skin shirts & trowsers, mockassins, etc. with plentiful mostacios and beards none the cleaner for exposure to weather) he took us to be some vagabond trappers wanting to eat fruit, and rec^d us rather rudely; but being reproved by Mr. Rich in good Spanish, his conduct so completely altered, that we not only visited the gardens to see peach, pear, apple & olive besides fig trees, but he insisted on our coming to his rooms, to eat the fruit, and drink a sample of the spirit distilled from the pears.

Reached San Fransicquito before dark, after riding 20 miles.

Tuesday Octr 26th The grass being good, and none to be had further on the road, it was concluded best to remain in camp today to recruit the horses for a "long camp"* tomorrow. Hunted & botanized.

Killed several geese, but having plenty of beef no

---

* "Long camp" and "short camp" are expressions I believe, although peculiar to the Hudson's Bay Company; and mean the journeys between two camps, being greater or less. It applys to the *march* and not the Camp.

Snow geese (Anser hyperborea)	In incredible numbers
White front^d geese (A- albifrons)	feeding on the plains
Porant (A-burnielu??)	and marshes. Yesterday
Sandhill cranes (Gras Canadensis)	saw some caugh with
Mallard (Anas boscha)	a lasso.
Buffil head	Green wing Teal
Mergansors (Mergus merganser)	
Hood^d Mergansors	
Icterus phoenicias & ferrugineas, in large flocks	
Strix brachyotus common	
Falco cyaneus common	
_____ sparverius—not common.	

one would eat them, and the wolves entered the camp during the night and carried them off. Found another species of Tobacco (Nicotia⎯⎯) and obtained the ripe fruit of a very fragrant species of Laurus. It is a beautiful tree 30–40 ft. high, regularly formed and close in foliage. Packed some of the nuts with dry clay in a goose skin, hopeing to introduce it at home. We found it first in the valley of the Umpqua river, and in the mountains where it must endure considerable cold in the winters. The foliage is so fragrant as to perfume the air to a considerable distance when heated by the sun. At dark it commenced raining and caused us to spend a wet night. We had guarded against the decending torrents of rain but forgot that we were on level ground & without floor to our tent.

Wednesday Oct' 27ᵗʰ Started early in a heavy rain, some over a level marshy prairie passing several Ranchos. A high wooded range of hills to our left, course about N. We were in hopes to have completed our Journey today but several horses gave out about the middle of the afternoon, and we had to halt on the borders of a marshy prairie between two ranges of hills about 12 miles short of our destination.

Having no more beef, we had to kill some Geese and Ducks for our supper. They are fortunately for us very abundant. The weather cleared a little, but not long enough to dry our blankets. It was chilly & we had a wet bed and but little food.

Thursday 28ᵗʰ Started a little after sunrise and in four hours reached "Yerba-buena," stopping at the Mission of Dolores by the way. It is a mission truly of Sorrow, and is nearly all in ruins, but 50 Indians are left in it who are the "picture of poverty." Yerba buena on the contrary presents quite a prosperous appearance having several neatly built frame houses & Stores—all English or American.

We found a boat waiting for us, and before night reached the Vincennes at Sansalito where the Brigs Oregon[26] & Porpoise also lay. Several trading vessels in port also.

----

[26] Wilkes had purchased the American brig, *Thomas H. Perkins*, at Astoria, to make up in part for the loss of the *Peacock*; the name was changed to the *Oregon*. Wilkes, *Narrative* 5: 115. The ships were engaged in a survey of the coast during the period when the Emmons' party made the overland trip.

Peale and the other members of the Scientific Corps who joined the Vincennes at this time were with her until the end of the expedition.

XI

Across the Pacific And To Singapore

Sunday Octr 31st Sailed from the port of San Francisco in the afternoon, and beat out the wind failing us just as we reached the bar at night. We anchored in 7 fathoms water, the sea very heavy.

Monday Novr 1st The sea increased during the night, and began to break around the ship. Several times it broke on board, injuring 3 boats, a part of the hammock rail, and killing one of the Marines, who was caught while decending the fore hatch by some loose spars. Weighed anchor in the morning and sought a better situation, where we lay to a kedge, during a thick fog. Buried the Marine, and when it cleared we stood to the Southward; the 2 Brigs in company.

Tuesday Novr 2^d Brig porpoise despatched with a letter bag, into the port of Monté Ray, and we stood to the westwards.

Wednesday Novr 17th Anchored off Honolulu, Oahu, this morning at 10 oclock. The Brig Porpoise joined comp^y and anchored 1 hour after us. Likewise the Oregon and schooner Flying fish from Columbia river.

Had the misfortune to have all our letters sent to Manilla recently.

The vessels were subsequently taken to the inner harbour, and many of us lived on shore.

Sat^y Novr 27th Left the Harbour in the morning and anchored outside. Joined by the rest of the Squadron (Origon, Porpoise & Flying fish) and weighed anchor again at sunset. Hove too at 12 p.m. and remained during Sunday morning distributing orders. The two Brigs left us, and were soon out of sight. Sail was then set and we stood before the wind but about 2 p.m. signal was made from the schooner for assistance. Hove too & sent a boat on board when it was reported that she had sprung her mainmast; the carpenters were sent on board of her and we made sail on our course.

Monday Novr 29th The damage on board the Schooner Flying fish was not found by the carpenters to be so serious as at first reported. Dr. Whittle was sent on board, and after some other assistance, she rec^d her orders and we parted company.

Our general course was westward. The weather pleasant, Sundry islands of doubtful existence were searched for, but nothing material occurred to change the usual monotony of a sea voyage untill

Monday Decemb^r 20 At daylight discovered Wake's Island, and at 9 a.m. the boats were lowered, a survey commenced and the Scientific Corps landed, while the ship stood off & on.

Island coral lunatus open to the N W. with a reef enclosing the lagoon about 3 miles long, and 12 feet above the sea; no cocoa nuts, Pandanus, or fresh water. The only remarkable part in the formation of this island is the enormous blocks of coral which have been thrown up by the violence of the Sea. One or two that I visited were quite 20 feet in diameter.

Rats were common

Diomeddea brachyurus	—were breeding, they lay an oblong white Egg.
Sula bassanus	
Sula —— (red leg^d sp^s	—just building on trees, but had not begun to lay.
Sula fusca	
Sterna fuliginosus	The bassanus always lays on the ground.
——alba	
Phaeton phoenicurus	—Either the Albatross or gannets suffer their hens to be lifted off their nest, and fight for them, even when there are no eggs.
Pelidna	
Scolopax	
Tachypetes aquileous	

Fish abound^d in the lagoon and were of the most varied and beautiful col^rs. Remained on shore untill ½ past 4 p.m. The sun powerfully hot, and the white coral sand very unpleasant.

Sat^y December 25th We have had thus far pleasant weather and trade winds, but having to look for sundry Islands & Shoals of doubtful existence, our progress towards Manilla has not been so rapid as our anxiety to get our letters from home leads us to wish.

Capt^{ns} Wilkes & Hudson dined with us in the ward room and our Christmas passed as pleasantly as could be expected for those who are accustomed to make it a *family* festival.

Wednesday 29th This morning saw the Island of Grigan one of the Ladrones, about fifteen miles south of us, but the weather was hazey and we had some rain, which spoiled our view. It is however very high, and from its form volcanic. Part of the day we lay becalmed. Passed the great volcano or "Assuncion" Island in the night, but it was still in view.

Thursday 30th Before sunrise had a clear view of "Assumpcion" to the N E of us 15 miles off. Its form is a regular truncated cone, about 5 or 6000 feet high, the stratified clouds resting about half way to its summit, from which at one time I thought I saw white vapour issueing—Soon after sunrise, the whole was covered with clouds forming a huge "bank."

Sat^y Jany 8th, 1842 For the last few days we have been sailing with a gentle southerly wind which is considered unusual at this season, as we expected to meet the N E "monsoon." With the dawn of day this morning we were able to discern the Bashee Islands, and passed to the southward in view of three or four of them, the two nearest being mountainous, and broken into irregular peaks, one of which was envelloped in clouds. They were all destitute of trees, and were sterile in appearance, evidently volcanic. The rocks nearest to us were of a dark chocolate col^r, others were very light col^d and decomposing. Between 9 and 10 crossed the path of a barque rigged vessel Standing to the North. On firing a gun she displayed English col^{rs}. Weather clear, gentle breese and but few birds seen.

Wednesday Jany 12th At the dawn of day were entering the bay of Manilla, but having the wind ahead, after beating untill nine at night, still found ourselves some miles from the anchorage at Caviti. Much to our surprise the schooner Flying fish appeared just after us, and we both anchored together. Shores of the bay picturesque and the rocks which skirt them apparently volcanic.

Thursday 13th Weighed at daylight and proceeded with a gentle breeze to the anchorage at 9 o'clock, where we found several other vessels. The Flying Fish came in by the Southern passage & was very near being lost on Cape "Espirito Santo" on to which she was swept by a strong current during the night. She has passed Scarboroughs and the Caroline Islands, without landing, but has communicated with the natives.

The members of the Scientific Corps were landed and Messrs Rich, Agate & Drayton with myself took lodgings at the Foncea of Seven Days [?]. No strangers are allowed to reside in the city of Manilla (proper) which is enclosed within the fortifications. In it all the houses are built of Stone, 2 stories high, and after the usual Spanish fashions. Population—nearly all Spaniards. Most of the stores out of the of town are kept by Chinese who are also the artisans. They are an acute race of dealers. They retain their native costume. The troops are all natives of the Islands, having Spanish officers. They are kept well clothed and present a very neat appearance. Their numbers are somewhat short of 20,000. Five regiments are now stationed in the City. They always keep six months advance of provisions on hand, and are in all other respects well provided for. The pay of a soldier is 4 dollars per month, and a ration of ½ a real (6¼ cents) per day.*

Tobacco is a government monopoly, and the manufactaries of segars are the great curiosities of the place. 15,000 persons are employed in these "factories," (Estancos), 8000 women & girls and 780 men are employed in one building. The opperations are conducted with good order without any confusion.

The City is intersected in various directions by canals, which afford great facilities to the market people who came mostly from the lagoon in canoes. The varieties of Fish and vegetables are very great but the meat is inferior. Coagulated blood is sold in cakes. Poultry excellent. As all the poorer people are extravagantly fond of Cock fighting, much care is taken in breeding them. Cock pits are licenced by the Government. Double edged curved "gaffs" are used. The natives are so fond of the amusement that they carry their birds under their arms whereever they go, so that at the musical entertainments in the plaza it was a great nuisance as the cocks would crow every time the music commenced.

Made an excursion to Maraguina, which is 8 or 10 miles from Manilla. The country was very beautiful, abounding in highly cultivated farms where the Natives produce rice, maize, sugar, etc. They are generally surrounded with bamboo groves with the stems of which the houses are built, fences made, and indeed almost every article, even floors & water buckets, etc. We crossed a river in our carriages on a raft of it guided by a single rattan at least 100 yds long. Buffalos are the only animals used in preparing the ground and in Carrying burthens. They are attached by a very simple yoke [fig. 76] which rests on the neck in front of the shoulders, and is attached to shafts on traces, by which they draw Sleds, trucks, ploughs and enormous bundles of Bamboos, being guided entirely by a cord run through & attached to the sceptum of the nose.

---

* The music of these regiments is under the direction of Frenchmen & Spaniards, but the performers are Natives, who appear to have a very correct ear—the pieces generally selected from the German & Italian operas. They perform twice a week in the plaza for the amusement of the public.

Their local name signifies Indian brother. They appear to have a special dislike to White poeple & Strangers but even the native children manage them with ease. Meat of the Buff not eaten excepting the young cows.

Maraquino has about 10,000 inhabitants, all of whom are Christians, though few speak the Spanish language. The houses are mostly built of Bamboo, & Mat trees and are all elevated 6–8 feet from the ground on posts, are kept very clean, the people appearing very contented and happy. Chinese intermixture is observable every where. They are easily told by the oblique eye.

Returned on board ship Thursday 20th of January after a pleasant week on shore.

Friday Jany 21st Sailed at daylight. Met two American vessels comeing in, and received a few late newspapers from them, which were particularly interesting to some of our younger officers, as they contained a list of Naval promotions.

22^d, 23^d 24th Sailing along the coast of the Island of Mindoro. The schooner was sent to survey a shoal on which a vessel has lately been wrecked. Island high with several very abrupt mountains, all from appearances volcanic, covered with vegetation to the waters edge. No birds excepting a few Terns seen. Fish abundant, and a small species of black Porpoise.

Monday 24th Ran over a very dangerous shoal called "Apo bank" in the charts. At one time we had less than 5 fathoms water. We could see the bottom distinctly, particularly where composed of white sand.

Wednesday 26th Beating all day amongst a group of small Islands to get around the S E end of Mindoro. The N E monsoon now blows steadily from the one quarter and is very strong. All the Islands are high and rocky with here and there a white sand beach. They are mostly clothed with a dense vegetation.

Schooner in sight to lee ward.

Thursday 27th Before the wind, standing along the W coast of the Island of Panay with a tolerably smooth sea.

Friday 28th Opposite San José, nearly calm. Several boats out Surveying, one or two landed at the village of Antija in which the Govr resides. He was out in the country and his wife, the only white lady in the place, was somewhat alarmed at the firing during the Survey. Her husband is a Captn of Infantry.

A small species of Delphinapterus passed us in a troup of hundreds. They were very active & leapt several feet above the water, and went with a velocity of near 20 miles per hour. They were almost entirely black, & not more than 3 feet long. No birds.

Sunday Jan 30th In the afternoon came in sight of the Isl^d of Mindoro and at night anchored in a small harbour opposite a fort a few miles west of Samboangu. The fort displayed a Spanish flag.

Monday 31st All the Scientific Corps landed at the fort, & boats were sent out to survey the harbour. The fort* is under the command of a Lt. of Infantry sent

FIG. 76.

by the Govr of Samboangu to protect the fishermen & wood cutters from the "Moors" (Malays) who have a village a few miles west of this. It was visited by a few of our party who were kindly rec^d by the inhabitants. Mes^{srs} Rich, Agate, Brackenridge & I made an excursion two or three miles into the hills, across a fine stream of water. The whole country is covered with a most profuse vegetation. We saw numbers of Monkeys (Semnopithecus entellus?) and Hornbills of several species, which made the woods resound with their hoarse voices. A few Buffaloe were wallowing in the mire. They seem to have a particular antipathy to white poeple. The officer in command of the fort told us that Boas were numerous (and of size sufficient to strangle Buffalo??). We however saw no traces of any, but Deer & wild hogs are evidently not uncommon. Amongst the shells collected were many specimens of Malleus nigra, which is here obtained as food. Many birds were obtained & some few Insects.

Samboangu is a penal settlement where convicts are sent from Manilla, etc. It has about 6000 inhabitants. The Govr is a Lt. of Infantry. There are natives on the Island who are neither Christians or Mahamedans. They are called by the Span^{ds} "gentiles." The Malays are of the same race but being Mahomedans** are distinguished by the title of "Moors." The original inhabitants are black, and keep distinct from the light col^d races. They live mostly in the mnts.

At sunset we returned on board and by daylight next morning, *Tuesday, Feb. 1st* Weighed anchor again, and stood off towards the Soloo Islands, in sight to the Southward & Westward. Becalmed soon after but the wind subsequently came from the Southward, and after beating untill night, we anchored. A strong current of nearly one and a half miles per hour flowing westwardly.

Wednesday 2^d Passed over a good deal of shoal water today, and were successful in taking a few Comatulie, Asteria, etc. with the dredge in about 8 fathoms. The Island of Sooloo was in sight, but we could not succeed in reaching it, and therefore anchored about 8 o'clock in 25 fathoms water. Many islets & high rocks were passed during the day. Large shoals of fish were seen, and a few flocks of Terns & Sula seen in in pursuit of them.

---

* Built 1784, to protect the small harbor in front of it called "la caldera."

** [No note.]

Thursday Feb. 3ᵈ Under sail by sunrise but it was nearly calm & we made but slow progress during the day. The boats were out towing, but at night we had to drop anchor just in sight of the City of "Sonng" Island of Sooloo. Had a heavy shower of rain in the evening.

The Island has a few mountain peaks generally envelloped in clouds. The land is generally "rolling" and presents a most picturesque appearance. Many "clearings" and highly cultivated portions giving diversity to its wild and luxuriant aspect. Many canoes were around us, but none ventured aboard.

Whales & a great variety of fish were seen.

Friday Febʸ 4ᵗʰ Dead calm, but the tide turning. About 9 oclock the anchor was weighed and we towed towards the town. The heat yesterday & today has been more oppressive than experienced heretofore. Anchored about 3/4th of a mile from Soung, and Lt. Budd was sent to call upon the Sultan and acquaint him with the objects of our visit. He did not return untill noon, and soon afterwards all the Scientific Corps were landed. We passed through the Town to the residence of the prime minister or "King" where we met the son of the Sultan.

Captⁿˢ Wilkes and Hudson had an interview with the Sultan, who refused permission for us to make excursions out of the town, and even in it there was interdicted portions. The most interesting places we visited were the work shops and market. 2/3ds of the town is built over the water* on piles and all the houses on shore elevated in the same manner. The common ones are bamboo thatched with palm leaves, and the better sorts of Slabs with carved lintils to the doors and windows. Canals intersect the town in every direction; some of them faced with Chinese granite.

Satʸ Feb. 5ᵗʰ The Sultan having refused his permission for us to land out of the town we this morning started with two boats and a marine guard to the Island opposite. We found the vegetation very much dried up for want of rain, while that on the Main Isᵈ appears in the greatest luxuriance oweing to the vicinity of the mountains, where the atmospheric condensation is profuse. A few fine plants were obtained, some bulimi and other shells, and a beautiful cream colᵈ Pigion, with black primaries, and a black terminal band on the tail. We spent most of the day unannoyed by natives untill we discovered a village built over a lagoon, near which we approached on a sand bar. Our presence seemed to create great uneasiness, and after

FIG. 77.

a little while a number of men in canoes came to us, but as they could not understand us in Spanish or English we could gain no information from them. They were all armed with Spears & Krisses, and had large wooden Shields, and appeared somewhat disposed to be quarrelsome. The Sultan was often named, & it is probable they were as much afraid of him as they were of us.* We therefore withdrew to our boats. The Island was generally low, & covered with Mangroves near the water, but several abrupt hills of about 300 feet elevation were composed of a volcanic conglomerate rock.

Saw numbers of Hirundo esculenta in the rocky caverns facing the sea, but could not discover any of their nests. There was a fungus like mucilaguous substance adhering to the rocks which they appeared to be collecting. At a distance we supposed it to be their nests but on an approach they abandoned the place entirely.

Sunday Febʸ 6ᵗʰ Left Soung early and with a gentle breese stood towards the strts of "Balibak."

Tuesday 8ᵗʰ Entered the Strts in the afternoon and anchored near the Isld of Mongsew. Several boats out Surveying. Preparations were made for surveying, and all the boats hoisted out.

Wednesday 9ᵗʰ All the boats excepting two were dispatched with forty-eight hours provisions to survey the neighbouring reefs & Islands. Frequent squalls of wind & heavy rain during the day. The Scientific Corps were landed off Mangsew. The small easternmost Island on which we landed was separated from the main one by a reef, dry at low water. It is rather more than a mile in circumference, thickly wooded with large trees of various species, and abounds in Nutmeg Pigions, (C. aenea) and Nicobar Pigions (C. Nicobarica), one of the most beautiful of its race. Contrary to my expectations I found here at least it was "arboreal," but this may be owing to the fruit on which it was feeding, which was only to be obtained on some of the tallest trees. Many curious plants, some shells, etc. were obtained. We were thoroughly soaked by the del-

---

* The Chinese part is entirely over the water, with a gateway on the land side, and guards were constantly patroling the avenue like an arcade closed over the top and extending like a long street from the land. Chinese, open fronted shops, on each side, back of which were their dwellings, and in front small tables with a very small assortment of goods, generally of very inferior quality.

Several black smith shops we visited were rather curious. They were open sheds. Charcoal was used for the fire, on the ground. The bellows were two wooden cyllinders having pistons moved by a man like two Churns. (The valves in the bottom). He was generally on an elevated seat and held a p [word unfinished].

---

* The people appeared to be fishermen, as numbers of their basket traps were lying on the point, apparently to dry off the barnacles with which they were entirely covered. They were 6 or 8 feet square, 18 inches high with mouse trap entrances. Large rolls *of fence* were also laid out to dry [fig. 77]. They are used for encircling places where the fish are caught at low water. Everything of this kind are made of bamboo and rattan; even the fishing lines are made of the latter.

uges of rains and as we found no water on the Island we filled a wine bottle in less than a minute from a stream decending the trunk of a tree. No Natives were seen on the Island, though traces were observed, showing that it was sometimes visited (a canoe & a house were found on the N side). Those in our boats must have rather an unpleasant night from the frequent and sudden squalls, without bedding & small boats to sleep in.

Thursday 10th Still annoyed by squalls & showers of rain. A party went on the reef at daylight, low water, to collect Shells, etc. Others subsequently landed on the Island. We obtained many birds, found 2 species of Megapodus, 3 Pigeons, a Swallow, Shrike besides others. The Island is not more than 2 or 3 hundred yards wide, but covered with heavy timber, amongst which the India fig is conspicuous. Amongst its numerous roots I found a new species of "Vampyre" bat Pteropus. The whole woods resounded with the cooings of Pigions, but notwithstanding many of our sportsmen were out, but few were killed, it being exceedingly difficult to see the birds in the dense & lofty foliage.

Friday 11th Again on shore, after the morning Showers. A party of men were occupied in cutting wood. All but the Launch and first cutter returned from surveying. They met but few natives, but they evinced hostile feelings and came on a sand bar occupied by Lt Perry with their Spears, Krisses, & Shields ready for a contest which Lt Perry declined and left them in possession of the bar, having concluded his survey.

Saty 12th The Launch (Lt Budd) and first cutter (Lt Perry) arrived about noon, & having completed the survey of the Balabak passage we weighed anchor and by dark were in the China Sea again. A proa [?] having 10 men in it paddled up to the 1st Cutter just before the occurrence on the Sand bar, and on arriving within a few yards each of the natives armed himself with Shield and Spear. The cutter's crew did the same with pistols, which the natives seeing declared themselves friends, but no further intercourse took place.

Saty Feby 19th Arrived at Singapore, and found that the Schooner Flying fish, and the two Brigs had arrived before us, the Brigs having been here four weeks, and what was quite as satisfactory, most of us recd communications from home, though most of the dates are old.

The first things which impress a stranger on landing in Singapore are the spacious and palace like building in the English portion, and the immence variety of the human race amongst its population:—Europeans, Malays, Bugis, Hindoos, Parsees, Chinese, Cochin Chinese, Siamese, etc., etc.—each in their respective & various costumes, and *all* in the free exercise of their own religious beliefs. There is an Episcopal Church, Catholic, Armenian, etc. for the Christians, a Mohamedan Mosque, a Chinese temple in full array of Idols, etc.

Our arrival is at the termination of the festivities for the New Year, but in time to see numerous Mohamedan & Chinese processions. "Hussan in search of Housain" was celebrated with great pomp at night. Lofty pagodas made of gilt and coloured paper over bamboo frames were carried by great numbers of men on a kind of bier accompanied by fire works, dancing and "vile" music, consisting of a kind of keyed trumpet accompanied by a "drone," drums, etc.

One of the best of the Chinese was an enormous transparent Dragon in pursuit of a Globe, which was admirable managed. The globe waved from one side of the street to the other while the dragon (40–50 feet long) pursued it opening its enormous Jaws, rolling its fiery eyes, etc, while the diablary music of gongs and harsh trumpets crushed forth their terrors at every effort of the monster.

Then there was processions of little children, dressed in the "full togs" of Chinese finery as the lanterns before and behind them, in imitation of the two halves of horses, with streaming paper tails. Some humourously were made to appear as if mounted on fish, with open mouths & wagging tongues. Lanterns and banners waved above while the little ones (each with adult leaders) marched and counter marched to the clang of gongs, etc.

Two theatres were opened in the streets for the benefit of the celestial public; one in front of the Temple. They were stages covered with mat roofs, without scenes, only a kind of dressing room in the rear. Dresses of the performers gorgeous; gesticulation extravagant; voices elevated and squeaking; hard to tell whether tragedy or comedy. Music almost incessant consisting of gongs, reed trumpets and a kind of Marble Drum, the sound of which was peculiar, and not unlike nicely managed castonettes.

Still vaulting and tumbling formed a part of the performance one evening; it was iminitable. The muscular power displayed surpassed anything of the kind I had previously seen.

THE END

REFERENCES

MANUSCRIPTS

ACADEMY OF NATURAL SCIENCES OF PHILADELPHIA

BONAPARTE, CHARLES LUCIEN. Manuscripts and letters.
LAWSON, ALEXANDER. Scrapbooks. (These scrapbooks include many original drawings and plate proofs.)
ORD, GEORGE. Letters.
PEALE, T. R., to Chairman, ANSP, Oct. 31, 1826. Drawings.
PICKERING, CHARLES. Journals. 2 v.
SAY, THOMAS. Letters to J. V. Melsheimer, Dec. 12, 1812, through Feb. 18, 1825; to P. S. Du Ponceau, Dec. 28, 1828.
Minutes of the Academy of Natural Sciences of Philadelphia:
    Vol. 2, Jan. 5, 1813–Dec. 26, 1820.
    Vol. 3, Jan. 2, 1821–Mar. 29, 1825.
    Vol. 4, Apr. 5, 1825–Oct. 23, 1827.
    Vol. 5, Oct. 30, 1827–Mar. 26, 1833.
    Vol. 6, Apr. 2, 1833–Mar. 26, 1839.

AMERICAN MUSEUM OF NATURAL HISTORY

HUDSON, WILLIAM L. Journal of William L. Hudson, Comdg. U. S. Ship Peacock—one of the vessels attached to the South Sea surveying and exploring expedition under the command of Charles Wilkes, Esqr., 1838–1840.
PEALE, TITIAN R. A catalogue of the specimens of mammalia and birds collected by the South Sea Surveying & Exploring Expedition during the years 1838, 39, 40, 41, 42.
——. Sketches, Mss. Notes & photographs.
——. The butterflies of North America, diurnal Lepidoptera, whence they come; where they go; and what they do. Illustrated and described by Titian R. Peale. 1 v. manuscript; 3 v. drawings and paintings.
PEALE, TITIAN R., and SAMUEL SEYMOUR. Plate proofs for Edwin James, *Account of an Expedition to the Rocky Mountains in 1819–20.*

AMERICAN PHILOSOPHICAL SOCIETY

Archives:

PEALE, TITIAN R., to A. D. Bache and John Ludlow. May 8, 1843.
——, to George Ord. February 11, 1845.
AUDUBON, JOHN JAMES. Correspondence.
BONAPARTE, CHARLES LUCIEN. Correspondence of American scientists with Charles Lucien Bonaparte, 1824–1855. Microfilm 542; originals in *Bibliothèque Nationale*, Paris.
FRAZER, JOHN FRIES. Papers: 28 letters, May 15, 1844 through April 16, 1854.

Coleman Sellers Mills Collection

Miscellaneous Manuscripts Collection:

PEALE, TITIAN R., to J. K. Kane. April 5, 1840.
——, to George Ord. March 14, 1843.
——, to R. M. Patterson. Nov. 13, 1838.
ORD, GEORGE. Letters to Charles Waterton, April 23, 1832, through Aug. 22, 1858.

Peale-Sellers Collection:

Museum material (black box).
PEALE C. W., autobiography. MSS and typed copy; MSS in 34 sections.
——. Belfield day book, Mar. 12, 1810, to Feb. 18, 1824.
——. Diaries:

    May 30–June 12, 1799.
    June 5–July 3, 1801.
    July 29–Sept. 25, 1801.
    May 29, 1804–April 28, 1805.
    March 24–April 24, 1813.
    May 23–June 14, 1817.

    Nov. 5, 1818–Jan. 29, 1819.
    Dec. 1826.

——. Letterbooks:
    3. May 11, 1791–Jan. 9, 1803.
    4. Jan. 9, 1803–Dec. 25, 1803.
    5. Jan. 6, 1804–Dec. 21, 1804.
    6. Jan. 6, 1805–Dec. 7, 1805.
    8. Jan. 8, 1807–Dec. 16, 1807.
    9. Jan. 15, 1808–Dec. 23, 1808.
    10. Jan. 10, 1809–Dec. 20, 1809.
    11. Jan. 7, 1810–Jan. 23, 1811.
    12. Jan., 1811–Dec. 28, 1813.
    13. Jan., 1814–Jan. 9, 1816.
    14. Jan. 9, 1816–Jan. 15, 1818.
    15. Jan. 3, 1818–Dec. 31, 1818.
    16. Jan. 1, 1819–Dec. 24, 1820.
    17. Jan. 14, 1821–May 21, 1824.
    18. Jan. 14, 1824–Dec. 28, 1824.
    20. Jan. 8, 1826–Feb. 19, 1827.

PEALE, FRANKLIN, and TITIAN R. PEALE. Letters, 1820–1868.
PEALE, RUBENS. Letterbooks. Autobiographical notes and New York museum records.
PEALE, TITIAN R. Biography of C. W. Peale. 2 v.
——. Manuscripts and sketches—new acquisition.
——. Sketchbook.
PILKINGTON, M. 1770. The gentleman's and connoisseur's dictionary of painters. London. (C. W. Peale copy, has a list of the births of members of the family recorded on flyleaf, and comments in margin throughout book.)
Sellers family papers. **4, 5, 6,** and **7.** (These papers contain manuscripts of different members of the Peale and Sellers families.)
SELLERS, GEORGE ESCOL. Memoirs. Typescript copy.
VAUGHAN, BENJAMIN. Papers: Benjamin Vaughan to Parker Cleveland, Sept. 23, 1829; Dec. 16, 1832; and Jan. 8, 1833.

BRINGHURST UNDERTAKERS, PHILADELPHIA

Files—1885.

MRS. JOSEPH CARSON COLLECTION

Cancelled check, to Titian R. Peale from Ja H. Booth, April 1, 1884.
Peale family memorabilia.

MISS IDA EDELSON COLLECTION

PEALE, TITIAN R. Paintings and drawings.
Peale family books.

HARRY PEALE HALDT COLLECTION

PEALE, C. W., to Titian R. Peale, May 29, 1823.
PEALE, T. R., to B. J. Lossing, May 21, 1881.
Peale family memorabilia.

HAVERFORD COLLEGE, HAVERFORD, PENNSYLVANIA

Charles Roberts Autographed Collection:

PEALE, T. R., to Reynell Coates, Nov. 17, 1836, and Sept. 14, 1837.

HISTORICAL SOCIETY OF PENNSYLVANIA

BARTRAM, WILLIAM. Drawings. Photostats. Originals at British Museum.

Dreer Collection:

PEALE, T. R., to John McAllister, May 21, 1870.

Gratz Collection:

PEALE, T. R., to Dr. Wroth, Nov. 3, 1873 and Dec. 24, 1873.
——, to F. M. Etting, Feb. 5, 1876.

GIBSON, CHAS. H., to Chas. P. Hayes, March 13, 1885 (Re TRP's death.)

LOGAN, DEBORAH. Journal. Vol. IX. Typescript copy.

Peale Collection:

PEALE, TITIAN R. Drawing Book. First sketches from nature, Titian Ramsay Peale, n.d., 12 pencil drawings.

Minutes of Philadelphia Museum, 1841–1845.

ORD, GEORGE, to T. R. Peale. Letters, Feb. 23, 1827, through March 17, 1854.

Peale's Museum, current expenditures, 1808–1819.

Philadelphia Museum Company, Manager's reports (T. R. Peale, Manager).
    Sept. 12, 1833.
    March 20, 1834.
    April 17, 1834.
    Oct. 16, 1834.
    Jan. 8, 1835.
    March 24, 1835.
    May 2, 1835.
    May 21, 1835.
    June 18, 1835.

Accession and record book of Peale's Museum, March, 1803, to Oct. 28, 1842.

PEALE, T. R., to James Shrigley, Sept. 27, 1871.

PEALE, W. J. Genealogy of the Peale family, 1892. In Genealogical Sections of Historical Society of Pennsylvania.

David McNeeley Stauffer Collection:

PEALE, T. R., to D. McN. Stauffer, Aug. 5, 1884, in extra illustrated edition of Westcott's history of Philadelphia. **18:** 1356.

United Bowmen Collection.

MISS JACQUELINE HOFFMIRE COLLECTION

PEALE, T. R. Drawings, paintings, and miscellaneous memorabilia.

LAUREL HILL CEMETERY, PHILADELPHIA

Records. T. R. Peale interred March 16, 1885.

LIBRARY COMPANY OF PHILADELPHIA

PEALE, T. R., to John A. McAllister. Sept. 27, 1871, and April 16, 1875.

LIBRARY OF CONGRESS

ELD, HENRY. Papers.

TAPPAN, BENJAMIN. Papers.

PEALE, TITIAN R. Journal of T. R. Peale, kept by Titian R. Peale, as assistant naturalist of Long's Expedition west of Rocky Mountains, May 3 to Aug. 1, 1819.

———. Journals kept on the U. S. Exploring Expedition to the South Seas:
    1. Aug. 1, 1838 to April 7, 1839.
    2. Apr. 12, 1839 to Oct. 10, 1839.
    3. Sept. 24, 1839 to June 13, 1840.
    5. Jan. 1, 1841 to July 18, 1841.
    7. Sept. 22, 1841 to Feb. 19, 1842.

WILKES, CHARLES. Papers. Letters from Mr. Drayton to Capt. Wilkes, March 10, 1850 to Dec. 30, 1851. Recommendations of the American Philosophical Society, October, 1836.

MUSEUM OF COMPARATIVE ZOOLOGY,
AT HARVARD UNIVERSITY

PEALE, T. R. Letters.

NEW-YORK HISTORICAL SOCIETY

PEALE, TITIAN RAMSAY, to an unknown correspondent, March 22, 1879.

NEW YORK PUBLIC LIBRARY

PEALE, T. R., to John Cropper, Nov. 8, 1884.

ROBERT R. PEALE COLLECTION

Notebook—Zoological Classification.

PENNSYLVANIA ACADEMY OF THE FINE ARTS

PEALE, T. R., to unknown correspondent. Undated MS.
Letters re T. R. Peale estate.

PHILADELPHIA CITY HALL

Philadelphia County, Records of Wills
    Peale, Caroline E. Girard, Will 804, 1875.
    Peale, Franklin, Will 317, 1870.
    Peale, Titian R., Will 504, 1885.

ST. JOHN'S CHURCH, 13TH AND MARKET, PHILADELPHIA

Records.

THE SMITHSONIAN INSTITUTION

Catalogue of specimens received on deposit at the Philadelphia Museum, from the U. S. Exploring Expedition, with receipts for same, signed by Franklin Peale.

Catalogue, Collections of the United States South Sea Surveying and Exploring Expedition, 1838, 9, 40, 41, & 42, By T. R. Peale, U. S. Patent Office, 1846.

PEALE, TITIAN R., to Charles Wilkes. Dec. 21, 1839.

———. List of miscellaneous curiosities collected by the Officers, and crew of the U. S. Ship Peacock, during her cruise from the Sandwich Islands to the Columbia River, from December 1840 to July 1841.

———. The South Sea Surveying and Exploring Expedition; its organization, equipment, purposes, results and termination.

U. S. NATIONAL ARCHIVES, WASHINGTON, D. C.

Department of Interior, Patent Office Records:

FITZGERALD, W. P. N., HENRY B. RENWICK, L. D. GALE, J. H. LANE and SAM COOPER to Alexander Stuart, Secretary of the Interior, May 5, 1852.

STUART, ALEXANDER, to above-named Patent Office Examiners, May 7, 1852.

PEALE, T. R., to O. H. Browning, Secretary of the Interior, July 21, 1868.

———, to President of the United States, March 12, 1869.

Department of the Navy:

Record Group 37, 272.24, ✗ 507. Anonymous Journal, *Vincennes*, Aug. 1838–Oct. 1840, with extracts from Sergt. Stearns' journal on an excursion into the interior of Otaheite accompanied by a number of scientific gentlemen and officers attached to the Ex.Ex.

Record Group 27, 272.24, ✗ 521. Surgeon's journal (Dr. Sickels), July 1838–Mar. 1840, on board the *Peacock*.

UNIVERSITY OF NORTH CAROLINA

Southern Historical Collection:

HUDSON, W. L. "Journal II," Aug. 11, 1840, to Feb. 19, 1842. Microfilm.

YALE UNIVERSITY LIBRARY

DANA, JAMES D. Letters to Edward Herrick.

Western Americana Manuscripts:

ELD, HENRY, JR. Journal, Sept. 6 to Oct. 29, 1841.

———. 3 Sketchbooks.

EMMONS, GEORGE FOSTER. Journals while attached to the South Sea Surveying and Exploring Expedition, 1838–1842.
——. 2 Sketchbooks.

NEWSPAPERS

Atkinson's Saturday Evening Post (Philadelphia), June 13, 1835.
Daily Evening Chronicle (Washington), Jan. 11, 1871.
Daily National Intelligencer (Washington), May 10, 1819.
Poulson's American Daily Advertiser (Philadelphia), May 16, 1821; Aug. 30, 1821.
Saturday Courier (Philadelphia), Jan. 23, 1847.
The National Gazette and Literary Register (Philadelphia), Oct. 28, 1820; Mar. 16, 1821; Nov. 3, 1824; June 26, 1832; Oct. 29, 1836.
The Press (Philadelphia), Oct. 26, 1858.
The United States Gazette (Philadelphia), Sept. 8, 1827.

BOOKS

ADAMS, EDGAR H., and WILLIAM H. WOODIN. 1913. United States pattern, trial and experimental pieces. New York, American Numismatic Society.
ALDINGTON, RICHARD. 1949. The strange life of Charles Waterton, 1782–1865. New York, Duell, Sloan and Pearce.
BARTRAM, WILLIAM. 1791. Travels through North & South Carolina, Georgia, East & West Florida, the Cherokee country, the extensive territories of the Muscogulges, or Creek confederacy, and the country of the Choctaws; containing an account of the soil and natural productions of those regions, together with observations on the manners of the Indians. Philadelphia.
BENNETT, WHITMAN. 1949. A practical guide to American nineteenth century color plate books. New York, Bennett Book Studios, Inc.
BLUNT, WILFRED. 1950. The art of botanical illustration. London, Collins.
BONAPARTE, CHARLES LUCIEN. 1825–1833. American ornithology; or the natural history of birds inhabiting the United States, not given by Wilson. 4 v. Philadelphia.
—— 1826. Observations on the nomenclature of Wilson's ornithology. Philadelphia.
CASSIN, JOHN. 1858. Mammalogy and ornithology. U.S. Exploring Expedition, 8. Philadelphia.
CATESBY, MARK. 1731. The natural history of Carolina, Florida, and the Bahama Islands. 2 v. London.
CLARK, JOSEPH G. 1848. Lights and shadows of sailor life, as exemplified in fifteen years' experience, including the more thrilling events of the U.S. exploring expedition, and reminiscences of an eventful life on the "mountain wave." Boston.
COLVOCORESSES, GEORGE M. 1852. Four years in a government exploring expedition. New York.
DARLINGTON, WILLIAM. 1849. Memorials of John Bartram and Humphrey Marshall. Philadelphia.
——, ed. 1843. Reliquiae Baldwinianae. Philadelphia.
DAVIDSON, ROBERT B. 1888. History of the United Bowmen of Philadelphia. Pamphlet. Philadelphia.
DE BOISDUVAL, J. B. A. D., and JOHN LE CONTE. 1829–1833. Histoire générale et iconographie des lepidoptéres et des chenilles de l'Amèrique Septentrionale. Paris.
DONOVAN, EDWARD. 1793–1801. The natural history of British Insects. 10 v. London.
DREPPERD, CARL W. 1930. Early American prints. New York, Century Co.
DRURY, CLIFFORD MERRILL. ed. 1957. Diary of Titian Ramsay Peale. Los Angeles, Glen Dawson.
EWAN, JOSEPH ANDORFER. 1950. Rocky Mountain naturalists. Denver, Univ. of Denver Press.
FORD, ALICE. 1952. Audubon's butterflies, moths and other studies. New York, Studio.
FULLER, HARLAN M., and LEROY R. HAFEN. 1957. The journal of Captain John R. Bell, official journalist for the Stephen H. Long expedition to the Rocky Mountains, 1820. Glendale, Calif., Arthur H. Clarke Co.

GILMAN, DANIEL C. 1899. The life of James Dwight Dana. New York and London.
GODMAN, JOHN D. 1826–1828. American natural history. 3 v. Philadelphia.
GRAEBNER, NORMAN A. 1955. Empire on the Pacific. New York, Ronald Press.
GRAUSTEIN, JEANNETTE A., ed. 1951. Nuttall's travels into the old northwest. Waltham, Mass., in *Chronica Botanica* 14.
GUIFFREY, JEAN, ed. 1933. Etats-Unis de 1816 à 1837 dessins de Ch. A. Lesueur. Paris, Daniel Tacomet & Cie.
HASKELL, DANIEL C. 1942. The United States exploring expedition, 1838–1842 and its publications 1844–1874—a bibliography. New York, New York Public Library.
HENDERSON, DANIEL. 1953. The hidden coasts. New York, Sloane.
IRWIN, R. A., ed. 1955. Letters of Charles Waterton of Walton Hall, near Wakefield. London, Rockliff Publishing Corporation Ltd.
JAMES, EDWIN. 1832. Account of an expedition from Pittsburgh to the Rocky Mountains. 2 v. and atlas of maps and plates. Philadelphia.
LEWIS, J. O. 1836. The aboriginal portfolio. Philadelphia.
LORANT, STEFAN, ed. 1946. The new world, the first pictures of America. New York, Duell, Sloan and Pearce.
McCRACKEN, HAROLD. 1952. Portrait of the old west. New York, McGraw-Hill.
MEISEL, MAX. 1924–1929. A bibliography of American natural history. 3 v. Brooklyn, Premier Publishing Co.
MELVILLE, HERMAN. 1955. Moby Dick. New York, Signet.
—— 1958. Typee. New York, Bantam.
PEALE, REMBRANDT. 1802. Account of the skeleton of the mammoth, a non-descript carnivorous animal of immense size found in America. London.
—— 1803. An historical disquisition on the mammoth, or great American incognitum, an extinct, immense, carnivorous animal whose fossil remains have been found in North America. London.
PEALE, TITIAN R. 1831. Circular of the Philadelphia Museum containing directions for the preparations and preservation of objects of natural history. Pamphlet. Philadelphia.
—— 1833. Lepidoptera Americana. Prospectus. Philadelphia. (In collection of Academy of Natural Sciences of Philadelphia.) Six unpublished lithographic page proofs also with this in ANSP collection.
—— 1848. Mammalia and ornithology. U.S. Exploring expedition, 8. Philadelphia. (Suppressed.)
Pennsylvania Academy of the Fine Arts. May, 1822. Catalogue. Eleventh annual exhibition of the Pennsylvania Academy of the Fine Arts. Philadelphia.
PHILLIPS, RICHARD. 1833. A dictionary of the arts of life and civilization. London.
RUTLEDGE, ANNA WELLS. 1949. Artists in the life of Charleston. Philadelphia, *Trans. Amer. Philos. Soc.* 39(2).
——, ed. 1955. Cumulative record of exhibition catalogues: the Pennsylvania Academy of the Fine Arts, 1807–1870; the Society of Artists, 1800–1814; the Artists' Fund Society, 1835–1845. Philadelphia, *Memoirs Amer. Philos. Soc.* 38.
SAY, THOMAS. Prospectus. 1817. American entomology. Philadelphia.
—— 1824–1828. American entomology, or descriptions of the insects of North America. 3 v. Philadelphia.
SELLERS, CHARLES COLEMAN. 1947. Charles Willson Peale. 2 v. Philadelphia. *Memoirs Amer. Philos. Soc.* 23(1 & 2).
—— 1951. Portraits and miniatures by Charles Willson Peale. Philadelphia. *Trans. Amer. Philos. Soc.* 42(1).
SMALLWOOD, WILLIAM MARTIN, and MABEL S. C. SMALLWOOD. 1941. Natural history and the American mind. New York, Columbia Univ. Press.
SMITH, HENRY NASH. 1950. Virgin land, the American West as symbol and myth. Cambridge, Mass., Harvard Univ. Press.
SMITH, JAMES EDWARD. 1797. The natural history of the rarer lepidopterous insects of Georgia, collected from the observations of Mr. John Abbot. 2 v. London.

TAYLOR, GEORGE ROGERS. 1951. The transportation revolution 1815–1860. New York, Rinehart.

THWAITES, R. G., ed. 1905. Early western travels. **14, 15** and **16.** Cleveland.

WATERTON, CHARLES. 1825. Wanderings in South America, the Northwest of the United States, and the Antilles in the years 1812, 1816, 1820, and 1824. London.

Webster's Geographical Dictionary. 1949. Springfield, Mass., G. & C. Merriam Co.

WEISS, HARRY B., and GRACE M. ZEIGLER. 1931. Thomas Say, early American naturalist. Baltimore, C. C Thomas.

WELKER, ROBERT HENRY. 1955. Birds and men, American birds in science, art, literature, and conservation, 1800–1900. Cambridge, Mass., Belknap Press of Harvard Univ. Press.

WILKES, CHARLES. 1845. The narrative of the United States exploring expedition. 5 v. Philadelphia. On reverse of title page: Stereotyped by J. Fagan. Printed by C. Sherman.

WILSON, ALEXANDER. 1808–1814. American ornithology or the natural history of the birds of the United States. 9 v. Philadelphia.

WITTLIN, ALMA. 1949. The museum, its history and its tasks in education. London, Routledge & K. Paul.

DIRECTORIES

DeSilver's directory. Philadelphia, 1825, 1828, 1829, 1830, 1831, 1833, 1835, 1837.

Gopsill's Philadelphia directory. Philadelphia, 1877, 1878, 1879, 1880, 1881, 1882, 1883, 1884, 1885, 1886.

McElroy's Philadelphia directory. Philadelphia, 1837, 1839, 1840, 1841, 1842, 1843, 1844, 1845, 1846, 1847, 1849.

ARTICLES

ABBOT, JACOB BATES. Oct. 1943. An artist looks at Wilson. *Frontiers* **8:** 11–13.

ABBOTT, R. TUCKER. 1955. The Titian R. Peale shell collection. *The Nautilus* **68:** 123–127.

ALLEN, ELSA G. 1937. New light on Mark Catesby. *The Auk* **54:** 349–363.

BARTLETT, HARLEY HARRIS. 1940. The reports of the Wilkes expedition, and the work of the specialists in science. *Proc. Amer. Philos. Soc.* **82:** 601–705.

BURNS, FRANK L. 1932. Charles W. and Titian R. Peale and the ornithological section of the old Philadelphia Museum. *Wilson Bulletin* **44:** 23–25.

—— 1917. Miss Lawson's recollections of ornithologists. *The Auk,* n.s., **34:** 275–282.

The cabinet of natural history and American rural sports. **1,** 1830; **2,** 1832; **3,** 1833.

CALLAHAN, J. M. 1901. America in the Pacific and the Far East. *Johns Hopkins Univ. Studies in Histor. and Pol. Sci.* **19:** 1–174.

CHINARD, GILBERT. 1949. The American sketchbooks of Charles Alexandre Lesueur. *Proc. Amer. Philos. Soc.* **93(2):** 114–118. (*Lib. Bull.* for 1949).

COLTON, HAROLD S. Sept. 1909. Peale's Museum. *Popular Science Monthly.* 221–238.

COOLEY, MARY E. 1940. The exploring expedition in the Pacific, *Proc. Amer. Philos. Soc.* **82(5):** 707–719.

DALL, WILLIAM H. 1888. Some American conchologists. *Proc. Biol. Soc. of Washington* **4:** 95–134.

ECKHARDT, GEORGE H. 1935. Early lithography in America. *Antiques* **28:** 249–252.

FAXON, WALTER. 1915. Relics of Peale's Museum. *Bull. Mus. Comp. Zoology at Harvard* **9:** 119–148.

GODMAN, JOHN D. 1826. Natural history. *The Franklin Journal and American Mechanics' Magazine* **1:** 16–17.

HAMY, E. T. 1904. Les voyages du naturaliste Ch. Alex. Lesueur dans l'Amérique du nord 1815–1837. *Jour. de la Société des Américanistes de Paris* **5.**

HARLAN, RICHARD. 1824. On a species of Lamantin resembling the Manatus senegalensis (Cuvier) inhabiting the coast of East Florida. *Jour. Acad. Nat. Sciences* **3:** 391–394.

HARTLAUB, G. 1851. Bericht über die Leistungen in der Naturgeschichte der Vogel wahrend des Jahres 1850. *Archiv. fur Naturgeschichte* **17:** 48.

—— 1852. R. Titian Peale's Vogel der 'United States Exploring Expedition,' in Auszuge mitgeheilt und mit Kritischen Anmerkungen. *Archiv fur Naturgeschichte* **18:** 93–138.

HOBBS, WILLIAM HERBERT. 1940. The discovery of Wilkes Land, Antarctica. *Proc. Amer. Philos. Soc.* **82(5):** 561–582.

JENSEN, OLIVER. April, 1955. The Peales. *American Heritage* **4:** 40–51; 97–101.

KEATING, WILLIAM H. July, 1825. Major Long's second expedition. *North American Review* **21:** 179.

[KELSO, LEON]. 1951. The six journals of Mr. Peale, naturalist, from the journals of Titian Ramsay Peale. *Biological Leaflet* No. 55: 1–3.

LEA, ISAAC. 1839. Description of new freshwater and land shells. *Trans. Amer. Philos. Soc.,* n.s., **6:** 1–109.

McCOSKER, M. J. 1941. Philadelphia and the genesis of the motion picture. *Penna. Mag. Hist. Biog.* **65:** 401–419.

McDERMOTT, JOHN F. 1952. Early sketches of T. R. Peale. *Nebraska History* **33:** 186–189.

MEANY, EDMOND S., ed. 1925–1926. Diary of Wilkes in the northwest. *Washington Hist. Quart.* **16:** 49–61, 137–145, 206–223, 290–301; **17:** 43–65, 129–149, 223–229.

MURPHY, ROBERT CUSHMAN. 1957. The sketches of Titian Ramsay Peale (1799–1885). *Proc. Amer. Philos. Soc.* **101:** 523–531.

Notes and queries. *Penna. Mag. Hist. Biog.* **1**(1877): 223. **9**(1885): 121–135. **16**(1892): 249.

PATTERSON, ROBERT. 1871. An obituary notice of Franklin Peale, read before the American Philosophical Society, Dec. 16, 1870. *Proc. Amer. Philos. Soc.* **11:** 597–604.

PEALE, ALBERT CHARLES. 1905. Titian R. Peale, 1800–1885. *Bull. Philos. Soc. Washington* **14:** 317–326.

PEALE, TITIAN R. 1862. Ancient mounds at St. Louis, Missouri, in 1819. *Annual Report of the Board of Regents of the Smithsonian Institution, 1861:* 386–391.

—— 1834. Black-tailed or mule deer, *Cervus macrotis. Advocate of science and annals of natural history* **1:** 11–13.

—— 1864. Method of preserving Lepidoptera. *Annual Report of the Board of Regents of the Smithsonian Institution, 1863:* 404–406.

—— 1871. On the uses of the brain and morrow of animals among the Indians of North America. *Annual Report of the Board of Regents of the Smithsonian Institution, 1870:* 390–391.

—— 1873. Pre-historic remains found in the vicinity of the City of Washington, D.C. *Annual Report of the Board of Regents of the Smithsonian Institution, 1872:* 430–432.

PEALE, TITIAN R., and JACOB GREEN. 1829. Description of two new species of the Linnaean Genus Lacerta. *Jour. Acad. Nat. Sciences* **6:** 231.

PHILLIPS, HENRY, JR. 1884. Old minutes of the Society, from 1743 to 1838. *Proc. Amer. Philos. Soc.* **22.**

PHILLIPS, MAURICE E. 1953. The Academy of Natural Sciences of Philadelphia. In: Historic Philadelphia. *Trans. Amer. Philos. Soc.* **43(1):** 266–274.

REHN, JAMES A. G. 1940. Connection of the Academy of Natural Sciences of Philadelphia with our first national exploring expedition. *Proc. Amer. Philos. Soc.* **82:** 543–549.

—— 1954. The John Eatton LeConte collection of paintings of insects, arachnids, and myriopods. *Proc. Amer. Philos. Soc.* **98:** 442–448.

Say's American entomology. July 1825. *North American Review* **21:** 251–252.

SELLERS, CHARLES COLEMAN. 1953. Peale's Museum. In: Historic Philadelphia. *Trans. Amer. Philos. Soc.* **43(1):** 253–259.

SELLERS, COLEMAN. 1888. An old photographic club. *Anthony's Photographic Bulletin,* 1–17.

STONE, WITMER. 1915. Titian Ramsey Peale. *Cassinia, Proc. Del. Valley Ornithol. Club* **19:** 1–13.

WEESE, ASA ORRIN, ed. 1947. The journal of Titian Ramsay Peale, pioneer naturalist. *Missouri Historical Review* **41:** 147–163; 266–284.

Index

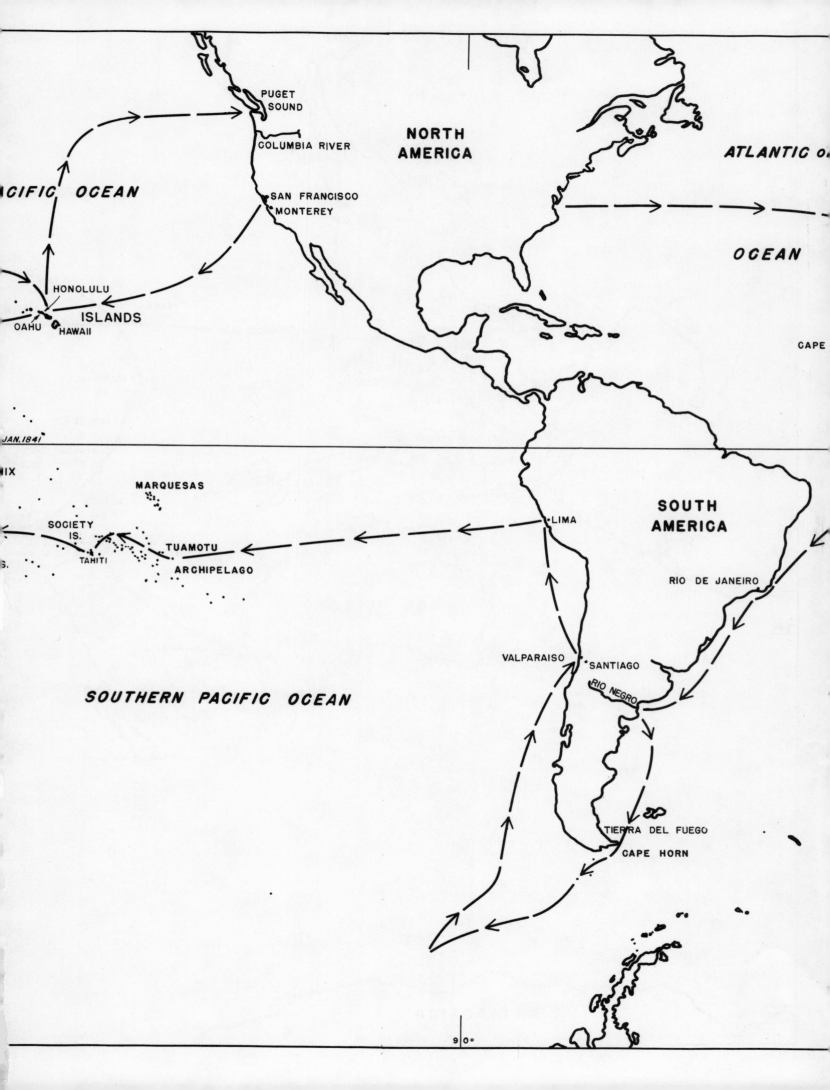

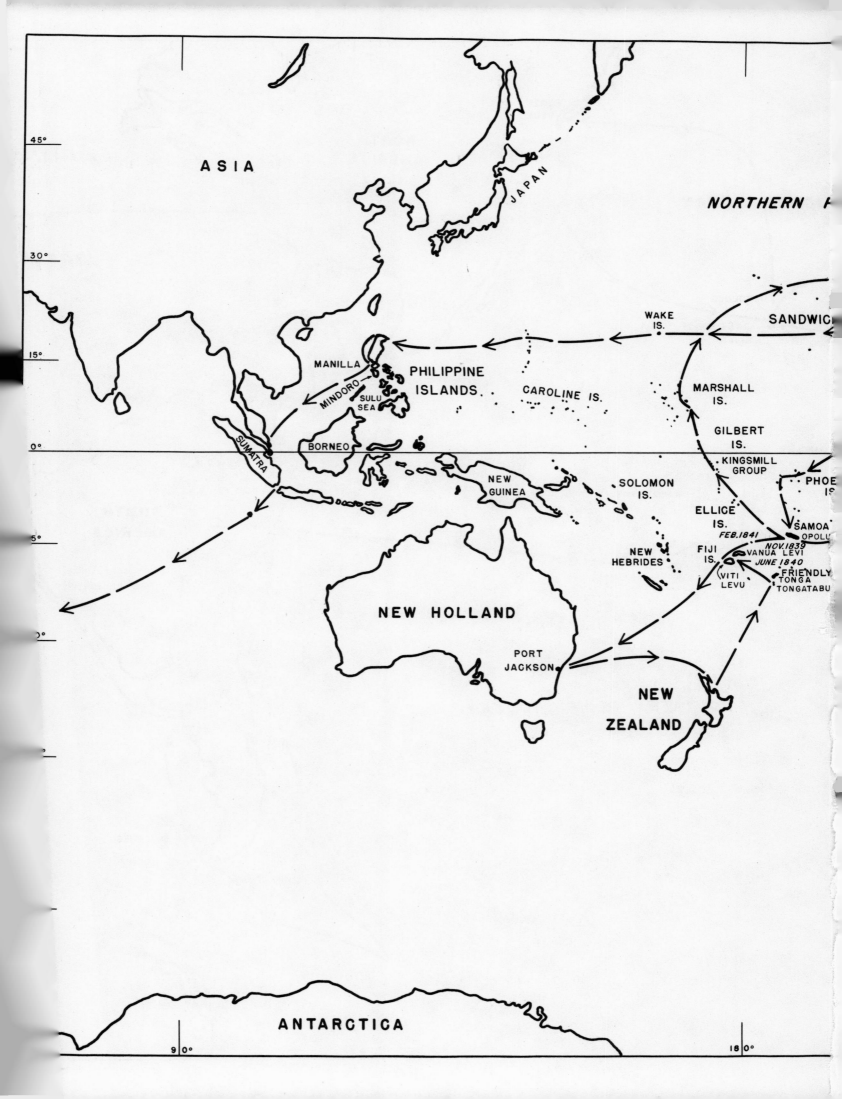

30°

45°

60°